GEOMETRY FOR TEACHERS

GEOMETRY
FOR TEACHERS

An Introduction to Geometrical Theories

G. Y. RAINICH

Professor of Mathematics, Emeritus
University of Michigan

S. M. DOWDY

Assistant Professor of Mathematics
Ball State University

JOHN WILEY AND SONS, INC., NEW YORK · LONDON · SYDNEY

Preface

This book originated from lectures given for several years to the Academic Year Institutes of the National Science Foundation at the University of Michigan and the University of Notre Dame. It does not attempt to tell teachers how to teach; instead, it is based on two convictions: that a teacher must know much more than just the material he is using in his classroom, and that the additional material should be clearly related to the subject matter of his teaching. Only these things will help him to understand more fully the elementary aspects that he is teaching.

To accomplish this objective, the book begins with the familiar subject of Euclidean geometry, but deals with it from what is a new point of view for many teachers: vectors. When a geometry other than Euclidean, projective, is first introduced, care is taken to present each new concept as a generalization or modification of a familiar concept in Euclidean geometry. An attempt is made to avoid too much sophistication (especially at the beginning) but, in later chapters when the experience of the student should have increased by working through the earlier material, the style of exposition changes; the last chapters are presented in a manner that would have been difficult for the reader if he had not carefully gone through the earlier parts of the book.

As the subtitle indicates, this text is an introduction to geometrical theories. This means that several geometries will be studied (Euclidean, projective, affine, inversive, hyperbolic, equiform, and equiaffine) from various points of view (using intuition, analytic methods, transformations, vectors, and the axiomatic approach). Although there are many cross-references within the book, several chapters could be read independently; for example, Chapters 3, 5, and 6 on projective geometry, inversive geometry, and hyperbolic geometry.

The exercises have been designed to help the reader understand the material in the text. Often, the exercises ask questions that arise from the material just presented or that fill in details omitted in the presentation. Some of the exercises apply the new material to particular situations and other exercises indicate ways that the material could be extended. The exercises are intended to be an integral part of the book, and many of them should be attempted if the reader is to get the maximum benefit from this text.

In keeping with the character of the book as a text, detailed references to original sources are not given but, for a reader who wants to go beyond the discussion in the book, a bibliography is given at the end.

G. Y. Rainich
S. M. Dowdy

Contents

GEOMETRY FOR TEACHERS

I
EUCLIDEAN GEOMETRY

1 Intuitive Vector Geometry

How does a mathematician develop a new theory? As a student, you have probably wondered about this. Over and over you see the finished product—precise, logical, almost elegant—maybe very difficult to understand. Where did it come from?

In this chapter, we want to develop vector geometry, not in an abstract polished way, but as it happened. (No one can really say exactly how it grew, but we can imagine that something like this must have gone through the minds of the many people who built vector geometry.)

Where do we begin? We start with three-dimensional Euclidean geometry. We already understand terms like point, line, plane, parallel, perpendicular, and distance. We know many properties of these terms. We are also familiar with the real numbers and the trigonometric functions. This is where we begin; we shall allow ourselves to use all of these ideas. In the world of Euclidean geometry, we shall search for some concepts that will lead to vector geometry. For the present, we shall not attempt to give formal definitions or proofs; this will be done in Chapter 2.

1.1 THE BASIC OBJECTS—POINTS AND VECTORS

What is geometry? Sometimes it is defined as the study of properties of figures that are not affected by change of position. At first this may not seem to be what geometry is about, but let us look at some examples. In Figure 1.1a, triangle ABC has three equal angles. If we change the position

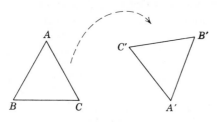

Fig. 1.1a

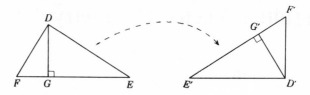

Fig. 1.1b

of triangle ABC to triangle $A'B'C'$, the angles are still equal. The property of having three equal angles *is* a geometric property.

Now look at Figure 1.1b. Triangle DEF has a vertical altitude DG. After many types of changes of position, such as the one shown, the resulting altitude $D'G'$ may not be vertical. Having a vertical altitude is *not* a geometric property.

This definition of geometry (the study of properties of figures that are not affected by change of position) will have to be revised later on, but for now it is useful because it does describe most of the geometry treated by Euclid.

Another big question is: What methods are used to study geometry? There is the method of Euclid—it deals directly with figures and derives some of their properties from other properties by logical reasoning. This method is called *synthetic*. There is a second method, called *analytic*. It uses a coordinate system, expresses properties of figures by numbers (coordinates), and some properties are derived from others by working with numerical expressions and equations, the numerical results being interpreted in terms of figures. Sometimes we speak of "synthetic geometry" and "analytic geometry." These are not different geometries because they deal ultimately with the same objects—the difference is in the method.

We want to find a third method of treating geometry, the *vector method*, or we could call it "vector geometry." The content will be the same as in synthetic or analytic geometry. The difference again is in the method. The vector method occupies a middle position between the synthetic and analytic methods. In common with the synthetic method, the vector method deals with figures directly (and not with their representations by numbers like the analytic method). It is like the analytic method because

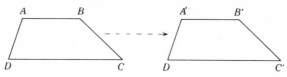

Fig. 1.1c

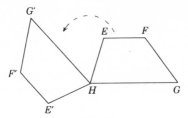

Fig. 1.1d

it derives properties from other properties by computation with expressions and equations (but the elements of these expressions and equations are mainly geometric objects and only incidentally numbers).

Since we have defined geometry in terms of change of position, it is reasonable to look here for a clue which will lead to vector geometry. When a change of position occurs two things can happen: either all the lines of three-space move parallel to themselves (that is, their final position is parallel to their original position), or some lines do not move parallel to themselves. For example, in Figure 1.1c, trapezoid *ABCD* has been shifted, or *translated*, to position *A′B′C′D′*. (Actually, we must imagine that all the points and lines of three-space are moving along with the trapezoid.) *In a translation, all lines move parallel to themselves.*

Notice that, in this last example, the line determined by the points *D* and *C* moves along itself. Sometimes this happens, sometimes not; if it does, we shall still say that the line moves parallel to itself. Even if the line stays fixed, we shall say that it moves parallel to itself.

In Figure 1.1d, trapezoid *EFGH* has been rotated about point *H* to the position *E′F′G′H*. A rotation is an example of a change of position in which lines usually do not move parallel to themselves.

What happens to two points under a change of position? The same thing occurs; either all of the lines (including the one determined by the two points) move parallel to themselves (Figure 1.1e) or they do not (Figure 1.1f).

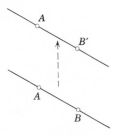

Fig. 1.1e

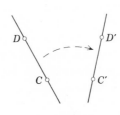

Fig. 1.1f

The pair of points A,B in Figure 1.1e can be moved to the pair of points A',B' in such a way that all lines move parallel to themselves (by a translation). This possible change of position forces the two pairs of points to be related to each other in a special way: A,B and A',B' lie on parallel lines, A and B are the same distance apart as A' and B', and the line through A and B is parallel to the line through A' and B'. (All of these properties are easy to prove and are the content of Exercise 2 at the end of this section.)

Because of these relations, we give a special name to *all the pairs of points that can be changed into each other by translation*. We call such a collection of pairs of points a *vector*. If A and B are one such pair of points, we shall call the vector AB. Notice that a vector is *represented* by a pair of points, but it is *not* a pair of points. The same vector may be represented by many different pairs of points; more specifically, if there is a translation that takes P and Q to points P' and Q', then we say PQ and $P'Q'$ represent the same vector, or the vector PQ is equal to $P'Q'$. Translation does not change a vector (it merely changes its representative); therefore, we are allowed to translate a vector—the result is the same vector. Other types of movements, like rotations, are not permitted. If we rotate a vector (that is, one of its representatives) we usually get a different vector.

Notice that AB is usually not the same vector as BA. The order of the points is important. The only case in which vector AB is the same as BA is if A is the same point as B. This vector is called the *zero vector*. There is only one zero vector; it is the collection of all the pairs of points in which the first and second point coincide.

Since the order of the points makes a difference, we can make our description of a vector more precise: *A vector is represented by an ordered pair of points*. There is a first point which we shall call the *tail*, and a second point which we shall call the *tip* of the vector. (In the case of the zero vector, the tail and tip coincide.) Often a vector is drawn as an arrow, illustrating the fact that we use a particular representative to deal with the vector.

Sometimes it is stated that every vector has a direction and a magnitude. This is not accurate because the zero vector has no definite direction. It is true that every vector has a magnitude, or *length*. (The length of zero vector is the number zero.) We shall discuss length a little later. As to direction, it is convenient to assign to every nonzero vector not only direction but also *sense*.

This is how we determine direction and sense. We bring two vectors together at their tails by a translation. If their common tail and two tips are then on one line, we shall say that the vectors have the *same direction*;

if, in addition, the common tail is between their tips, we shall say that they have *opposite sense*—and we shall say that they have the *same sense* in the other case (when either one tip is between the common tail and the other tip, or the tips coincide).

Now that we have some idea of what a vector is, we should mention that, in developing vector geometry, we would like to use points and vectors as our primary geometrical objects. This is different from both synthetic and analytic geometry, in which points and lines are the primary objects.

Exercises

1. Using your knowledge of Euclidean geometry, prove that if a translation (a change of position that moves *all* lines parallel to themselves) moves at least one point, then it moves every point.
2. Prove that, if a point A is translated to a point A', and A' is not on the line determined by two distinct points A and B, then the translation moves B to a point B' which is the vertex of a parallelogram $ABB'A'$ (the vertices are listed consecutively).
3. Does a rotation ever leave a line fixed? If not, why not? If so, in which cases? Does a rotation ever leave a vector unchanged?
4. Describe some changes of position which would preserve the Euclidean properties of size of an angle and length of a line segment; you need not restrict yourself to a plane. Are vectors changed by any of these movements? Which ones?
5. Show that two different ordered pairs of points which represent the same vector determine the same direction, sense, and length. (We shall use "show" synonymously with "prove.")
6. Prove that, if point A is not the same point as B (vector AB is not the zero vector), then vector AB is not equal to vector BA.
7. Let AB be a fixed vector. Prove that a change of position which takes every point P to a point P' such that vector PP' is equal to AB is a translation.

1.2 ADDITION AND SUBTRACTION OF VECTORS

In vector geometry, we want to derive propositions about geometric objects by computation. This is the way we prove propositions in algebra and arithmetic. Since we are familiar with the rules of arithmetic, it would be convenient if vector geometry had similar rules. Let us try to find a way to add vectors so that this addition will resemble arithmetic as much as possible.

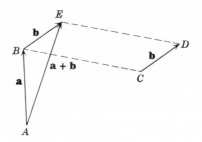

Fig. 1.2*a*

Thus far, we have used two capital italic letters to represent vectors. We could use only one letter, a bold lower case roman letter. We will do this and call vector *AB* simply **a**.

Given two vectors **a** = *AB* and **b** = *CD*, the first step in finding their sum will be to translate the vector **b** so that *C* goes to *B* (Figure 1.2*a*). If the new position of *D* is then *E*, *AE* will be called the sum of *AB* and *CD*. In other words, we move **b** so that its tail coincides with the tip of **a**, then the tail of **a** and the tip of **b** determine their sum.

Strictly speaking it is necessary to prove that this addition is independent of the representatives of the vectors. This means that, if we translate vectors **a** and **b** to new positions (but so that the tip of **a** coincides with the tail of **b**), the sum (defined as the vector whose tail is the tail of **a** and whose tip is the tip of **b**) will be the same vector as defined before. Using your knowledge of translations and their relationship to parallelograms developed in the exercises of the last section, you should be able to find your own proof.

Addition of vectors, as we have just described it, does obey the laws of arithmetic. It is associative, commutative, and has a zero element. Proofs of these laws are not difficult and will be asked for at the end of this section.

The next natural step is subtraction. Using the operations on numbers as our guide, we define the difference **a** − **b** to be the vector **x** which added to **b** gives **a**; that is, **x** = **a** − **b** if **a** = **b** + **x** (Figure 1.2*b*).

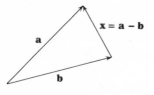

Fig. 1.2*b*

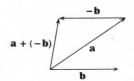

Fig. 1.2*c*

An alternate approach would be to interchange the tip and tail of the vector **b**. This gives a new vector which we call the opposite, or *negative*, of **b**. From the definition of addition, it is easy to see that the sum of a vector and its negative is the zero vector **0**. Putting both of these approaches together, we can say that the negative of **b** is **0** − **b**; that is, **0** − **b** is equal to that vector which added to **b** gives **0**. We usually omit the **0** and just write −**b** for the negative of **b**. Now, instead of subtracting a vector **b** from **a**, we can add its negative, **a** − **b** = **a** + (−**b**) (Figure 1.2c).

Exercises

1. Prove that, instead of the definition of addition given above, we get the same result if we do the following. Bring the tails of the two vectors together: draw the parallelogram having the two vectors as adjacent sides; then draw the diagonal from the common tail to the opposite vertex; this diagonal, considered as a vector with tail at the common tail and tip at the opposite vertex, is the sum of the two vectors.
2. Show that the two approaches to subtraction described in this section give the same result.
3. Prove that addition of vectors satisfies the commutative and associative laws: **a** + **b** = **b** + **a** and (**a** + **b**) + **c** = **a** + (**b** + **c**).
4. Prove that the addition of the zero vector to any vector **a** does not change **a**, or in formula **a** + **0** = **a**. Also prove that no other vector besides the zero vector has this property.
5. Show that for all vectors **a**, **a** − **a** = **0**. Also prove that, for any two vectors **a** and **b**, −(**a** + **b**) = −**a** − **b**.
6. Show that **a** + (**b** − **c**) = (**a** + **b**) − **c**, and that (**a** + **b**) − (**c** + **d**) = (**a** − **c**) + (**b** − **d**) for all vectors **a**,**b**,**c**, and **d**.
7. Is vector subtraction associative? Why or why not?

1.3   MULTIPLICATION OF VECTORS BY NUMBERS

Thus far, we have been able to avoid the concept of the length of a vector. You will notice that length is not mentioned in the definition of addition or subtraction. When we begin to multiply, we shall no longer be able to avoid this concept. We shall agree, before we begin, that the length of a vector means the distance between its endpoints (tip and tail). This presupposes that we have chosen a unit of length—we shall assume that we have chosen it.

In arithmetic, we have only one kind of element—numbers; therefore, we have only one kind of multiplication. In vector geometry, we have two kinds of elements that may occur in multiplication—vectors and numbers; therefore, several kinds of multiplication with vectors are possible. We could multiply vectors and numbers, or vectors and vectors (in the second case the result could be a number or a vector). We shall talk about multiplying vectors by numbers now and postpone a discussion of the product of vectors until later. Following the pattern of arithmetic, in all kinds of multiplication we shall want the distributive law to hold; that is, to multiply a sum, we shall multiply each term separately and then add to get the result.

To decide on a reasonable way to multiply vectors by numbers, we first look at the case where the multiplier is an integer. It is reasonable to assume that $1\mathbf{a} = \mathbf{a}$. The distributive law tells us that

$$2\mathbf{a} = (1 + 1)\mathbf{a} = 1\mathbf{a} + 1\mathbf{a} = \mathbf{a} + \mathbf{a}.$$

Applying the distributive law several times, to multiply by a positive integer n we must "add $\mathbf{a}$ to itself n times"; for example, $4\mathbf{a} = \mathbf{a} + \mathbf{a} + \mathbf{a} + \mathbf{a}$. The vector which is the product $n\mathbf{a}$ has the same direction and sense as $\mathbf{a}$, and its length is the length of $\mathbf{a}$ multiplied by n. Since this is the rule for positive integers, we extend it to all positive numbers. If α is a positive real number and $\mathbf{a}$ is a vector, then the product $\alpha\mathbf{a}$ is a vector with the same direction and sense as $\mathbf{a}$ and with length α times the length of $\mathbf{a}$.

What about $0\mathbf{a}$, the number zero times a vector? Since zero times any length is zero, we suspect that $0\mathbf{a} = \mathbf{0}$. This agrees with the distributive law because $\alpha + 0 = \alpha$ and $\alpha\mathbf{a} = (\alpha + 0)\mathbf{a} = \alpha\mathbf{a} + 0\mathbf{a}$; then, from Exercise 4 of Section 1.2, it follows that $0\mathbf{a}$ must be the zero vector.

We still have not talked about negative numbers. Let us try to use the distributive law again: $\alpha\mathbf{a} + (-\alpha)\mathbf{a} = [\alpha + (-\alpha)]\mathbf{a} = 0\mathbf{a} = \mathbf{0}$. Because of this, we say that $(-\alpha)\mathbf{a} = -(\alpha\mathbf{a})$; this means that, to multiply a vector by a negative number, we multiply by the absolute value of the number and then take the negative of the resulting vector.

It is easy to see that any vector $\mathbf{b}$ that has the same direction as a vector $\mathbf{a}$ may be written as a multiple of $\mathbf{a}$, say $\alpha\mathbf{a}$. If $\mathbf{b}$ has the same sense as $\mathbf{a}$, α will be a positive number, and α will be a negative number when $\mathbf{a}$ and $\mathbf{b}$ have opposite senses.

You may have noticed in this section that, in a product, we always wrote the number on the left and the vector on the right. This is not necessary. Sometimes we shall write the product the other way and we shall agree that $\alpha\mathbf{a} = \mathbf{a}\alpha$.

Exercises

1. Let α and β be any real numbers, **a** and **b** any vectors. Show that the following are true:

(a) $\alpha(\mathbf{a} + \mathbf{b}) = \alpha\mathbf{a} + \alpha\mathbf{b}$
(b) $\alpha(-\mathbf{a}) = (-\alpha)\mathbf{a} = -(\alpha\mathbf{a})$
(c) $\alpha(\mathbf{a} - \mathbf{b}) = \alpha\mathbf{a} - \alpha\mathbf{b}$
(d) $\alpha(\beta\mathbf{a}) = (\alpha\beta)\mathbf{a}$
(e) $\alpha\mathbf{0} = \mathbf{0}$.

2. Prove that the definition of multiplication of a vector by a number does not depend upon the representative of the vector.

1.4 LINEAR COMBINATIONS AND LINEAR DEPENDENCE

The operations of addition of vectors and multiplication of vectors by numbers are closely related; we saw that multiplication by an integer is a special case of addition.

It is natural to combine these two operations another way. Given n vectors, $\mathbf{a}_1, \mathbf{a}_2, \ldots, \mathbf{a}_n$, and n numbers, $\alpha_1, \alpha_2, \ldots, \alpha_n$, we can form the sum of the products, $\alpha_1\mathbf{a}_1 + \alpha_2\mathbf{a}_2 + \cdots + \alpha_n\mathbf{a}_n$. We call this a *linear combination* of $\mathbf{a}_1, \mathbf{a}_2, \ldots, \mathbf{a}_n$.

We could define a linear combination in arithmetic, but there it would not give us anything new; in vector geometry, it has an important significance which we shall discuss now.

Consider a linear combination $\alpha\mathbf{a} + \beta\mathbf{b}$ with fixed vectors **a**,**b** and variable coefficients α, β. If **a** and **b** have the *same* direction, then $\alpha\mathbf{a} + \beta\mathbf{b}$ will have that direction also (Figure 1.4a). If **a** and **b** have *different* directions, then $\alpha\mathbf{a} + \beta\mathbf{b}$ is in the plane of the two vectors. In fact, an expression of the form $\alpha\mathbf{a} + \beta\mathbf{b}$ can represent any vector in the plane determined by **a** and **b**. To see this, translate **a** and **b** so that they have their tails at a common point O; let **c** be any other vector, it can be

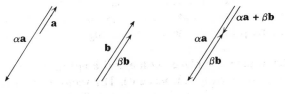

Fig. 1.4a

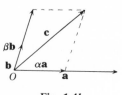

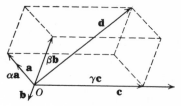

Fig. 1.4b

Fig. 1.4c

translated so that its tail is at O also (Figure 1.4b). If **c** does not have the same direction as **a** or **b**, draw lines parallel to **a** and **b** through the tip of **c**; the vector **c** now coincides with a diagonal of a parallelogram which has sides in the directions of **a** and **b**. These sides are multiples of **a** and **b**, say α**a** and β**b**; by the definition of addition, $\mathbf{c} = \alpha\mathbf{a} + \beta\mathbf{b}$. If **c** has the direction of $\mathbf{a}, \mathbf{c} = \alpha\mathbf{a} + 0\mathbf{b}$ for some real number α; similarly if **c** has the direction of **b**.

We can interpret a linear combination of three vectors in a similar way. If **a,b,c** all have the same direction, $\alpha\mathbf{a} + \beta\mathbf{b} + \gamma\mathbf{c}$ has that direction; if **a,b,c** are in the same plane, then $\alpha\mathbf{a} + \beta\mathbf{b} + \gamma\mathbf{c}$ is in that plane; but if **a,b,c** are not in the same plane, then $\alpha\mathbf{a} + \beta\mathbf{b} + \gamma\mathbf{c}$ can be any vector in three-space. To see this, let **a,b,c** be translated so that they have their tails at O (Figure 1.4c); let **d** be any other vector, translate **d** to O also. If **d** is not in one of the planes determined by **a,b,c**, consider planes through the tip of **d** and parallel to the planes of **a** and **b**, **b** and **c**, **a** and **c**. Then **d** coincides with the diagonal of a parallelopiped with edges in the directions of **a,b,c**; for some α, β, γ, $\mathbf{d} = \alpha\mathbf{a} + \beta\mathbf{b} + \gamma\mathbf{c}$. If **d** is in one of the planes determined by **a,b,c**, we can find the coefficients in a similar way to that used above for two vectors.

Closely related to the concept of a linear combination is that of linear dependence. We say that a set of vectors is *linearly dependent* if there exists a linear combination of these vectors with coefficients not all zero, which is equal to the zero vector. If this is not true, we say that the set of vectors is *linearly independent*. (This means that, if a linear combination of linearly independent vectors is the zero vector, then all of the coefficients are zero.)

Let us look at some examples. If **a** and **b** have the same direction, we can find a number ρ such that $\mathbf{b} = \rho\mathbf{a}$. This can be rewritten as $\rho\mathbf{a} + (-1)\mathbf{b} = \mathbf{0}$. Since $-1 \neq 0$, this says that **a** and **b** are linearly dependent; more precisely, the set consisting of **a** and **b** is linearly dependent.

Let **a,b,c** be in the same plane, with **a** and **b** not in the same direction (or, as we say now, linearly independent). The vector **c** can be expressed as a linear combination of **a** and **b**, $\mathbf{c} = \alpha\mathbf{a} + \beta\mathbf{b}$ for some α and β. We can change this to read $\alpha\mathbf{a} + \beta\mathbf{b} + (-1)\mathbf{c} = \mathbf{0}$. According to the above definition, $\mathbf{a},\mathbf{b},\mathbf{c}$ are linearly dependent.

What about four vectors $\mathbf{a},\mathbf{b},\mathbf{c},\mathbf{d}$ in three-space? Let us consider $\mathbf{a},\mathbf{b},\mathbf{c}$ first. Either $\mathbf{a},\mathbf{b},\mathbf{c}$ are linearly independent, or they are not. If $\mathbf{a},\mathbf{b},\mathbf{c}$ are independent, then we have shown before that $\mathbf{d}$ can be written as $\mathbf{d} = \alpha\mathbf{a} + \beta\mathbf{b} + \gamma\mathbf{c}$. It follows that $\alpha\mathbf{a} + \beta\mathbf{b} + \gamma\mathbf{c} + (-1)\mathbf{d} = \mathbf{0}$ and $\mathbf{a},\mathbf{b},\mathbf{c},\mathbf{d}$ are linearly dependent. In the second case, if $\mathbf{a},\mathbf{b},\mathbf{c}$ are linearly dependent, $\alpha\mathbf{a} + \beta\mathbf{b} + \gamma\mathbf{c} = \mathbf{0}$ where α,β,γ are not all zero. Then we can write $\alpha\mathbf{a} + \beta\mathbf{b} + \gamma\mathbf{c} + 0\mathbf{d} = \mathbf{0}$. Again from the definition, $\mathbf{a},\mathbf{b},\mathbf{c},\mathbf{d}$ are linearly dependent. What we have just shown is that, in three-space, any four vectors are linearly dependent.

Exercises

1. In what special case is a linear combination simply addition of vectors? When does a linear combination reduce to multiplication of a vector by a number?
2. Show that the sum of two linear combinations $\alpha\mathbf{a} + \beta\mathbf{b}$ and $\gamma\mathbf{a} + \delta\mathbf{b}$ is again a linear combination. Is it true for any number of vectors?
3. Show that the product of a linear combination of n vectors and a number is still a linear combination.
4. Let $\mathbf{a},\mathbf{b},\mathbf{c}$ be a set of linearly independent vectors. Show that $\mathbf{a} + \mathbf{b}$, $\mathbf{a} + \mathbf{c}$, and $\mathbf{b} + \mathbf{c}$ is also a linearly independent set.
5. The notion of linear dependence applies to sets of vectors. We can apply it to a set consisting of a single vector $\mathbf{a}$. If $\mathbf{a}$ is not the zero vector, we say that the set is linearly independent; if $\mathbf{a} = \mathbf{0}$, we say that the set is linearly dependent. Justify this convention.
6. Show that $\mathbf{0}$ and any other vector $\mathbf{a}$ are linearly dependent. Why was it reasonable in Section 1.1 to say that the zero vector has no definite direction?
7. How could linear dependence be used to test whether a set of vectors is one, two, or three dimensional? (Since we are considering only three-space, this means that all the vectors are parallel to a line, parallel to a plane, or neither of these cases.)

1.5   LINES AND PLANES

We have been discussing vectors and operations on them. You may feel that we have neglected the other primitive element, *point*; there is very little we can say about a point considered by itself. Any point has the same properties as any other point—it is only the mutual relationship

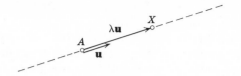

Fig. 1.5a

between different points that makes them interesting. The simplest interesting concept is two points; we know that the relationship between two points is expressed by a vector. Two points determine a vector (of which they are the tip and tail); given a point A and a vector $\mathbf{u}$, they determine another point, that is, the point B which is the tip of $\mathbf{u}$ if we place its tail at A. This relationship will be expressed by considering the vector $\mathbf{u}$ as the *difference* of the two points. We shall write $B - A = \mathbf{u}$, and also $B = A + \mathbf{u}$. We could say that the *sum* of a point A and a vector $\mathbf{u}$ is the point B. We can also subtract a vector $\mathbf{u}$ from a point A by finding the sum $A + (-\mathbf{u})$.

There are several operations possible with points. We can add a vector to a point—the result is a point. We can also subtract a vector from a point—the result is a point—it may be obtained by adding the negative of the vector to the point. We can subtract points from points—the result is a vector. However, we shall *not* define the sum of two points.

This notation gives us a way to represent lines. Let $X = A + \lambda\mathbf{u}$ where A and $\mathbf{u}$ are fixed and λ is a variable real number. For each different value of λ, we get a different point of a line which passes through A and has the direction of $\mathbf{u}$ (Figure 1.5a). Since λ can be both positive and negative, the equation represents the whole line (it extends in both senses from A). The number λ has a simple geometric meaning if we choose $\mathbf{u}$ to be a vector of length one, a *unit vector*; λ gives the distance of a point X from the point A.

A line may also be given by two points A and B; a line through these two points can be written in the form above if we let $\mathbf{u} = B - A$;

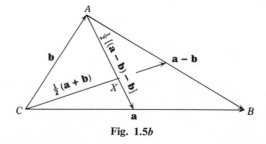

Fig. 1.5b

$A + \lambda\mathbf{u} = X$ is then the required line. If $\lambda = 0$, we get the point A; for $\lambda = 1$, we get the point B because $B - A$ is the vector with tail at A and tip at B so that $A + (B - A) = B$.

This form of representing a straight line can be used to prove many theorems in elementary geometry. For example, *the medians of a triangle intersect at a point which is two-thirds the distance from each vertex to the opposite side.* Let the triangle be ABC (Figure 1.5b). Let $A - C = \mathbf{b}$ and $B - C = \mathbf{a}$, then $B - A = \mathbf{a} - \mathbf{b}$. The medians from A and C determine the vectors $\frac{1}{2}[(\mathbf{a} - \mathbf{b}) - \mathbf{b}]$ and $\frac{1}{2}(\mathbf{a} + \mathbf{b})$. We shall show that, if these medians do intersect, it is at a point X which is in the required position. Assume that the medians from A and C intersect in some point X (the other pairs of medians could be dealt with in a similar way). For some α, $X - C = \frac{1}{2}\alpha(\mathbf{a} + \mathbf{b})$; for some β, $X - C = \mathbf{b} + \frac{1}{2}\beta[(\mathbf{a} - \mathbf{b}) - \mathbf{b}]$. Combining these two equations,

$$\alpha(\mathbf{a} + \mathbf{b}) = 2\mathbf{b} + \beta(\mathbf{a} - 2\mathbf{b}), \qquad \text{or} \qquad (\alpha - \beta)\mathbf{a} = (2 - 2\beta - \alpha)\mathbf{b}.$$

We now notice that $\mathbf{a}$ and $\mathbf{b}$ are linearly independent vectors (why?); it follows that the only solution is that both of the coefficients $\alpha - \beta$ and $2 - 2\beta - \alpha$ are zero. We now have two linear equations in two unknowns α and β: $\alpha - \beta = 0$ and $2 - 2\beta - \alpha = 0$. You can now check that $\alpha = \beta = \frac{2}{3}$.

Can we represent planes by points and vectors? We have shown (in the previous section) that any vector in a plane can be expressed as a linear combination of two linearly independent vectors in that plane. It follows that $X = A + \lambda\mathbf{u} + \mu\mathbf{v}$ (where A is a fixed point, $\mathbf{u}$ and $\mathbf{v}$ are two fixed linearly independent vectors, and λ and μ are variables) represents any point in the plane through A and parallel to the vectors $\mathbf{u}$ and $\mathbf{v}$. Every pair of real numbers λ, μ gives a point, so they play the parts of coordinates of the point.

Finally, any point X of three-space can be expressed in terms of three linearly independent vectors $\mathbf{u}, \mathbf{v}, \mathbf{w}$ and a fixed point A,

$$X = A + \lambda\mathbf{u} + \mu\mathbf{v} + \nu\mathbf{w}$$

where λ, μ, ν are real numbers.

Exercises

1. Let $X = A + \lambda\mathbf{u}$ and $Y = B + \mu\mathbf{v}$. Under what conditions do these formulas represent parallel lines? Under what conditions do they represent the same line?

2. Using vectors, show that the diagonals of a parallelogram bisect each other.

3. Prove that the line joining the midpoints of two sides of a triangle is parallel to the third side and has length equal to one-half the length of the third side.

4. Show that the midpoints of consecutive sides of any quadrilateral are the vertices of a parallelogram.

5. Show that the line that joins one vertex of a parallelogram to the midpoint of an opposite side divides the diagonal in a ratio of 1 to 2 and is divided in the same way by it.

6. A more general form of Problem 5 can be stated. Let a line join one vertex of a parallelogram to a point on an opposite side, the point dividing that side in a ratio of m to n; derive an expression in terms of m and n for the ratio into which the diagonal is divided by this line.

7. Find some other theorems from high-school geometry which can be proved using vectors. (Most of the theorems about parallel lines, parallel planes, and ratios of lengths can be proved with the tools developed so far.) Prove them.

1.6 DOT PRODUCT

Many properties of lines and planes can be expressed using only the notation and operations introduced thus far. In order to talk about distance (other than as a ratio), angle, and perpendicularity, we need another kind of multiplication in which both factors are vectors. Here again we are not introducing anything that is essentially new, but we are reformulating—formulating in terms of vectors—the knowledge that we already have.

We have already mentioned the idea of a unit vector (that is, a vector of length one) and the idea of distance. Products of two vectors require more preparation along these lines.

We shall represent the length of a vector **a** by the symbol $|\mathbf{a}|$, similar to the notation that we use to indicate the absolute value of a number. If **a** is not the zero vector, its length $\alpha = |\mathbf{a}|$ is not zero; $(1/|\mathbf{a}|)\mathbf{a}$ is then a unit vector (a vector of length one), and if we denote this unit vector by **i**, we can write $\mathbf{a} = \alpha\mathbf{i}$. In this way, any vector can be written as a multiple of a unit vector. Since it is the length of a vector, α is a positive number; **i** has the same direction and sense as **a**.

We would like a similar representation for any second vector. Consider two nonzero vectors **a**,**b** and place them in such a position that their tails coincide at the point O (Figure 1.6a). Drop a perpendicular from the tip B of **b** to **a** and call its foot F; $\mathbf{b} = OF + FB$. OF has the direction of **a** and therefore of **i** and may be written as $\beta\mathbf{i}$ for some real number β. FB is perpendicular to **a**; if we denote a unit vector perpendicular to **i** by **j**, we can say $FB = \gamma\mathbf{j}$ for some real number γ. Of course, there are two

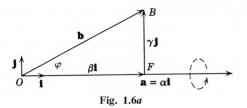

Fig. 1.6*a*

vectors in the plane of **a** and **b** perpendicular to **i** (they differ from each other in sense); we can always choose one of them so that γ is positive, or if **b** has the same direction as **a**, the number γ is zero. Now

$$\mathbf{b} = \beta\mathbf{i} + \gamma\mathbf{j}$$

where $\gamma \geq 0$. We cannot say a similar thing about β; in fact, from our knowledge of trigonometry, we see that $\beta/|\mathbf{b}|$ is the cosine of the directed angle φ from **a** to **b**, so if the angle is obtuse, β will be negative. In all cases, we know that the given vectors **a** and **b** can be written as $\mathbf{a} = \alpha\mathbf{i}$ and $\mathbf{b} = \beta\mathbf{i} + \gamma\mathbf{j}$ where **i** and **j** are two mutually perpendicular unit vectors, $\alpha > 0$, $\gamma \geq 0$, $\beta = |\mathbf{b}| \cos \varphi$, and $\gamma = |\mathbf{b}| \sin \varphi$, φ is the directed angle from **a** to **b** and $\beta\mathbf{i}$ is the projection of **b** on the direction of **a**.

Now we are ready to multiply with both factors being vectors. Our purpose, as before, is to derive geometrical propositions by computations with rules of operations that differ from the familiar rules for numbers as little as possible. Since it is not possible to keep all of the rules, we must decide which are essential and which we are ready to sacrifice.

There are two subcases of multiplication of vectors by vectors; the product of such a multiplication could be a number or it could be a vector. If the product of two vectors is a number, this is the *dot product* (sometimes called inner product or scalar product); if it is a vector, we are speaking of the *cross product* (outer product or vector product).

In this section, we shall discuss the first case and we shall write **a** · **b** to represent the dot product of **a** and **b**. We could simply define this right now; instead, we shall try to see how the definition came about.

Two properties that we want when we multiply are the distributive law $(\mathbf{a} + \mathbf{b}) \cdot \mathbf{c} = \mathbf{a} \cdot \mathbf{c} + \mathbf{b} \cdot \mathbf{c}$, and a modified associative law $(\alpha\mathbf{a}) \cdot \mathbf{c} = \alpha(\mathbf{a} \cdot \mathbf{c}) = \mathbf{a} \cdot (\alpha\mathbf{c})$.

We have just seen that any two vectors **a**,**b** can be written as $\mathbf{a} = \alpha\mathbf{i}$ and $\mathbf{b} = \beta\mathbf{i} + \gamma\mathbf{j}$. Applying the two essential laws $\mathbf{a} \cdot \mathbf{b} = (\alpha\mathbf{i}) \cdot (\beta\mathbf{i} + \gamma\mathbf{j}) = (\alpha\mathbf{i}) \cdot (\beta\mathbf{i}) + (\alpha\mathbf{i}) \cdot (\gamma\mathbf{j}) = (\alpha\beta)(\mathbf{i} \cdot \mathbf{i}) + (\alpha\gamma)(\mathbf{i} \cdot \mathbf{j})$. Thus, to find a definition of dot product which is distributive and has a modified associative law, all we have to do is to decide what $\mathbf{i} \cdot \mathbf{i}$ and $\mathbf{i} \cdot \mathbf{j}$ should be.

We want to use our operations to derive geometrical propositions (that is, propositions that do not depend on position) so our definitions must not depend on position. In Section 1.2, you have already been asked to prove this independence of position, or the representatives, for addition of vectors. In Exercise 2 of 1.3, the definition of multiplication of vectors by numbers was shown to be independent of the representatives of the vector. We want to apply this idea now to the new case of multiplication. Our definition of dot product must be *invariant* under change of position.

If we rotate the configuration containing **a** and **b** (Figure 1.6*a*) through 180° around the straight line containing the vector **i** (remember that we are in three-space so this is a possible change of position), this does not affect the vector **i**, but it changes the vector **j** into its negative −**j**. Since our definition of **i · j** must be invariant under changes of position of this figure, we must have **i · j** = **i · (−j)**. By the modified associative law, **i · (−j)** = **i · (−1)j** = **(−1)(i · j)** = **−(i · j)**. Combining these two results **i · j** = **−(i · j)**, which says that the number **i · j** should equal its negative. There is only one real number which is equal to its negative, the number zero. So we have no choice, we must define **i · j** = 0.

We still must find—or define—**i · i**. Actually, we are free to define it as any number and still keep all the properties that we wanted. To keep things simple, we define **i · i** = 1, then

$$\mathbf{a} \cdot \mathbf{b} = (\alpha\beta)(\mathbf{i} \cdot \mathbf{i}) + (\alpha\gamma)(\mathbf{i} \cdot \mathbf{j}) = \alpha\beta.$$

Since α is the length of **a** and β is the length of **b** times the cosine of the directed angle between **a** and **b**,

$$\mathbf{a} \cdot \mathbf{b} = |\mathbf{a}|\,|\mathbf{b}|\cos\varphi.$$

If **a** and **b** have the same sense, φ is zero and $\cos\varphi = 1$, so **a · b** = |**a**| |**b**|. If **a** = **b**, then **a · a** = |**a**| |**a**| = |**a**|². We can denote **a · a** by **a²**, then $\mathbf{a}^2 = |\mathbf{a}|^2$.

Since $\cos\varphi = \cos(-\varphi)$, the dot product does not change if we interchange the factors, so **a · b** = **b · a**; we say that dot multiplication is *commutative*.

The perpendicularity of **a** to **b** can now be expressed by **a · b** = 0; the commutativity of dot multiplication then implies that perpendicularity means mutual perpendicularity.

The dot product can be applied to many geometrical problems. We shall look at two problems: the cosine law, and a condition for a line to be perpendicular to a plane.

For the cosine law, we look at a triangle *PQR* and let $R - P = \mathbf{a}$, $Q - P = \mathbf{b}$, $R - Q = \mathbf{c}$ (Figure 1.6*b*). Then **a** = **b** + **c** or **a** − **b** = **c**. Let us dot multiply both sides of this last equation by itself:

$$(\mathbf{a} - \mathbf{b}) \cdot (\mathbf{a} - \mathbf{b}) = \mathbf{c} \cdot \mathbf{c}.$$

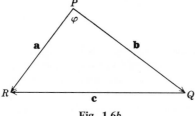

Fig. 1.6*b*

Using the distributive and commutative laws, this may be written as

$$\mathbf{a} \cdot \mathbf{a} + \mathbf{b} \cdot \mathbf{b} - 2\mathbf{a} \cdot \mathbf{b} = \mathbf{c} \cdot \mathbf{c}.$$

Finally, using the notation introduced above,

$$|\mathbf{a}|^2 + |\mathbf{b}|^2 - 2\mathbf{a} \cdot \mathbf{b} = |\mathbf{c}|^2,$$

and

$$|\mathbf{a}|^2 + |\mathbf{b}|^2 - 2\,|\mathbf{a}|\,|\mathbf{b}|\cos\varphi = |\mathbf{c}|^2,$$

or, in other words, the square of the length of a side of a triangle is equal to the sum of the squares of the lengths of the other two sides minus twice the product of their lengths times the cosine of the angle between them. The angle φ may be acute or obtuse (if it is obtuse, the cosine is negative) or it may be a right angle (in which case this reduces to the Pythagorean theorem).

For our second example, we take the following proposition. *A line perpendicular to each of two distinct intersecting lines is perpendicular to every line in their plane.* The lines pass through the same point. In terms of vectors, what we must show is that, if $\mathbf{a} \cdot \mathbf{c} = 0$ and $\mathbf{b} \cdot \mathbf{c} = 0$, then $\mathbf{x} \cdot \mathbf{c} = 0$ where $\mathbf{x}$ is any vector in the plane determined by $\mathbf{a}$ and $\mathbf{b}$, or in other words, $\mathbf{x} = \alpha\mathbf{a} + \beta\mathbf{b}$ (Figure 1.6c). Using the distributive and modified associative law, $\mathbf{x} \cdot \mathbf{c} = (\alpha\mathbf{a} + \beta\mathbf{b}) \cdot \mathbf{c} = \alpha(\mathbf{a} \cdot \mathbf{c}) + \beta(\mathbf{b} \cdot \mathbf{c})$. Since $\alpha(\mathbf{a} \cdot \mathbf{c}) + \beta(\mathbf{b} \cdot \mathbf{c}) = 0$ follows from $\mathbf{a} \cdot \mathbf{c} = 0$ and $\mathbf{b} \cdot \mathbf{c} = 0$, $\mathbf{x} \cdot \mathbf{c} = 0$ and the line determined by $\mathbf{c}$ is perpendicular to any line in the plane of $\mathbf{a}$ and $\mathbf{b}$.

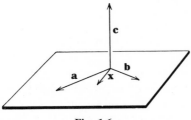

Fig. 1.6*c*

Exercises

1. Verify that dot product defined by $\mathbf{a} \cdot \mathbf{b} = |\mathbf{a}|\,|\mathbf{b}| \cos \varphi$ (where φ is the angle from $\mathbf{a}$ to $\mathbf{b}$) does satisfy the distributive and modified associative laws.
2. Show that $|\mathbf{a}| = (\mathbf{a}^2)^{\frac{1}{2}}$. What change would have to be made if we had defined $\mathbf{i} \cdot \mathbf{i} = \delta$ where $\delta > 0$ and $\delta \neq 1$? Could we have defined $\mathbf{i} \cdot \mathbf{i} = 0$? Using $|\mathbf{a}| = (\mathbf{a}^2)^{\frac{1}{2}}$, prove that $|\mathbf{a}| = 0$ if, and only if, $\mathbf{a} = \mathbf{0}$.
3. Prove that if $\mathbf{x} \cdot \mathbf{a} = 0$ for all $\mathbf{x}$, then $\mathbf{a} = \mathbf{0}$.
4. Prove that the diagonals of a rhombus are perpendicular to each other.
5. Prove that the three altitudes of a triangle intersect at a common point.
6. Prove that an angle inscribed in a semicircle is a right angle.
7. Find some other elementary geometry theorems which can be proved using dot product. Prove them.

1.7   EQUIVALENT TRIPLES OF VECTORS

If $\mathbf{a},\mathbf{b},\mathbf{c}$ are three linearly independent vectors, we saw in Section 1.4 that any vector in three-space can be written as a linear combination of $\mathbf{a},\mathbf{b},\mathbf{c}$. Consider three other vectors $\mathbf{a}',\mathbf{b}',\mathbf{c}'$; there exist real numbers $\alpha,\beta,\gamma,\lambda,\mu,\nu,\rho,\sigma,\tau$, such that

$$\mathbf{a}' = \alpha\mathbf{a} + \beta\mathbf{b} + \gamma\mathbf{c},$$

$$\mathbf{b}' = \lambda\mathbf{a} + \mu\mathbf{b} + \nu\mathbf{c},$$

$$\mathbf{c}' = \rho\mathbf{a} + \sigma\mathbf{b} + \tau\mathbf{c}.$$

If $\mathbf{a}',\mathbf{b}',\mathbf{c}'$ are linearly independent, it must also be possible to express $\mathbf{a},\mathbf{b},\mathbf{c}$ as linear combinations of $\mathbf{a}',\mathbf{b}',\mathbf{c}'$; this means that the above system of equations can be solved considering $\mathbf{a},\mathbf{b},\mathbf{c}$ as the unknowns. We know how to solve a system of three first-degree equations with three unknowns in numbers; although we are talking about vectors here, the steps are the same and, fortunately, the rules of algebra which we use hold for vectors. From algebra, we know that a necessary and sufficient condition for the existence of a solution (in our language, for the linear independence of the vectors $\mathbf{a}',\mathbf{b}',\mathbf{c}'$) is that

$$\Delta = \begin{vmatrix} \alpha & \beta & \gamma \\ \lambda & \mu & \nu \\ \rho & \sigma & \tau \end{vmatrix} \neq 0.$$

There are two different ways in which a determinant may be different from zero: it may be positive or negative. This permits us to divide triples of linearly independent vectors into two classes (relative to three given linearly independent vectors). If Δ is positive, we say $\mathbf{a}',\mathbf{b}',\mathbf{c}'$ are right-handed with respect to $\mathbf{a},\mathbf{b},\mathbf{c}$; if Δ is negative, $\mathbf{a}',\mathbf{b}',\mathbf{c}'$ are left-handed. Of course, the sign of the determinant depends on our initial choice of the three fixed vectors and the order in which we consider the triples; thus, we can arbitrarily call one ordered triple right-handed, then classify all other triples relative to it. We shall say that *two ordered triples of linearly independent vectors are equivalent if the determinant of one with respect to the other is positive.* We shall put together into one class all the triples that are equivalent to each other.

What we have here is a special case of something that occurs often in mathematics. Other examples of equivalence are congruent figures, equality of vectors, and equivalent equations (equations with the same roots). In all these cases, the following three properties hold.

1. An object is equivalent to itself,
2. If one object is equivalent to a second, then the second is equivalent to the first,
3. If two objects are equivalent to a third, they are equivalent to each other.

It is not hard to verify that our definition of equivalent vector triples does satisfy these statements.

Exercises

1. Verify properties 1, 2, and 3 above for equivalent vector triples, congruent figures, equal vectors, and equivalent equations.
2. Property 3 is frequently stated as follows. (3′) If one object is equivalent to a second and the second is equivalent to a third, then the first object is equivalent to the third. Using 2, prove that 3 implies 3′ and that 3′ implies 3.
3. Show that replacing one vector of a triple by its negative changes the class of a triple.
4. Show that a cyclic permutation of the vectors of a triple does not change its class. In other words, if $\mathbf{a},\mathbf{b},\mathbf{c}$ are right-handed (or left-handed), then so are $\mathbf{b},\mathbf{c},\mathbf{a}$ and $\mathbf{c},\mathbf{a},\mathbf{b}$.
5. Consider all vectors having a common initial point (tail). Let $\mathbf{a}$ and $\mathbf{b}$ be two fixed vectors in this collection. Show that all vectors $\mathbf{x}$ which are independent of $\mathbf{a}$ and $\mathbf{b}$ (that is, $\mathbf{x},\mathbf{a},\mathbf{b}$ is a linearly independent set) may be divided into two classes so that $\mathbf{c}$ and $\mathbf{d}$ belong to the same class if there is no point of the $\mathbf{a},\mathbf{b}$ plane between the tips of $\mathbf{c}$ and $\mathbf{d}$.
6. Find some other examples of equivalence other than those mentioned in this section.

1.8   CROSS PRODUCT

We shall now examine the second case of multiplication of a vector by a vector. In this case, the product is a vector; we shall call it the *cross product* and denote it by $\mathbf{a} \times \mathbf{b}$.

We shall try to find a definition of cross product using an approach similar to the one that we used for dot product. Again, $\mathbf{a}$ and $\mathbf{b}$ can be written as $\alpha\mathbf{i}$ and $\beta\mathbf{i} + \gamma\mathbf{j}$ where $\alpha > 0$, $\gamma \geq 0$, and $\mathbf{i}$ and $\mathbf{j}$ are two mutually perpendicular unit vectors in the plane of $\mathbf{a}$ and $\mathbf{b}$. We want the distributive law and modified associative law to hold for cross product also; because of this,

$$\mathbf{a} \times \mathbf{b} = (\alpha\mathbf{i}) \times (\beta\mathbf{i} + \gamma\mathbf{j}) = (\alpha\mathbf{i}) \times (\beta\mathbf{i}) + (\alpha\mathbf{i}) \times (\gamma\mathbf{j})$$
$$= (\alpha\beta)(\mathbf{i} \times \mathbf{i}) + (\alpha\gamma)(\mathbf{i} \times \mathbf{j}).$$

Again all we need to do is to define $\mathbf{i} \times \mathbf{i}$ and $\mathbf{i} \times \mathbf{j}$ and make our definitions invariant under change of position.

Begin with $\mathbf{i} \times \mathbf{i}$. If we rotate around the line containing $\mathbf{i}$, the vector $\mathbf{i}$ is not changed; that is, both factors of the product $\mathbf{i} \times \mathbf{i}$ are not changed; therefore, by the principle of invariance, the product $\mathbf{i} \times \mathbf{i}$ must not be changed; the vector $\mathbf{i} \times \mathbf{i}$ is then a vector that is not affected by rotation around the line containing $\mathbf{i}$; but any vector that makes an angle with a line is affected by a rotation around the line; so the vector $\mathbf{i} \times \mathbf{i}$ must be parallel to that line or be the zero vector. We must decide between these two possibilities. We rotate through 180° around an axis perpendicular to $\mathbf{i}$. This rotation brings each factor $\mathbf{i}$ and $\mathbf{i}$ into its opposites $-\mathbf{i} = (-1)\mathbf{i}$; in other words, each factor is multiplied by -1. From the modified associative law, the product $\mathbf{i} \times \mathbf{i}$ is multiplied by -1 *twice*, and this means that it is not affected. The principle of invariance tells us that $\mathbf{i} \times \mathbf{i}$ must not be affected by a rotation of 180° around $\mathbf{i}$; but if $\mathbf{i} \times \mathbf{i}$ is in the direction of $\mathbf{i}$, and a rotation through 180° around $\mathbf{i}$ changes it into its opposite, the only possibility is for $\mathbf{i} \times \mathbf{i}$ to be the zero vector; thus, $\mathbf{i} \times \mathbf{i} = \mathbf{0}$.

We now look at $\mathbf{i} \times \mathbf{j}$. Again we rotate around the line containing $\mathbf{i}$, this time through 180°; this rotation does not affect the first factor but it replaces the second factor $\mathbf{j}$ by $-\mathbf{j} = (-1)\mathbf{j}$. By the modified associative law, it must multiply the product by -1; so a rotation around the line containing $\mathbf{i}$ through 180° replaces $\mathbf{i} \times \mathbf{j}$ by its opposite. This can only mean that $\mathbf{i} \times \mathbf{j}$ is perpendicular to the axis of the rotation, that is, to the line of $\mathbf{i}$ and so to $\mathbf{i}$. Similarly, we may conclude that it must be perpendicular to $\mathbf{j}$. So we know the direction of $\mathbf{i} \times \mathbf{j}$—it is the common perpendicular to $\mathbf{i}$ and $\mathbf{j}$.

There are two unit vectors that are perpendicular to both $\mathbf{i}$ and $\mathbf{j}$; they have the same direction but *differ in sense*. If we choose one of them,

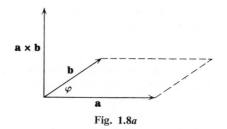

Fig. 1.8a

the triple formed by it and the vectors **i** and **j** will be right-handed and, for the other choice, the triple will be left-handed (see Exercise 3 of Section 1.7). Mathematically, there is no difference between these two cases, but in order to make our statements definite, we must choose one of the possibilities. We shall assume that it has been decided which triples are right-handed and we shall choose **k** so that the triple **i**,**j**,**k** is right-handed. From Exercise 4 of Section 1.7, we know that **j**,**k**,**i** and **k**,**i**,**j** will also be right-handed.

Then we may write $\mathbf{i} \times \mathbf{j} = \xi\mathbf{k}$. ξ is arbitrary considering the conditions that we have imposed on the cross product, but things will be simplest with respect to the chosen unit of length if we let $\xi = 1$, then $\mathbf{i} \times \mathbf{j} = \mathbf{k}$ and $\mathbf{a} \times \mathbf{b} = \alpha\gamma\mathbf{k}$. Since α is the length of **a** and γ is the length of **b** multiplied by the sine of φ (the angle from **a** to **b**), we have our definition of cross product

$$\mathbf{a} \times \mathbf{b} = |\mathbf{a}|\,|\mathbf{b}|\sin\varphi\,\mathbf{k}.$$

There is a geometrical interpretation of the cross product (Figure 1.8a). The length of $\mathbf{a} \times \mathbf{b}$ is the absolute value of $|\mathbf{a}|\,|\mathbf{b}|\sin\varphi$, that is, the area of the parallelogram whose two adjacent sides coincide with **a** and **b**. The direction of $\mathbf{a} \times \mathbf{b}$ is perpendicular to both **a** and **b**; the sense is determined in a somewhat complicated way by the fact that **k** forms a right-handed system with **i** and **j**, and **i** and **j** are related to **a** and **b** by the formulas $\mathbf{a} = \alpha\mathbf{i}$, $\mathbf{b} = \beta\mathbf{i} + \gamma\mathbf{j}$ with $\alpha > 0$ and $\gamma \geq 0$.

Notice that the cross product is *not* commutative because $\sin\varphi \neq \sin(-\varphi)$; however, $-\sin\varphi = \sin(-\varphi)$ so we can conclude that the vector product is anticommutative (or skew), $\mathbf{a} \times \mathbf{b} = -\mathbf{b} \times \mathbf{a}$.

Exercises

1. Why is it impossible in two-space to define a cross product that is distributive and obeys the modified associative law?

2. Show that if vectors **a** and **b** are linearly independent, then the ordered triple **a**, **b**, $\mathbf{a} \times \mathbf{b}$ is right-handed (relative to the ordered triple **i**,**j**,**k**).

3. Prove that the area of the parallelogram with sides **a** and **b** is $|\mathbf{a} \times \mathbf{b}|$. In our definition of cross product if we had chosen $\xi > 0$ but $\xi \neq 1$, what modification would be necessary in this statement?

4. Prove the modified associative law for cross product. (You may also try to prove the distributive law, but you will find a proof from our definition quite difficult. It may be better to try it after the next section.)

5. Prove the sine law for triangles using the cross product.

6. Show that adding a multiple of a vector **b** to a vector **a** does not change $\mathbf{a} \times \mathbf{b}$; that is, $\mathbf{a} \times \mathbf{b} = (\mathbf{a} + \rho\mathbf{b}) \times \mathbf{b}$ for all real numbers ρ. What is the geometrical significance of this statement?

7. Prove that $(\mathbf{a} \times \mathbf{b})^2 + (\mathbf{a} \cdot \mathbf{b})^2 = \mathbf{a}^2\mathbf{b}^2$.

1.9   TRIPLE PRODUCTS

In arithmetic, we have the associative law; it expresses a relationship (equality) between two products, each of which contains the same factors but combined in different ways. For example, $(5 \cdot 7) \cdot 3 = 5 \cdot (7 \cdot 3)$. We have a similar situation for vectors in the modified associative laws:

$$(\alpha\mathbf{a}) \cdot \mathbf{b} = \alpha(\mathbf{a} \cdot \mathbf{b}), \qquad (\alpha\beta)\mathbf{a} = \alpha(\beta\mathbf{a}), \qquad \text{and} \qquad (\alpha\mathbf{a}) \times \mathbf{b} = \alpha(\mathbf{a} \times \mathbf{b}).$$

There are cases in which all the factors are vectors. The three types of ternary (or triple) products are:

$$(\mathbf{a} \times \mathbf{b}) \cdot \mathbf{c}, \qquad (\mathbf{a} \cdot \mathbf{b})\mathbf{c}, \qquad \text{and} \qquad (\mathbf{a} \times \mathbf{b}) \times \mathbf{c}.$$

Look first at the product of the type $(\mathbf{a} \times \mathbf{b}) \cdot \mathbf{c}$, the *triple scalar product*. We can find a geometrical meaning of this product. In forming the product, we first cross multiply two of the vectors and then form the dot product of the resulting vector and the third. The first multiplication gives $\mathbf{a} \times \mathbf{b}$ whose direction is the common perpendicular of **a** and **b**. Denoting a unit vector perpendicular to **a** and **b** by **k**, $\mathbf{a} \times \mathbf{b} = \sigma\mathbf{k}$ where the absolute value of σ is equal to the area of the parallelogram with adjacent sides **a** and **b**. This we dot multiply with **c**. The result is a number which is the product of the length of **c**, the length of $\mathbf{a} \times \mathbf{b}$ (which is σ), and the cosine of φ the angle between **k** and **c**. If the cosine is positive, the number may be considered as the product of the length of $\mathbf{a} \times \mathbf{b}$ and the projection of the vector **c** on the direction **k**. If we visualize the parallelopiped with adjacent edges **a**,**b**,**c** (Figure 1.9*a*), we see that this projection is the altitude of the parallelopiped with base determined by **a** and **b**. The product $(\mathbf{a} \times \mathbf{b}) \cdot \mathbf{c}$ gives, in this case, the volume of the parallelopiped.

We may also consider, instead of the parallelopiped, the tetrahedron (triangular pyramid) with base determined by **a** and **b** and with one edge **c**

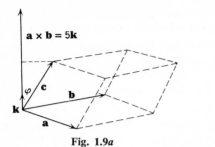

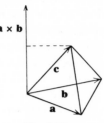

Fig. 1.9*a*   Fig. 1.9*b*

(Figure 1.9*b*). The product $(\mathbf{a} \times \mathbf{b}) \cdot \mathbf{c}$ represents six times the volume of this tetrahedron.

If $\cos \varphi$ is negative, that is if the vectors $\mathbf{a} \times \mathbf{b}$ and $\mathbf{c}$ form an obtuse angle, then the absolute value of $(\mathbf{a} \times \mathbf{b}) \cdot \mathbf{c}$ gives the volume in question.

If the vectors $\mathbf{a},\mathbf{b},\mathbf{c}$ are a right-handed triple, we shall show that $(\mathbf{a} \times \mathbf{b}) \cdot \mathbf{c}$ is positive. From Exercise 2 of Section 1.8, we know that $\mathbf{a},\mathbf{b},\mathbf{a} \times \mathbf{b}$ are right-handed if $\mathbf{a}$ and $\mathbf{b}$ are linearly independent, which of course they are in this case. Furthermore, $\mathbf{a}$, $\mathbf{b}$, and $\mathbf{a} \times \mathbf{b}$ linearly independent means that $\mathbf{c}$ can be expressed as a linear combination $\mathbf{c} = \alpha\mathbf{a} + \beta\mathbf{b} + \gamma(\mathbf{a} \times \mathbf{b})$. Since $\mathbf{a},\mathbf{b},\mathbf{a} \times \mathbf{b}$ are right-handed, if $\mathbf{a},\mathbf{b},\mathbf{c}$ are right-handed the determinant

$$\begin{vmatrix} 1 & 0 & 0 \\ 0 & 1 & 0 \\ \alpha & \beta & \gamma \end{vmatrix} = \gamma$$

must be greater than zero. On the other hand, if we dot multiply $\mathbf{c}$ by $\mathbf{a} \times \mathbf{b}$, we get

$$\begin{aligned} (\mathbf{a} \times \mathbf{b}) \cdot \mathbf{c} &= (\mathbf{a} \times \mathbf{b}) \cdot [\alpha\mathbf{a} + \beta\mathbf{b} + \gamma(\mathbf{a} \times \mathbf{b})] \\ &= \alpha(\mathbf{a} \times \mathbf{b}) \cdot \mathbf{a} + \beta(\mathbf{a} \times \mathbf{b}) \cdot \mathbf{b} + \gamma(\mathbf{a} \times \mathbf{b})^2 \\ &= \gamma(\mathbf{a} \times \mathbf{b})^2 \end{aligned}$$

because $\mathbf{a} \times \mathbf{b}$ is perpendicular to both $\mathbf{a}$ and $\mathbf{b}$. This shows us that the sign of $(\mathbf{a} \times \mathbf{b}) \cdot \mathbf{c}$ is the same as that of γ, so that the right-handedness of $\mathbf{a},\mathbf{b},\mathbf{c}$ does imply that $(\mathbf{a} \times \mathbf{b}) \cdot \mathbf{c}$ is positive.

Since cyclic interchange does not affect equivalence of vector triples (Exercise 4 of Section 1.7), the products

$$(\mathbf{a} \times \mathbf{b}) \cdot \mathbf{c}, \qquad (\mathbf{b} \times \mathbf{c}) \cdot \mathbf{a}, \qquad \text{and} \qquad (\mathbf{c} \times \mathbf{a}) \cdot \mathbf{b}$$

all have the same sign; when we consider their absolute value, each one represents six times the volume of the same tetrahedron—so they are all equal. Besides this, $(\mathbf{b} \times \mathbf{c}) \cdot \mathbf{a} = \mathbf{a} \cdot (\mathbf{b} \times \mathbf{c})$ because of the commutativity of dot product, so $(\mathbf{a} \times \mathbf{b}) \cdot \mathbf{c} = \mathbf{a} \cdot (\mathbf{b} \times \mathbf{c})$. This means that the triple scalar product is not changed when we interchange the symbols $\cdot$ and $\times$. We shall therefore omit these symbols and just write $(\mathbf{abc})$ when no confusion is likely to occur.

We now come to the two other triple products with values that are vectors: $(\mathbf{a} \cdot \mathbf{b})\mathbf{c}$ and $(\mathbf{a} \times \mathbf{b}) \times \mathbf{c}$. We call this latter form the *triple vector product* (the first form has no special name). We may expect that there is some relationship between these two types of products, and there is, but its form is somewhat unexpected:

$$(\mathbf{a} \times \mathbf{b}) \times \mathbf{c} = (\mathbf{a} \cdot \mathbf{c})\mathbf{b} - (\mathbf{b} \cdot \mathbf{c})\mathbf{a}.$$

To prove this, we use $\mathbf{a} = \alpha\mathbf{i}$ and $\mathbf{b} = \beta\mathbf{i} + \gamma\mathbf{j}$ as before. Then simple computations show that $(\mathbf{a} \times \mathbf{b}) \times \mathbf{c} = \alpha\gamma[(\mathbf{i} \times \mathbf{j}) \times \mathbf{c}]$ and

$$(\mathbf{a} \cdot \mathbf{c})\mathbf{b} - (\mathbf{b} \cdot \mathbf{c})\mathbf{a} = \alpha\gamma[(\mathbf{i} \cdot \mathbf{c})\mathbf{j} - (\mathbf{j} \cdot \mathbf{c})\mathbf{i}].$$

(Can you do the computations?)

It remains to show that the two expressions in square brackets are equal for all values of $\mathbf{c}$. Substituting consecutively for $\mathbf{c}$ the values $\mathbf{i},\mathbf{j},\mathbf{k}$, we obtain respectively

$$(\mathbf{i} \times \mathbf{j}) \times \mathbf{i} = \mathbf{k} \times \mathbf{i} = \mathbf{j} \qquad\qquad (\mathbf{i} \cdot \mathbf{i})\mathbf{j} - (\mathbf{j} \cdot \mathbf{i})\mathbf{i} = \mathbf{j}$$

$$(\mathbf{i} \times \mathbf{j}) \times \mathbf{j} = \mathbf{k} \times \mathbf{j} = -\mathbf{i} \quad\text{and}\quad (\mathbf{i} \cdot \mathbf{j})\mathbf{j} - (\mathbf{j} \cdot \mathbf{j})\mathbf{i} = -\mathbf{i}$$

$$(\mathbf{i} \times \mathbf{j}) \times \mathbf{k} = \mathbf{k} \times \mathbf{k} = 0 \qquad\qquad (\mathbf{i} \cdot \mathbf{k})\mathbf{j} - (\mathbf{j} \cdot \mathbf{k})\mathbf{i} = 0.$$

The relation is proved, therefore, for these particular values of $\mathbf{c}$. Besides this, both dot and cross product have the distributive law and a modified associative law and any $\mathbf{c}$ can be written as a linear combination of $\mathbf{i},\mathbf{j},\mathbf{k}$; for instance, $\mathbf{c} = \rho\mathbf{i} + \sigma\mathbf{j} + \tau\mathbf{k}$. Using these facts, we can easily calculate the product for any $\mathbf{c}$ so the two expressions in square brackets are equal.

Exercises

1. Why did we not consider triple products of the form $\mathbf{a} \times (\mathbf{b} \cdot \mathbf{c})$ or $\mathbf{a} \cdot (\mathbf{b} \cdot \mathbf{c})$?
2. Let $\mathbf{c} = \rho\mathbf{i} + \sigma\mathbf{j} + \tau\mathbf{k}$ and verify that $(\mathbf{i} \times \mathbf{j}) \times \mathbf{c} = (\mathbf{i} \cdot \mathbf{c})\mathbf{j} - (\mathbf{j} \cdot \mathbf{c})\mathbf{i}$. What does this prove?
3. Prove that the distributive law holds for cross product over addition.
4. Consider the operations of $+$ and $\times$ on vectors. Which properties of addition and multiplication of real numbers do these vector operations have?

5. Prove that $\mathbf{a} \times (\mathbf{b} \times \mathbf{c}) = (\mathbf{a} \cdot \mathbf{c})\mathbf{b} - (\mathbf{a} \cdot \mathbf{b})\mathbf{c}$.

6. Show that $\mathbf{a} \times (\mathbf{b} \times \mathbf{c}) \neq (\mathbf{a} \times \mathbf{b}) \times \mathbf{c}$.

7. Show that $\mathbf{a} \times (\mathbf{b} \times \mathbf{c}) + \mathbf{b} \times (\mathbf{c} \times \mathbf{a}) + \mathbf{c} \times (\mathbf{a} \times \mathbf{b}) = \mathbf{0}$.

8. Prove that

$$\begin{vmatrix} \mathbf{a} \cdot \mathbf{a} & \mathbf{a} \cdot \mathbf{b} \\ \mathbf{a} \cdot \mathbf{b} & \mathbf{b} \cdot \mathbf{b} \end{vmatrix} = |\mathbf{a} \times \mathbf{b}|^2.$$

9. Show that $\mathbf{a}(\mathbf{bcd}) - \mathbf{b}(\mathbf{cda}) + \mathbf{c}(\mathbf{dab}) - \mathbf{d}(\mathbf{abc}) = \mathbf{0}$. If $\mathbf{a},\mathbf{b},\mathbf{c}$ are linearly independent, how can this form be used to find the coefficients necessary to express any fourth vector $\mathbf{d}$ in terms of $\mathbf{a},\mathbf{b},\mathbf{c}$?

10. Show that the existence of a vector product implies that the number of dimensions we are dealing with is three.

2 Axiomatic Vector Geometry

In the first chapter, we saw how Euclidean geometry can be expressed in terms of vectors and points. The discussion relied heavily on our intuition and previous knowledge of Euclidean geometry. Now we want to forbid any direct use of intuition and even restrict to a minimum the number of propositions that we shall assume. We want to build vector geometry again. This time, everything must be expressed in terms of vectors and points and based on a few propositions that we shall decide to accept: the *axioms*. We do not even have to know what points and vectors are; they are simply two sets of objects that have the properties described in the axioms and any other properties which we can find by correctly applying logic to the axioms.

This approach to geometry is called *formal* because we do not worry about what the objects are; we just study how certain sets with certain properties behave. The question of whether a proposition is *true* cannot be asked in a formal treatment because we do not attach our objects to anything in real life. We do not have to know what "true" means to develop the theory. We *can* ask whether certain propositions are *valid*; that is, whether we can derive them from the axioms by using logic.

We must admit that, although we act as if our objects are unrelated to any real situation, in the back of our minds we have some ideas. The ideas may be vague, but somehow they do relate this formal world to the real world. There is satisfaction in deriving results on purely logical grounds—but it is the ideas in the back of our heads that cause our interest in the formal system.

We must make another admission before we set up our axioms. In the first chapter, we talked about Euclidean geometry in terms of vectors and points, but we also used the real numbers. In our axiomatic treatment, we shall do the same. We shall assume that we know about the real numbers from algebra and analysis. Things would be nicer (more geometrical) if we could avoid this and introduce numbers from the geometric axioms; we shall discuss this possibility in Chapter 9.

2.1 AXIOMS FOR VECTOR GEOMETRY

We begin with three sets of objects: a set of points, a set of vectors, and the real numbers. We shall accept the following groups of axioms.

Group 1. Vector Addition

(a) To every two vectors **a** and **b** there corresponds a unique vector **u** called their sum. We write $\mathbf{a} + \mathbf{b} = \mathbf{u}$.

(b) Vector addition is commutative and associative; that is, for all vectors **a,b,c**, $\mathbf{a} + \mathbf{b} = \mathbf{b} + \mathbf{a}$ and $(\mathbf{a} + \mathbf{b}) + \mathbf{c} = \mathbf{a} + (\mathbf{b} + \mathbf{c})$.

(c) Vector subtraction is always possible; that is, to every two vectors **a** and **b**, there corresponds a unique vector **x** called their difference. We write $\mathbf{a} - \mathbf{b} = \mathbf{x}$, or equivalently $\mathbf{a} = \mathbf{b} + \mathbf{x}$.

(d) $\mathbf{a} - \mathbf{a}$ is independent of **a** and is denoted by $\mathbf{0} = \mathbf{a} - \mathbf{a}$.

Group 2. Multiplication of Vectors by Numbers

(a) The real numbers have all their usual properties (a complete ordered field).

(b) To every real number α and every vector **a** there corresponds a unique product which is a vector **x**. We write $\alpha\mathbf{a} = \mathbf{x} = \mathbf{a}\alpha$.

(c) For all vectors **a**, $1\mathbf{a} = \mathbf{a}$.

(d) The modified associative law holds; that is, for all real numbers α, β and all vectors **a**, $\alpha(\beta\mathbf{a}) = (\alpha\beta)\mathbf{a}$.

(e) Two distributive laws hold: $\alpha(\mathbf{a} + \mathbf{b}) = \alpha\mathbf{a} + \alpha\mathbf{b}$ and $(\alpha + \beta)\mathbf{a} = \alpha\mathbf{a} + \beta\mathbf{a}$ for all real numbers α, β and all vectors **a,b**.

(f) For all vectors **a**, $(-1)\mathbf{a} = -\mathbf{a}$ and $\mathbf{a} + (-\mathbf{a}) = \mathbf{0}$.

Definition. *A set of vectors* $\mathbf{a}_1, \mathbf{a}_2, \ldots, \mathbf{a}_n$ *is linearly dependent if there exists numbers* $\alpha_1, \alpha_2, \ldots, \alpha_n$ *not all zero such that* $\alpha_1\mathbf{a}_1 + \alpha_2\mathbf{a}_2 + \cdots + \alpha_n\mathbf{a}_n = \mathbf{0}$. *A set of vectors is linearly independent if this is not true.*

Group 3. Number of Dimensions

For a fixed positive integer n:

(a) Any $n + 1$ vectors are linearly dependent.

(b) There exists a set of n linearly independent vectors.

For different values of n, we shall get different axiom systems. The number n is called the *number of dimensions*. For ordinary Euclidean space, n is 3.

Group 4.   Dot Product

(a) To every two vectors **a** and **b** there corresponds a unique number α called their dot product. We write $\mathbf{a} \cdot \mathbf{b} = \alpha$.

(b) Dot multiplication is commutative; that is, for all vectors **a**,**b**, $\mathbf{a} \cdot \mathbf{b} = \mathbf{b} \cdot \mathbf{a}$.

(c) The modified associative law holds for dot multiplication; that is, for all real numbers α and all vectors **a**,**b**, $\alpha(\mathbf{a} \cdot \mathbf{b}) = (\alpha\mathbf{a}) \cdot \mathbf{b}$.

(d) The distributive law holds for dot product; that is, for all vectors **a**,**b**,**c**, $\mathbf{a} \cdot (\mathbf{b} + \mathbf{c}) = \mathbf{a} \cdot \mathbf{b} + \mathbf{a} \cdot \mathbf{c}$.

(e) For all vectors **a**, if $\mathbf{a} \neq \mathbf{0}$, then $\mathbf{a} \cdot \mathbf{a} > 0$.

What we have now is a Euclidean vector space. If we want *geometry* we must introduce points into the axioms; this we do in the remaining group.

Group 5.   Points and Vectors

(a) To any two points A and B there corresponds a unique vector **u**; we write $A - B = \mathbf{u}$, or equivalently $A = B + \mathbf{u}$ or $A - \mathbf{u} = B$.

(b) To any point B and any vector **u** corresponds a unique point A such that $B + \mathbf{u} = A$.

(c) To any point A and any vector **u** corresponds a unique point B such that $A - \mathbf{u} = B$.

(d) For any three points X,Y,Z, $(X - Y) + (Y - Z) + (Z - X) = \mathbf{0}$.

You may have noticed that cross-multiplication does not appear in our axioms. The reason for not including it is that a cross product is peculiar to three-space; there is no analog to it in either two or higher dimensions (see Exercise 10 of Section 1.9). If we include cross product, we are forcing n to be three and depriving the axiom system of the flexibility it now has with respect to dimension.

Exercises

1. Using the axioms of Group 1, show that for all vectors **b**, $\mathbf{b} + \mathbf{0} = \mathbf{b} = \mathbf{0} + \mathbf{b}$.

2. Use the axioms of Groups 1 and 2 to show that for all vectors **a**,**b** and all numbers α:

(a) $\mathbf{a} - \mathbf{b} = \mathbf{a} + (-\mathbf{b})$

(b) $-\mathbf{0} = \mathbf{0}$

(c) If $\alpha\mathbf{a} = \mathbf{0}$, then either $\alpha = 0$ or $\mathbf{a} = \mathbf{0}$ (or both).

3. Show that Axiom 2c can be proved from the other axioms of Groups 1 and 2. Show that $(-1)\mathbf{a} = -\mathbf{a}$ can be proved from the other axioms. (This tells us

that we could drop *one* of these statements from the axioms because it would still be in the system as a theorem.)
4. Can we conclude from the axioms that dot product is associative? Why, or why not?
5. What is the geometrical significance of axiom 5*d*?

2.2 IMMEDIATE CONSEQUENCES OF THE AXIOMS

The set of axioms given above completely describes a Euclidean geometry of any dimension. To prove this rigorously would be a huge task. We shall set a more modest goal. We shall let $n = 3$ in Group 3 and then introduce lines and planes, prove Euclid's parallel postulate, define distance and measure of angle, and finally set up solid analytic geometry. All the propositions of Euclid can be proved analytically, so this should convince us that our axioms do give Euclidean geometry.

Before we introduce lines and planes, let us consider some properties that follow immediately from our axioms. From 5*a*, we know that every pair of points A,B is associated with a unique vector $\mathbf{u} = A - B$. If the axioms have been set up correctly, a vector with its tip and tail coinciding will be the zero vector; in other words, if A is any point, $A - A = \mathbf{0}$. We also expect that, if we interchange the tip and tail of a vector, the result is a vector which is the negative of the original, or $A - B = -(B - A)$. We shall prove both of these statements.

Theorem 1. *For all points A, $A - A = 0$.*

Proof. From Axiom 5*d*, $(A - A) + (A - A) + (A - A) = \mathbf{0}$, or $3(A - A) = \mathbf{0}$. Exercise 2*c* of Section 2.1 then tells us that $(A - A) = \mathbf{0}$. | (We shall use a vertical bar to indicate the end of a proof.)

Perhaps you have noticed that Axioms 5*a*, 1*b*, 2*c*, and 2*e* are also necessary in the proof of Theorem 1. They have not been mentioned because we shall often indicate only the main steps in the proofs of this chapter. The details are left for you to complete.

Theorem 2. *For all points A,B, $A - B = -(B - A)$.*

Proof. From 5*d*, $(A - B) + (B - B) + (B - A) = \mathbf{0}$; Theorem 1, Axiom 1*b*, and Exercise 1 of Section 2.1 reduce this to

$$(A - B) + (B - A) = \mathbf{0};$$

Axiom 1*a* allows us to add $-(B - A)$ to both sides, then

$$[(A - B) + (B - A)] + [-(B - A)] = \mathbf{0} + [-(B - A)].$$

Finally, from Axiom 2*f*, Axiom 1*b*, and Exercise 1 of Section 2.1, $A - B = -(B - A)$. |

We can think of a parallelogram as a quadrilateral with two adjacent vertices representing the same vector as the opposite two adjacent vertices. We then expect the other two pairs of similarly situated vertices to represent a second vector. If we translate this into the language of our axioms we get Theorem 3.

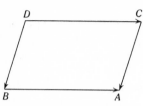

Fig. 2.2a

Theorem 3. *If A,B,C,D are any four points and A − B = C − D, then A − C = B − D (Figure 2.2a).*

Proof. From Axiom 5*d*, we can write $(A - B) + (B - D) + (D - A) = 0$ and $(D - C) + (C - A) + (A - D) = 0$. Adding these two equations and using the associative and commutative properties of vector addition, we get

$$[(A - B) + (D - C)] + [(B - D) + (C - A)] + [(D - A) + (A - D)] = 0.$$

From the hypothesis, Theorem 2, and Axiom 2*f*, the first and last terms reduce to the zero vector, so $(B - D) + (C - A) = 0$. You should be able to complete the steps to show that $A - C = B - D$ now follows. |

Exercises

1. Prove that for any point X and any two vectors **a**,**b**,

$$(X + \mathbf{a}) + \mathbf{b} = (X + \mathbf{b}) + \mathbf{a}.$$

2. In the first chapter, vectors had the property of "free mobility"; they were unchanged by translations. How does our axiom system guarantee that we have this property?

3. If n is a positive integer and $n \neq 3$, do Theorems 1 to 3 still hold? Why, or why not?

4. Is Theorem 3 valid if A,B,C,D are all on the same line? Why?

2.3   LINES AND PLANES

Lines and planes do not appear in the axioms; but because they are a part of Euclidean geometry, we want to define them. In Chapter 1, we found this quite easy in terms of vectors and points. A line was the set of all points $X = A + \lambda\mathbf{u}$ where A was a fixed point, $\mathbf{u}$ a fixed vector, and λ a variable real number. A plane was defined similarly by all points $X = A + \lambda\mathbf{u} + \mu\mathbf{v}$. We must now define lines and planes in such a way that it is possible to arrive at these equations from the axioms.

One approach would be to say that a line is characterized by the fact that it satisfies all of our axioms except that n in Group 3 must be 1; a plane satisfies all of our axioms except that n must be 2. This would give us an abstract line and plane. What we really want is to consider lines and planes as a part of three-space. We want to modify these abstract characterizations and derive the equations of Chapter 1.

Definition. *A line is a maximal set of points of three-space such that, if A,B,C,D are any four points of the set, then $A - B$ and $C - D$ are a linearly dependent set of vectors.* (A set is *maximal* if there is no larger set containing it and also having the required property.)

To get the equation of a line, let A and B be two distinct fixed points of a set as described above and let X be an arbitrary point of it. $X - A$ and $B - A$ are linearly dependent from the definition. Using the definition of linearly dependent vectors, we can arrive at $X - A = \lambda(B - A)$ for some real number λ. If we denote $B - A$ by $\mathbf{u}$, then any point of the line may be written as $X = A + \lambda\mathbf{u}$, where A is any fixed point of the line, $\mathbf{u}$ is a fixed vector of the line (that is, the difference of two distinct points of the line), and λ a variable real number; to each value of λ corresponds a different point of the line. The fixed vector $\mathbf{u}$ need not be $B - A$, but the difference of *any* two points of the set; this is because the line is one dimensional and any vector $\mathbf{v}$ on the line can be written as $\mathbf{v} = \sigma\mathbf{u}$, so that $X = A + \mu\mathbf{v} = A + (\mu\sigma)\mathbf{u} = A + \lambda\mathbf{u}$ if we let $\lambda = \mu\sigma$. (We can do this since, as μ runs through all real values, so does $\mu\sigma$.) The important idea to notice here is that the same line has many different representations.

Definition. *A plane is a maximal set of points of three-space which is not a line and such that if A,B,C,D,E,F are any six points of the set, then the vectors $A - B, C - D, E - F$ are a linearly dependent set of vectors.*

Any point of a plane can then be written in terms of three noncollinear points A,B,C as $X = A + \lambda(B - A) + \mu(C - A)$ or if we let $B - A = \mathbf{u}$ and $C - A = \mathbf{v}$, then $X = A + \lambda\mathbf{u} + \mu\mathbf{v}$ (where A is a fixed point of the plane, $\mathbf{u}$ and $\mathbf{v}$ are fixed linearly independent vectors of the plane, and λ and μ are variable real numbers). Again $\mathbf{u}$ and $\mathbf{v}$ may be any two fixed linearly independent vectors of the plane so that the same plane has many different representations.

Exercises

1. Why is the word "maximal" necessary in the definitions of line and plane?

2. Prove that, if A and B are distinct points of a line and X is any point on the line, there is a real number λ such that $X - A = \lambda(B - A)$.

3. Carry out the details of the remark above that any point of a plane can be written as $X = A + \lambda(B - A) + \mu(C - A)$.

4. Prove that in the last problem any two linearly independent vectors of the plane can be used instead of $B - A$ and $C - A$.

5. If we had chosen $n = 2$, what modifications would be necessary in this section? If $n = 5$, are any changes necessary in the definition of line and plane? What other analogous definitions would be possible in five-space?

2.4 THE PARALLEL POSTULATE

There is one statement that is so characteristic of Euclidean geometry that it is sometimes called "Euclid's parallel postulate": *Through a point not on a line there is one and only one line parallel to the given line.*

Euclid proved the existence part ("there is one") of this statement from his first four axioms, but the uniqueness part ("and only one") must either be postulated directly or can be proved if some other statement just as strong is in the axiom system. (For example, *the sum of the measures of the angles of any triangle is equal to π radians.*) The question of whether or not a special axiom was necessary for the uniqueness part bothered mathematicians for centuries. Eventually, this led to the discovery of non-Euclidean geometry where uniqueness does not hold. We shall discuss this further in Chapter 6.

If our axiom system does give Euclidean geometry, we have to be able to prove Euclid's parallel postulate. Since a special axiom is required for uniqueness in the ordinary development, it will be interesting to see just what it is in our axiom system that makes such a proof possible.

To prove that Euclid's parallel postulate holds, we must know what parallel lines are in our system; they are defined as in the usual development.

Definition. *Two lines in a plane are parallel if they have no point in common.*

To know whether two lines are parallel, we must find a necessary and sufficient condition for two lines to intersect.

Theorem 4. *Two lines $A + \sigma\mathbf{u}$ and $B + \tau\mathbf{v}$ have a point in common, if and only if, there exist real numbers λ and μ such that $(A - B) + \lambda\mathbf{u} - \mu\mathbf{v} = \mathbf{0}$.*

Proof. From the definition of a line, if $A + \sigma\mathbf{u}$ and $B + \tau\mathbf{v}$ intersect in a point P, then there exist real numbers λ and μ such that $A + \lambda\mathbf{u} = P = B + \mu\mathbf{v}$, or $P - A = \lambda\mathbf{u}$ and $P - B = \mu\mathbf{v}$ by Axiom 5a. Using Axiom 5d, $(A - B) + (B - P) + (P - A) = \mathbf{0}$; then, from Theorem 2, and commutativity, $(A - B) + \lambda\mathbf{u} - \mu\mathbf{v} = \mathbf{0}$. Conversely, if there exist numbers λ and μ such that $(A - B) + \lambda\mathbf{u} - \mu\mathbf{v} = \mathbf{0}$, then $A + \lambda\mathbf{u} = B + \mu\mathbf{v}$ (why?) and the lines do have a point in common. |

Theorem 5. *Lines $A + \lambda\mathbf{u}$ and $B + \mu\mathbf{v}$ in the same plane with B not on $A + \lambda\mathbf{u}$ do not intersect, if and only if, $\mathbf{u}$ and $\mathbf{v}$ are linearly dependent.*

Proof. Since $A + \lambda\mathbf{u}$ and $B + \mu\mathbf{v}$ lie in the same plane, the vectors $A - B$, $\mathbf{u}$, and $\mathbf{v}$ are linearly dependent; that is, there exist α, β, γ not all zero such that $\alpha(A - B) + \beta\mathbf{u} + \gamma\mathbf{v} = \mathbf{0}$. Since the lines do not intersect, from Theorem 4, for all σ, τ it is impossible to have $(A - B) + \sigma\mathbf{u} - \tau\mathbf{v} = \mathbf{0}$. This means that $\alpha = 0$. Then it follows that $\beta\mathbf{u} + \gamma\mathbf{v} = \mathbf{0}$ and, since β and γ are not both zero, $\mathbf{u}$ and $\mathbf{v}$ are linearly dependent.

The converse is left as an exercise. |

Euclid's parallel postulate now follows as a corollary of Theorem 5.

Corollary. *If a point B is not on the line $A + \lambda\mathbf{u}$, then there exists one and only one line $B + \sigma\mathbf{v}$ which is parallel to $A + \lambda\mathbf{u}$.*

Proof. From Theorem 5, if B is not on $A + \lambda\mathbf{u}$, then $B + \mu\mathbf{u}$ is parallel to $A + \lambda\mathbf{u}$ (that is, the existence part of Euclid's parallel postulate). Using the other part of Theorem 5, any line through B which does not intersect $A + \lambda\mathbf{u}$ is of the form $B + \sigma\mathbf{v}$ where $\mathbf{v}$ is dependent on $\mathbf{u}$, so we could write $B + \sigma\mathbf{v} = B + \mu\mathbf{u}$ (similar to what we did in Section 2.3) and so there is only one parallel through B (the uniqueness part). |

It seems that it is the identity $(X - Y) + (Y - Z) + (Z - X) = \mathbf{0}$ that makes it possible to prove Euclid's postulate.

Exercises

1. Complete the proof of Theorem 5.
2. Show that, through a point not on a plane, there is one and only one plane parallel to the given plane.
3. Let $n = 4$ and see if you can find a generalization of the parallel postulate for hyperplanes (the three-dimensional analog of a plane in four-space).

2.5   LENGTH AND BETWEENNESS

Thus far, we have used only the vector axioms of Groups 1 to 3 and the point-vector axioms of Group 5. The properties that we have derived (collinear points, coplanar points, and parallelism) are called *affine properties*. Affine geometry will be considered in Chapter 3. The notions of distance and magnitude of angle have not been introduced yet; for these, we need the dot product axioms of Group 4. Distance and magnitude of an angle have to do with measurement and are known as *metric properties*. We say that a geometry in which we consider these properties "has a metric."

We have already decided to allow real numbers into our geometry (even though this is not the purest geometric approach); metric properties supply some of the applications of numbers to geometry. When we measure, we assign numbers to geometric objects; for instance, the length of segments, the magnitude of angles, the area of regions, and the volume of solids. Outside of mathematics, we use numbers to measure weight, energy, and amount of heat. In all of these cases, the measures can be added and we observe the rule that the number assigned to the combination of two objects is the sum of the numbers assigned to each of the objects alone. This property is called *additivity*, or distributivity.

We want to introduce distance and measure of angle on the basis of our axioms and then check to see if they have the property of additivity.

From our experience with vectors in Chapter 1, we would expect to be able to define the distance between two points A and B as follows.

Definition.   *The distance between two points A and B is the principal square root of the dot product of the vector $A - B$ with itself. We write* $|A - B| = \sqrt{(A - B) \cdot (A - B)} = \sqrt{(A - B)^2}$.

If length is additive and A,B,C are points on the same line, then of the three lengths $|A - B|$, $|B - C|$, and $|C - A|$, one of them must be the sum of the other two. (Intuitively, we see that this depends on which point is between the other two.)

Theorem 6.   *If, A,B,C are distinct collinear points, then one of $|A - B|$, $|B - C|$, and $|C - A|$ is the sum of the other two.*

Proof.   Since A,B,C are all on the same line, from the definition of a line, $A - B$, $B - C$, and $C - A$ are all multiples of some vector $\mathbf{u}$, $\mathbf{u} \neq \mathbf{0}$. Let $A - B = \lambda\mathbf{u}$, $B - C = \mu\mathbf{u}$, and $C - A = \nu\mathbf{u}$. From Axiom 5d, $(A - B) + (B - C) + (C - A) = \mathbf{0}$, so $\lambda\mathbf{u} + \mu\mathbf{u} + \nu\mathbf{u} = \mathbf{0}$ or from Axioms 1b, 2e, and 2a, $(\lambda + \mu + \nu)\mathbf{u} = \mathbf{0}$ and therefore $\lambda + \mu + \nu = 0$

by Exercise 2c of Section 2.1. Since none of λ, μ, ν are equal to zero, two of the numbers must be of one sign and the other one of opposite sign. Assume that λ and μ are positive and ν is negative (the proof is similar in the other cases). We can write $\nu = -\rho$, where $\rho > 0$, then $A - B = \lambda \mathbf{u}$, $B - C = \mu \mathbf{u}$, and $A - C = \rho \mathbf{u}$ where λ, μ, ρ are all positive and $\lambda + \mu = \rho$. Finally,

$$
\begin{aligned}
|A - B| + |B - C| &= \sqrt{(A - B)^2} + \sqrt{(B - C)^2} \\
&= \sqrt{(\lambda \mathbf{u})^2} + \sqrt{(\mu \mathbf{u})^2} \\
&= (\lambda + \mu)\sqrt{\mathbf{u}^2} \\
&= \sqrt{(\rho \mathbf{u})^2} \\
&= \sqrt{(C - A)^2} \\
&= |C - A|. \quad |
\end{aligned}
$$

The concept of betweenness (or order) is closely related to additivity. We can define betweenness by saying that if points A, B, C are collinear and the distance from A to C is the sum of the distances from A to B and B to C, then B is between A and C; that is, the points have the order A, B, C or C, B, A.

Definition. *For any three distinct points A, B, C, B is between A and C if A, B, C are collinear and $|A - B| + |B - C| = |A - C|$.*

Sometimes the following criterion for betweenness is more useful.

Theorem 7. *If A, B, C are three points and B is between A and C, then*

$$(A - B) \cdot (B - C) > 0.$$

Proof. If B is between A and C, then from the definition, A, B, C are distinct collinear points and $|A - B| + |B - C| = |A - C|$. Squaring both sides of the equation, we get

$$|A - B|^2 + 2|A - B||B - C| + |B - C|^2 = |A - C|^2.$$

Since distance is positive, this tells us that $|A - B|^2 + |B - C|^2 < |A - C|^2$, or $(A - B)^2 + (B - C)^2 < (A - C)^2$. From Axiom 5d, we know that $(A - B) + (B - C) = (A - C)$, so

$$(A - B)^2 + 2(A - B) \cdot (B - C) + (B - C)^2 = (A - C)^2.$$

Combining these results, we have $2(A - B) \cdot (B - C) > 0$ or

$$(A - B) \cdot (B - C) > 0. \quad |$$

Strictly speaking the idea of betweenness could be treated without the notion of distance. It is not possible to get a metric from betweenness alone, but whenever a metric is present betweenness can be defined similar to the method described above.

Exercises

1. In the spirit of Chapter 1, let $\mathbf{a} \cdot \mathbf{b} = |\mathbf{a}|\,|\mathbf{b}|\cos\varphi$ and prove Theorem 7.

2. Using only our axioms, prove the Schwarz inequality: for any two vectors $\mathbf{u}$ and $\mathbf{v}$, $(\mathbf{u} \cdot \mathbf{v})^2 \leq |\mathbf{u}|^2\,|\mathbf{v}|^2$.

3. Prove the triangular inequality for any three distinct points A, B, C:
$$|A - B| + |B - C| \geq |A - C|.$$

4. Prove the converse of Theorem 7.

5. Show that betweenness, as we have defined it, has the usual properties:
   (a) If B is between A and C, then B is between C and A.
   (b) If B is between A and C, then C is not between A and B.
   (c) If A and B are two distinct points, then there exists a point C that is between A and B and a point D such that B is between A and D.

6. If $n = 4$, would any changes be necessary in this section?

2.6 MEASURE OF ANGLE AND BETWEENNESS

It is more difficult to define the measure of an angle on the basis of our axioms than it was to define length. We begin with what we found in Chapter 1, where $\mathbf{a} \cdot \mathbf{b} = |\mathbf{a}|\,|\mathbf{b}|\cos\varphi$. If $\mathbf{a}$ and $\mathbf{b}$ are not the zero vector, then $|\mathbf{a}| > 0$ and $|\mathbf{b}| > 0$ from Axiom 4e, so it seems that we could define $\cos\varphi = \mathbf{a} \cdot \mathbf{b}/|\mathbf{a}|\,|\mathbf{b}|$ and use this to get at the angle with measure φ. Of course, we cannot use the geometric definition of the cosine as a ratio of two lengths; we must consider $\cos\varphi$ as a real-valued function defined on the real numbers and independent of geometry; we shall define $\cos\varphi$ by the power series

$$\cos\varphi = 1 - \varphi^2/2! + \varphi^4/4! - \dots.$$

From our knowledge of this power series (from analysis) for every number r such that $r^2 < 1$ there is one and only one real number φ such that $\cos\varphi = r$ and $0 < \varphi < \pi$; if $r^2 = 1$, then φ is 0 or π. If φ is to be the measure of an angle, we must check that

$$\left[\frac{\mathbf{a} \cdot \mathbf{b}}{|\mathbf{a}|\,|\mathbf{b}|}\right]^2 \leq 1 \qquad \text{or} \qquad \frac{(\mathbf{a} \cdot \mathbf{b})^2}{\mathbf{a}^2\mathbf{b}^2} \leq 1.$$

Theorem 8. *If* $\mathbf{a} \cdot \mathbf{b}$ *are two nonzero vectors, then* $(\mathbf{a} \cdot \mathbf{b})^2/\mathbf{a}^2\mathbf{b}^2 \leq 1$.

Proof. If $\mathbf{a},\mathbf{b}$ are linearly independent, then for all real α, $\alpha\mathbf{a} + \mathbf{b} \neq \mathbf{0}$, thus, by Axiom 4*e* for all α, $(\alpha\mathbf{a} + \mathbf{b})^2 = \mathbf{a}^2\alpha^2 + 2\mathbf{a} \cdot \mathbf{b}\alpha + \mathbf{b}^2 > 0$. Thus the quadratic equation $\mathbf{a}^2\alpha^2 + 2\mathbf{a} \cdot \mathbf{b}\alpha + \mathbf{b}^2 = 0$ with real coefficients that has no real roots. This means that the expression under the radical in the quadratic formula is negative, $(2\mathbf{a} \cdot \mathbf{b})^2 - 4\mathbf{a}^2\mathbf{b}^2 < 0$, or $(\mathbf{a} \cdot \mathbf{b})^2/\mathbf{a}^2\mathbf{b}^2 < 1$.

If $\mathbf{a}$ and $\mathbf{b}$ are dependent, then for some α, $\mathbf{a} = \alpha\mathbf{b}$, and

$$(\mathbf{a} \cdot \mathbf{b})^2/\mathbf{a}^2\mathbf{b}^2 = (\alpha\mathbf{b} \cdot \mathbf{b})^2/(\alpha\mathbf{b})^2\mathbf{b}^2 = 1.$$

Thus, for all $\mathbf{a},\mathbf{b}$, $(\mathbf{a} \cdot \mathbf{b})^2/\mathbf{a}^2\mathbf{b}^2 \leq 1$. |

This shows that we can define the measure of an angle in terms of dot product.

Definition. *If* $\mathbf{a}$ *and* $\mathbf{b}$ *are any two nonzero vectors, then the measure of the angle between* $\mathbf{a}$ *and* $\mathbf{b}$ *is* φ *where* $\cos \varphi = \mathbf{a} \cdot \mathbf{b}/|\mathbf{a}|\,|\mathbf{b}|$ *and* $0 \leq \varphi \leq \pi$.

It should be noticed that this definition gives only the magnitude of an angle and does not distinguish between the angle from $\mathbf{a}$ to $\mathbf{b}$ and the angle from $\mathbf{b}$ to $\mathbf{a}$.

It is quite easy to show that the measure of the angle between two vectors is not changed if we multiply the vectors by arbitrary numbers. This permits us to define the measure of the angle between two lines.

Definition. *Given two lines* $A + \lambda\mathbf{u}$ *and* $B + \mu\mathbf{v}$, *the measure of the angle between these lines is the measure of the angle between* $\mathbf{u}$ *and* $\mathbf{v}$.

If the measure of an angle has been defined correctly, it must have the property of additivity. We shall prove this now for measures between 0 and $\pi/2$. If we consider angles of measure greater than $\pi/2$, we come upon a difficulty connected with the periodicity of the trigonometric functions. The difficulty is not very great and the solution of it will be left as an exercise.

Theorem 9. *If* $A + \alpha\mathbf{a}$, $B + \beta\mathbf{b}$ *and* $C + \gamma\mathbf{c}$ *are three coplanar lines, and the three angles determined by these lines have measures between* 0 *and* $\pi/2$, *then one of the measures is equal to the sum of the other two.*

Proof. Instead of considering the lines, from the definition of the measure of the angle between two lines, we may consider the corresponding vectors $\mathbf{a},\mathbf{b},\mathbf{c}$. We have the cosines of these measures:

$$\cos \varphi = \mathbf{a} \cdot \mathbf{b}/|\mathbf{a}|\,|\mathbf{b}|, \quad \cos \psi = \mathbf{b} \cdot \mathbf{c}/|\mathbf{b}|\,|\mathbf{c}|, \quad \text{and} \quad \cos \omega = \mathbf{c} \cdot \mathbf{a}/|\mathbf{c}|\,|\mathbf{a}|.$$

We must prove that one of these measures is the sum of the other two.

Since we have no idea of what condition on the three cosines is *sufficient* to guarantee additivity of the measures, we shall work in the opposite direction. Temporarily, we shall assume that one of the measures is the sum of the other two, say $\omega = \varphi + \psi$, and we shall find a *necessary* condition for additivity, if we are lucky, it may also turn out to be sufficient.

If $\omega = \varphi + \psi$, from our knowledge of analysis, we have $\cos \omega = \cos \varphi \cos \psi - \sin \varphi \sin \psi$, where sine is also a real-valued function defined on the reals by a power series. We can write $\cos \varphi \cos \psi - \cos \omega = \sin \varphi \sin \psi$; squaring and using the identity $\cos^2 \theta + \sin^2 \theta = 1$, we get $1 + 2 \cos \varphi \cos \psi \cos \omega - \cos^2 \varphi - \cos^2 \psi - \cos^2 \omega = 0$. This is the condition that we hope is also sufficient. We know it can be written

$$(\cos \varphi \cos \psi - \cos \omega)^2 = \sin^2 \varphi \sin^2 \psi,$$

or

$$\cos \omega = \cos \varphi \cos \psi \pm \sin \varphi \sin \psi,$$

or

$$\cos \omega = \cos (\varphi \mp \psi).$$

If the cosines of two numbers are equal, then the numbers are equal in absolute value, so we have four possibilities:

$$\omega = \varphi - \psi, \quad \omega = \varphi + \psi, \quad -\omega = \varphi - \psi, \quad \text{and} \quad -\omega = \varphi + \psi.$$

The fourth of these equalities contradicts our assumption that $0 \leq \varphi \leq \pi/2$ and $0 \leq \psi \leq \pi/2$. Each of the remaining equalities means that one number is the sum of the other two. So

$$1 + 2 \cos \varphi \cos \psi \cos \omega - \cos^2 \varphi - \cos^2 \psi - \cos^2 \omega = 0$$

is a necessary and sufficient condition for one of φ, ψ, ω to be the sum of the other two.

We must now show that our measures do satisfy this condition. Since the lines are coplanar, so are the vectors **a,b,c** and, therefore, there exist α, β, γ not all zero such that $\alpha \mathbf{a} + \beta \mathbf{b} + \gamma \mathbf{c} = \mathbf{0}$. Dot multiplying this in succession by **a,b,c**, we get

$$\mathbf{a}^2 \alpha + \mathbf{a} \cdot \mathbf{b} \beta + \mathbf{a} \cdot \mathbf{c} \gamma = 0$$

$$\mathbf{a} \cdot \mathbf{b} \alpha + \mathbf{b}^2 \beta + \mathbf{b} \cdot \mathbf{c} \gamma = 0$$

$$\mathbf{a} \cdot \mathbf{c} \alpha + \mathbf{b} \cdot \mathbf{c} \beta + \mathbf{c}^2 \gamma = 0.$$

Since α, β, γ are not all zero this system of homogeneous equations could be solved for α, β, γ, this means that

$$\begin{vmatrix} a^2 & a \cdot b & a \cdot c \\ a \cdot b & b^2 & b \cdot c \\ a \cdot c & b \cdot c & c^2 \end{vmatrix} = 0.$$

Since $|a|$, $|b|$, and $|c|$ are not zero (why?), we can divide the first row by $|a|$, the second by $|b|$, the third by $|c|$, do the same thing to the columns, and then substitute the cosines and expand the determinant. This gives the required condition

$$1 + 2 \cos \varphi \cos \psi \cos \omega - \cos^2 \varphi - \cos^2 \psi - \cos^2 \omega = 0. \quad |$$

We have mentioned the connection between additivity of distances and betweenness. There is also a concept of betweenness for angles if we restrict ourselves to angles of measure not greater than $\pi/2$; it is related to the additivity of the measures of angles.

We have just shown that, given three coplanar vectors **a,b,c**, we can define the measures of the angles between them and, if none of the measures are greater than $\pi/2$, then one of these magnitudes is the sum of the other two. This permits us to define betweenness for angles.

Definition. *If **a,b,c** are three coplanar vectors such that no two of them are linearly dependent and the magnitude of each of the three angles determined by them does not exceed $\pi/2$, then vector **b** is between vector **a** and **c** if the magnitude of the angle between **a** and **c** is the sum of the magnitudes of the angles between **a** and **b** and **b** and **c**.*

Theorem 10. *If **a,b,c** are any three coplanar vectors such that the magnitude of the three angles determined by them is each not greater than $\pi/2$, then **b** is between **a** and **c** if $(a \cdot b)(b \cdot c) - b^2(a \cdot c) > 0$ and conversely.*

Proof. Let $\cos \omega = a \cdot c/|a|\,|c|$, $\cos \varphi = a \cdot b/|a|\,|b|$, and $\cos \psi = b \cdot c/|b|\,|c|$. If **b** is between **a** and **c** we have

$$\omega = \varphi + \psi \quad \text{and} \quad \cos \omega = \cos \varphi \cos \psi - \sin \varphi \sin \psi.$$

Since $0 < \varphi \leq \pi/2$ and $0 < \psi \leq \pi/2$, $\sin \varphi \sin \psi > 0$ and

$$\cos \omega < \cos \varphi \cos \psi \quad \text{or} \quad a \cdot c/|a|\,|c| < (a \cdot b/|a|\,|b|)(b \cdot c/|b|\,|c|).$$

Finally, $(a \cdot b)(b \cdot c) > b^2(a \cdot c)$. The converse is left as an exercise. $\quad |$

We now have betweenness for distance and betweenness for angles; the natural question is whether there is a connection between them. Such a connection does exist and was taken for granted by Euclid. In Euclid's proofs, we find him making use of this property (which he never formally assumed): *If a straight line enters a triangle through a vertex it intersects the opposite side.* M. Pasch in 1882 was the first to formulate the proposition explicitly.

Another proposition from which this one can be proved is: *A line which intersects one side of a triangle but does not pass through any of the vertices of the triangle must also intersect another side of the triangle.* This latter form is now called the Axiom of Pasch.

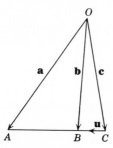

In our terminology, the converse of the first of these propositions becomes Theorem 11.

Theorem 11. *If A,O,C are three noncollinear points and B is a point between A and C, then the vector B − O is between the vectors A − O and C − O (Figure 2.6a).*

Fig. 2.6a

Proof. Since *B* is between *A* and *C*, by Theorem 7, $(B − A) \cdot (C − B) > O$. Let $A − O = \mathbf{a}, B − O = \mathbf{b}$, and $C − O = \mathbf{c}$, then from Axiom 5d (and other known properties which you should be able to list)

$$B − A = (B − O) − (A − O) = \mathbf{b} − \mathbf{a}$$
and
$$C − B = (C − O) − (B − O) = \mathbf{c} − \mathbf{b}.$$

It now follows that $(\mathbf{b} − \mathbf{a}) \cdot (\mathbf{c} − \mathbf{b}) > 0$. Since *B* is between *A* and *C*, *A,B,C* are collinear and we can write $A − B = \lambda\mathbf{u}$ and $B − C = \mu\mathbf{u}$ with λ and μ positive (see proof of Theorem 6), so $\mu(\mathbf{a} − \mathbf{b}) = \lambda(\mathbf{b} − \mathbf{c})$, or $(\lambda + \mu)\mathbf{b} = \mu\mathbf{a} + \lambda\mathbf{c}$. Solving this for **b** and substituting it into the left hand side of the condition for betweenness of angles (Theorem 10), we get $\lambda\mu[\mathbf{a}^2\mathbf{c}^2 − (\mathbf{a} \cdot \mathbf{c})^2]/(\lambda + \mu)^2$. The expression in square brackets is always positive (see proof of Theorem 8) when **a** and **c** are linearly independent, which they are in this case. So the whole expression is positive if $\lambda\mu$ is positive, but this follows because λ and μ are each positive. Thus, from Theorem 10, we do know that **b** is between **a** and **c**; that is, $B − O$ is between $A − O$ and $C − O$. |

Exercises

1. Prove that the measure of the angle between two vectors is not changed if we multiply the vectors by arbitrary nonzero numbers.

2. Show that the notion of measure of an angle is additive even if we speak of angles of measure greater than $\pi/2$.

3. Complete the proof of Theorem 10.
4. In the spirit of Chapter 1, show that the Axiom of Pasch implies the following proposition: If a straight line enters a triangle through a vertex it intersects the opposite side.
5. Using only our axioms prove the proposition in Exercise 4 (notice that this is the converse of Theorem 11).
6. Is the restriction of $n = 3$ necessary in this section?

2.7 TRANSITION TO ANALYTIC GEOMETRY

We shall now show how our axioms can be used to introduce analytic geometry. Since all Euclidean propositions can be proved analytically, this should convince us that three-dimensional Euclidean geometry can be set up on the basis of our axioms.

First we need an origin, a fixed point that we shall use to locate any other point. Let O be a fixed point, then by Axiom 5a any point X can be represented by the difference $X - O$ which is a vector that we shall call **x**. Instead of operating with points like X and Y, we can work with vectors $\mathbf{x} = X - O$, $\mathbf{y} = Y - O$. For instance, if we want to find the distance between X and Y, we can use $\mathbf{x} - \mathbf{y}$. This is based on Axiom 5d which gives us the relation $(X - Y) + (Y - O) + (O - X) = \mathbf{0}$, then from Theorem 2 we can write $X - Y = \mathbf{x} - \mathbf{y}$. Of course, there is nothing special about the point O; we could have used any other point O' just as well and then represent X, Y by the vectors $\mathbf{x}' = X - O'$, $\mathbf{y}' = Y - O'$.

The second step consists in representing any vector **x** as a linear combination of three fixed independent vectors. From Axiom 3b, there exist three linearly independent vectors **a**,**b**,**c**; from Axiom 3a, any four vectors are linearly dependent. These axioms tell us that there exist α,β,γ such that $\mathbf{x} = \alpha\mathbf{a} + \beta\mathbf{b} + \gamma\mathbf{c}$, or $X = O + \alpha\mathbf{a} + \beta\mathbf{b} + \gamma\mathbf{c}$. We call α,β,γ the coordinates of the point X with respect to the system $(O,\mathbf{a},\mathbf{b},\mathbf{c})$; **a**,**b**,**c** are like three coordinate axes. If we want rectangular coordinate axes, all we must do is use three mutually perpendicular unit vectors in place of **a**,**b**,**c**. (In the language of our axioms, two vectors are perpendicular if their dot product is zero.) We shall now prove that three such vectors always exist.

We have three mutually independent vectors **a**,**b**,**c** from Axiom 3b. It is easy to prove that these vectors are not the zero vector and so their lengths are different from zero; therefore, we can form the vector $\mathbf{i} = (1/|\mathbf{a}|)\mathbf{a}$ with length one. We next let $\mathbf{b}' = \mathbf{b} - \mathbf{i}(\mathbf{i} \cdot \mathbf{b})$ (Figure 2.7a) and prove that its dot product with **i** is zero, that is, $\mathbf{b}'$ is perpendicular to **i**. On the other hand, $\mathbf{b}'$ is not zero because if $\mathbf{b}'$ were zero, **b** would be a multiple of **i** and, therefore, also of **a** and this contradicts the assumption of independence. Now we can form $\mathbf{j} = (1/|\mathbf{b}'|)\mathbf{b}'$ and show that **j** is a unit vector perpendicular to **i**. We have $\mathbf{i}^2 = \mathbf{j}^2 = 1$ and $\mathbf{i} \cdot \mathbf{j} = 0$.

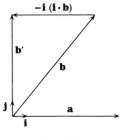

Fig. 2.7a

We next let $\mathbf{c}' = \mathbf{c} - \mathbf{i}(\mathbf{i} \cdot \mathbf{c}) - \mathbf{j}(\mathbf{j} \cdot \mathbf{c})$. $\mathbf{c}'$ is perpendicular to **i** and **j** and $\mathbf{c}' \neq \mathbf{0}$, so we can form $\mathbf{k} = (1/|\mathbf{c}'|)\mathbf{c}'$, which satisfies the rest of the requirements; that is, $\mathbf{k}^2 = 1$, $\mathbf{k} \cdot \mathbf{i} = 0$, and $\mathbf{k} \cdot \mathbf{j} = 0$. Finally, Axiom 3a tells us that, for any vector **x**, there exist α, β, γ such that $\mathbf{x} = \alpha\mathbf{i} + \beta\mathbf{j} + \gamma\mathbf{k}$. It follows that any point X may be represented by $X = 0 + \alpha\mathbf{i} + \beta\mathbf{j} + \gamma\mathbf{k}$. In order to conform to usage (and deviate from the rule of denoting numbers by Greek letters which we have been observing most of the time), we could use the letters x, y, z for the coordinates of the point X and write $X = 0 + x\mathbf{i} + y\mathbf{j} + z\mathbf{k}$, or simply $X = (x, y, z)$.

Exercises

1. Prove that, if **a**,**b**,**c** is a set of linearly independent vectors, then **a**,**b**,**c** are mutually independent; that is, no two vectors of the set are linearly dependent.
2. Prove that, if **a**,**b**,**c** are linearly independent vectors, then none of these vectors is the zero vector.
3. For any vector $\mathbf{a} \neq \mathbf{0}$ show that $\mathbf{i} = (1/|\mathbf{a}|)\mathbf{a}$ has length one.
4. Prove that $\mathbf{b}' \cdot \mathbf{i} = 0$ if $\mathbf{b}' = \mathbf{b} - \mathbf{i}(\mathbf{i} \cdot \mathbf{b})$ and **i** is as in Problem 3.
5. Prove that for any vector **c**, if we define $\mathbf{c}' = \mathbf{c} - \mathbf{i}(\mathbf{i} \cdot \mathbf{c}) - \mathbf{j}(\mathbf{j} \cdot \mathbf{c})$ where $\mathbf{i}^2 = \mathbf{j}^2 = 1$ and $\mathbf{i} \cdot \mathbf{j} = 0$, then $\mathbf{c}' \cdot \mathbf{i} = 0$ and $\mathbf{c}' \cdot \mathbf{j} = 0$.
6. Draw a diagram to illustrate the formation of vector $\mathbf{c}'$ in Problem 5.
7. Let $X = O + x\mathbf{i} + y\mathbf{j} + z\mathbf{k}$ and show that this representation of X is unique with respect to $(O, \mathbf{i}, \mathbf{j}, \mathbf{k})$; that is, if r, s, t are also coordinates of X, then $r = x$, $s = y$, and $t = z$.
8. Show that the origin has coordinates $(0, 0, 0)$.
9. Let $n = 4$ and show that four mutually perpendicular unit vectors exist. Could other values of n be used?

2.8   DOT AND CROSS PRODUCTS IN TERMS OF COORDINATES

In Chapter 1, using our previous knowledge, we talked about how we could construct Euclidean vector geometry. Thus far, in Chapter 2, we built vector geometry formally from a set of axioms. It remains now to consider some of the advantages of the vector method. In these last two sections, we shall consider a number of problems from solid analytic geometry and use vectors to find solutions. If you have already had a course in solid analytic geometry, you may decide to skip these sections; however, it still may be interesting for you to see familiar problems solved a new way. If you have never studied this part of mathematics, this would be a good opportunity to begin.

As we solve these problems, what are we going to allow ourselves to use? We could continue in the formal style of the first part of this chapter, but there is not much to be gained for these problems by this approach. Instead, we shall return to the spirit of Chapter 1. We shall permit ourselves to use any facts that we know from Euclidean geometry and any facts about vectors that we have developed thus far. We shall assume that we have chosen an origin and have found three mutually perpendicular unit vectors, which we use to get the coordinates of any point.

We already know that any point A can be represented by coordinates x,y,z where $A = O + x\mathbf{i} + y\mathbf{j} + z\mathbf{k}$, O is a fixed point, and $\mathbf{i},\mathbf{j},\mathbf{k}$ are three mutually perpendicular unit vectors. To be brief, we shall simply write $A = (x,y,z)$ since the coordinates are a unique representation of the point with respect to the chosen coordinate system.

We can also speak of the coordinates of a vector. Let $\mathbf{u}$ be a vector with its tail at the origin O and its tip at $B = (l,m,n)$; then $\mathbf{u} = B - O = l\mathbf{i} + m\mathbf{j} + n\mathbf{k}$. The vector $\mathbf{u}$ is completely determined by the triple l,m,n. We shall write $\mathbf{u} = \{l,m,n\}$, using braces to distinguish vector coordinates from point coordinates. Since any vector can be translated to the origin, we can always find the vector coordinates in this way; they are the same as the point coordinates of the tip after the tail is translated to the origin. It is also possible to find the coordinates of a vector without translating the vector to the origin; we shall leave this as an exercise.

Dot Product

We now want a formula for the dot product of two vectors in terms of their coordinates. Let $\mathbf{u} = \{l,m,n\}$ and $\mathbf{v} = \{l',m',n'\}$, then $\mathbf{u} \cdot \mathbf{v} = (l\mathbf{i} + m\mathbf{j} + n\mathbf{k}) \cdot (l'\mathbf{i} + m'\mathbf{j} + n'\mathbf{k})$. If we use the properties of dot product (distributive law, modified associative law, etc.), and the facts that $\mathbf{i}^2 = \mathbf{j}^2 = \mathbf{k}^2$ and $\mathbf{i} \cdot \mathbf{j} = \mathbf{j} \cdot \mathbf{k} = \mathbf{k} \cdot \mathbf{i} = 0$, we can derive the formula $\mathbf{u} \cdot \mathbf{v} = ll' + mm' + nn'$.

Cross Product

We would like a similar formula for the cross product of two vectors. Again, let $\mathbf{u} = \{l,m,n\}$ and $\mathbf{v} = \{l',m',n'\}$, then

$$\mathbf{u} \times \mathbf{v} = (l\mathbf{i} + m\mathbf{j} + n\mathbf{k}) \times (l'\mathbf{i} + m'\mathbf{j} + n'\mathbf{k}).$$

If we expand this, using the properties of the cross product and the facts that $\mathbf{i} \times \mathbf{i} = \mathbf{j} \times \mathbf{j} = \mathbf{k} \times \mathbf{k} = 0$ and $\mathbf{i} \times \mathbf{j} = \mathbf{k}$, $\mathbf{j} \times \mathbf{k} = \mathbf{i}$, and $\mathbf{k} \times \mathbf{i} = \mathbf{j}$ (we assume that we have decided that $\mathbf{i},\mathbf{j},\mathbf{k}$ is right-handed), then $\mathbf{u} \times \mathbf{v} = \mathbf{i}\,(mn' - nm') + \mathbf{j}(nl' - ln') + \mathbf{k}(lm' - ml')$. An easy way to remember this is to expand the determinant

$$\begin{vmatrix} \mathbf{i} & \mathbf{j} & \mathbf{k} \\ l & m & n \\ l' & m' & n' \end{vmatrix}$$

as if $\mathbf{i},\mathbf{j},\mathbf{k}$ were numbers.

Exercises

1. Let $\mathbf{u} = A - B$ where $A = (x,y,z)$ and $B = (x',y',z')$. Show that $\mathbf{u} = \{x - x', y - y', z - z'\}$.
2. Let every point A of three-space with coordinates (x,y,z) be moved to a new position $A' = (x - g, y - h, z - k)$. Show that this change is a translation and that every translation can be represented this way.
3. Prove that the coordinates of a vector are invariant under translations (this means that although many ordered pairs of points may represent the same vector, the coordinate representation of a vector is unique).
4. Carry out the details to prove that $\mathbf{u} \cdot \mathbf{v} = ll' + mm' + nn'$ if $\mathbf{u} = \{l,m,n\}$ and $\mathbf{v} = \{l',m',n'\}$.
5. Why is $\mathbf{i} \times \mathbf{i} = \mathbf{j} \times \mathbf{j} = \mathbf{k} \times \mathbf{k} = 0$ and $\mathbf{i} \times \mathbf{j} = \mathbf{k}$, $\mathbf{j} \times \mathbf{k} = \mathbf{i}$, and $\mathbf{k} \times \mathbf{i} = \mathbf{j}$?
6. Carry out the details to prove that

$$\mathbf{u} \times \mathbf{v} = \begin{vmatrix} \mathbf{i} & \mathbf{j} & \mathbf{k} \\ l & m & n \\ l' & m' & n' \end{vmatrix}$$

if $\mathbf{u} = \{l,m,n\}$ and $\mathbf{v} = \{l',m',n'\}$.

7. Find a coordinate representation of the triple scalar product and a simple way to remember it.
8. Prove that

$$(\mathbf{abc})(\mathbf{pqr}) = \begin{vmatrix} \mathbf{a} \cdot \mathbf{p} & \mathbf{a} \cdot \mathbf{q} & \mathbf{a} \cdot \mathbf{r} \\ \mathbf{b} \cdot \mathbf{p} & \mathbf{b} \cdot \mathbf{q} & \mathbf{b} \cdot \mathbf{r} \\ \mathbf{c} \cdot \mathbf{p} & \mathbf{c} \cdot \mathbf{q} & \mathbf{c} \cdot \mathbf{r} \end{vmatrix}.$$

2.9   DISTANCE AND MEASURE OF ANGLE IN TERMS OF COORDINATES

We now have at our disposal all the tools necessary to answer the elementary questions of solid analytic geometry. As we look at each problem that follows, we shall first handle it with vectors and then translate the result into the language of coordinates.

The Distance between Two Points

Let $A = (x,y,z)$ and $B = (x',y',z')$ be two given points. We would like to find a formula for the distance from A to B in terms of their coordinates. We know that the length of the vector $A - B$ is given by $|A - B| = \sqrt{(A - B)^2}$. From Exercise 1 of Section 2.8, we know that $A - B = \{x - x', y - y', z - z'\}$. Using these facts and the coordinate form of the dot product, $|A - B| = \sqrt{(x - x')^2 + (y - y')^2 + (z - z')^2}$.

The Angle between Two Vectors

The measure of an angle between two vectors can be written in coordinate form in two different ways. Let $\mathbf{u} = \{l,m,n\}$ and $\mathbf{v} = \{l',m',n'\}$, then if the angle between $\mathbf{u}$ and $\mathbf{v}$ is φ, we have

$$\cos \varphi = \mathbf{u} \cdot \mathbf{v}/|\mathbf{u}|\,|\mathbf{v}| \qquad \text{and} \qquad \sin \varphi = |\mathbf{u} \times \mathbf{v}|/|\mathbf{u}|\,|\mathbf{v}|.$$

In coordinate form, these become

$$\cos \varphi = \frac{ll' + mm' + nn'}{\sqrt{l^2 + m^2 + n^2}\sqrt{l'^2 + m'^2 + n'^2}}$$

and

$$\sin \varphi = \frac{\sqrt{(mn' - nm')^2 + (nl' - ln')^2 + (lm' - ml')^2}}{\sqrt{l^2 + m^2 + n^2}\sqrt{l'^2 + m'^2 + n'^2}}.$$

The Equations of a Line

We already know that a straight line can be given by a point-vector formula $X = A + \lambda\mathbf{u}$, where A is a fixed point on the line, $\mathbf{u}$ is a fixed vector in the line, and λ is a variable real number. We would like to find a coordinate representation of a line in three-space. Let $A = (a,b,c)$, $\mathbf{u} = \{l,m,n\}$, and $X = (x,y,z)$; then our formula becomes

$$X = O + (x\mathbf{i} + y\mathbf{j} + z\mathbf{k}) = O + (a\mathbf{i} + b\mathbf{j} + c\mathbf{k}) + \lambda(l\mathbf{i} + m\mathbf{j} + n\mathbf{k}).$$

Because $\mathbf{i},\mathbf{j},\mathbf{k}$ are linearly independent, this leads to three numerical equations $x = a + \lambda l$, $y = b + \lambda m$, and $z = c + \lambda n$. This is called the parametric form of the equations of a line. If none of l,m,n are zero, it is possible to eliminate λ and combine these three equations to get

$$\frac{x - a}{l} = \frac{y - b}{m} = \frac{z - c}{n}.$$

The three numbers l,m,n (which are the coordinates of a vector in the line) are known as a set of *direction numbers* of the line. Since any vector in the line can be used for this development, any multiple of the triple, as kl,km,kn where $k \neq 0$, is also a set of direction numbers for the line.

The Angle between Two Lines

If

$$\frac{x - a}{l} = \frac{y - b}{m} = \frac{z - c}{n} \quad \text{and} \quad \frac{x - a'}{l} = \frac{y - b'}{m'} = \frac{z - c'}{n'}$$

are any two lines, the smaller of the two angles between them, which is φ, $0 \leq \varphi \leq \pi/2$, is given by

$$\cos \varphi = \frac{|ll' + mm' + nn'|}{\sqrt{l^2 + m^2 + n^2}\sqrt{l'^2 + m'^2 + n'^2}}$$

because this is the cosine of the angle between the vectors $\{l,m,n\}$ and $\{l',m',n'\}$. We are using here the definition of the angle between two lines which we developed in Section 2.6. (Why do we consider the smaller of the two angles?) Even if it is not possible to express the equations of the lines in the combined form above, this formula may still be used on the direction numbers of the lines. If the lines are parallel, $\cos \varphi = 1$ and so $\varphi = 0$; if the lines are skew (nonparallel and nonintersecting), then the angle between them still has a meaning and is the same as the angle between one of the lines and an intersecting line parallel to the second.

The Angle between a Line and a Plane

Now let us find the angle φ between the line $A + \lambda\mathbf{u}$ and the plane $B + \mu\mathbf{v} + \nu\mathbf{w}$ where $0 \leq \varphi \leq \pi/2$. The angle will be the complement of the angle between the line and the perpendicular to the plane (Figure 2.9a).

Since the vector $\mathbf{r} = \mathbf{v} \times \mathbf{w}$ is perpendicular to the plane, and since the cosine of an angle is the sine of its complement, we can use either of two formulas:

$$\sin \varphi = \frac{|\mathbf{u} \cdot \mathbf{r}|}{|\mathbf{u}|\,|\mathbf{r}|} \quad \text{or} \quad \cos \varphi = \frac{|\mathbf{u} \times \mathbf{r}|}{|\mathbf{u}|\,|\mathbf{r}|}.$$

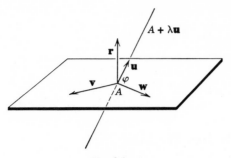

Fig. 2.9a

(Why do we consider the absolute value of $\mathbf{u} \cdot \mathbf{r}$?) If $\mathbf{u} = \{a,b,c\}$, $\mathbf{v} = \{l,m,n\}$, and $\mathbf{w} = \{l',m',n'\}$, we have $\mathbf{r} = \{mn' - nm', nl' - ln', lm' - ml'\}$ and

$$\sin \varphi = \frac{|a(mn' - nm') + b(nl' - ln') + c(lm' - ml')|}{\sqrt{a^2 + b^2 + c^2}\sqrt{(mn' - nm')^2 + (nl' - ln')^2 + (lm' - ml')^2}}.$$

We can also get a formula for $\cos \varphi$.

The Distance from a Point to a Plane

Let $P = (x,y,z)$ and $X = A + \lambda\mathbf{u} + \mu\mathbf{v}$ with $A = (a,b,c)$, $\mathbf{u} = \{l,m,n\}$, and $\mathbf{v} = \{l',m',n'\}$. We would like to find the distance from the point P to the plane $A + \lambda\mathbf{u} + \mu\mathbf{v}$. Since the distance is measured along a perpendicular to the plane, we introduce $\mathbf{w} = \mathbf{u} \times \mathbf{v}$ (Figure 2.9b). $|\mathbf{w} \cdot (P - A)| = |\mathbf{w}| \, |P - A| \, |\cos \varphi|$; that is, the absolute value of the dot product of $\mathbf{w}$ and $P - A$ is the length of $\mathbf{w}$ times the projection of $P - A$ on the direction of $\mathbf{w}$. This projection is the required distance; thus,

$$\frac{|\mathbf{w} \cdot (P - A|}{|\mathbf{w}|} = \frac{|\mathbf{u} \times \mathbf{v} \cdot (P - A)|}{|\mathbf{u} \times \mathbf{v}|}$$

is the distance of P from the plane $A + \lambda\mathbf{u} + \mu\mathbf{v}$. In coordinate form, the

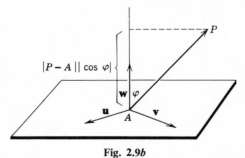

Fig. 2.9b

distance is

$$\left| \frac{\begin{vmatrix} x - a & y - b & z - c \\ l & m & n \\ l' & m' & n' \end{vmatrix}}{\sqrt{(mn' - nm')^2 + (nl' - ln')^2 + (lm' - ml')^2}} \right|. \qquad \text{(Why?)}$$

The Distance between Two Lines

Let $A = (a,b,c)$, $B = (a',b',c')$, $\mathbf{u} = \{l,m,n\}$, and $\mathbf{v} = \{l',m',n'\}$. We would like to find a formula for the distance between $A + \lambda\mathbf{u}$ and $B + \mu\mathbf{v}$. If the lines are not parallel (skew), we introduce the vector $\mathbf{w} = \mathbf{u} \times \mathbf{v}$ (Figure 2.9c); $\mathbf{w}$ is perpendicular to both lines and the required distance is the projection of $A - B$ on $\mathbf{w}$. To see this, let CD be the common perpendicular of the two lines, and $ABDE$ a parallelogram, then

$$|C - D| = |E - D|\,|\cos \varphi|$$

$$= |A - B|\,|\cos \varphi|$$

$$= \frac{|(A - B) \cdot \mathbf{w}|}{|\mathbf{w}|}$$

$$= \frac{|(A - B) \cdot \mathbf{u} \times \mathbf{v}|}{|\mathbf{u} \times \mathbf{v}|}.$$

This can be translated into coordinate form and will be left as an exercise.

If the lines are parallel, $\mathbf{v}$ may be taken the same as $\mathbf{u}$; in this case, $\mathbf{u} \times \mathbf{v} = 0$ and the above formula does not work. The cross product $(A - B) \times \mathbf{u}$ has length numerically equal to the area of the parallelogram

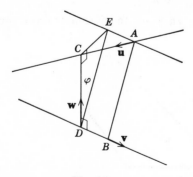

Fig. 2.9c

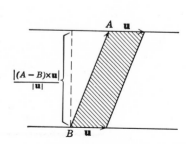

Fig. 2.9d

formed by the vectors $A - B$ and $\mathbf{u}$ (Figure 2.9d). This area is also equal to the length of $\mathbf{u}$ times the length of the altitude of the parallelogram; this altitude is the distance between the lines. Thus, the distance that we want is

$$\frac{|(A - B) \times \mathbf{u}|}{|\mathbf{u}|}.$$

Exercises

1. Show how the linear independence of $\mathbf{i},\mathbf{j},\mathbf{k}$ leads to the parametric form of the equation of a line as developed in this section.

2. In the formula for the angle between two lines, why is it necessary to consider the length of $\mathbf{u} \times \mathbf{v}$?

3. Prove that the angle between two lines with direction numbers l,m,n and l',m',n' is also given by

$$\sin \varphi = \frac{\sqrt{(mn' - nm')^2 + (nl' - ln')^2 + (lm' - ml')^2}}{\sqrt{l^2 + m^2 + n^2}\sqrt{l'^2 + m'^2 + n'^2}}.$$

4. Find the coordinate form of the $\cos \varphi$, where φ is the angle between a line and a plane.

5. Show that, if two lines are parallel, then the angle between them is zero.

6. Let $X = A + \lambda\mathbf{u} + \mu\mathbf{v}$ be a plane through $A = (a,b,c)$ with $\mathbf{u} = \{l,m,n\}$ and $\mathbf{v} = \{l',m',n'\}$. Using the fact that $X - A$ is perpendicular to $\mathbf{u} \times \mathbf{v}$, find the equation of the plane in terms of coordinates only.

7. If $\alpha x + \beta y + \gamma z + \delta = 0$ is the coordinate form of the equation of a plane, find the coordinates of two linearly independent vectors in this plane.

8. Let $\varphi_1, \varphi_2, \varphi_3$ be the angles between a line with direction numbers l,m,n and the lines $O + \lambda\mathbf{i}$, $O + \mu\mathbf{j}$, and $O + \nu\mathbf{k}$ respectively. Find a formula for $|\cos \varphi_1|$, $|\cos \varphi_2|$, and $|\cos \varphi_3|$ in terms of the direction numbers of the line.

9. Find the formula for the distance between two lines in terms of coordinates.

10. Find a formula in terms of coordinates for the distance of a point $P = (x,y,z)$ from the line $X = A + \lambda\mathbf{u}$ where $A = (a,b,c)$ and $\mathbf{u} = \{l,m,n\}$.

II

GEOMETRIES OTHER THAN EUCLIDEAN

Until the first half of the 19th century, the term "geometry" implied "Euclidean geometry." Since that time, because of attempts to answer questions about Euclidean geometry, mathematicians have investigated other possibilities. In this second part of our study, we shall discuss some of these other geometries without breaking the connection—in fact, we shall emphasize the connection with Euclidean geometry.

Once again, we shall assume an acquaintance with Euclidean geometry and shall begin on this familiar ground. There are several ways in which we can develop new geometries; we shall use three of these ways. We could restrict ourselves and concentrate on only a few notions of Euclidean geometry; this is how we shall get projective geometry. We could do just the opposite and use all of Euclidean geometry and even add some new ideas to it; inversive geometry will be built this way. Still another approach is not to use Euclidean geometry in any direct way, but to begin a new geometry independent of Euclid's; this is how we shall develop hyperbolic geometry. We must admit, however, that even here we shall look back now and then at Euclidean geometry in order to get ideas about how to proceed in this strange new non-Euclidean world.

3 Projective Geometry

3.1 AFFINE GEOMETRY

To build projective geometry, we shall need a new technique. This technique will be understood better if we first use it to build another geometry—plane affine geometry. Let us do this.

We know that Euclidean geometry studies those properties of figures or bodies that do not depend on position. There are other properties of bodies that we disregard when we study geometry: color, weight, and texture are some of them. In studying anything, we never attempt to study all of its aspects at the same time; we separate them. This is an efficient procedure. Imagine how complicated things would be if we tried to study mechanics or some other branch of physics and had to learn all about the geometric properties of size and shape at the same time.

Within geometry there are different properties which are studied: perpendicularity, parallelism, and distance are a few. It might be interesting and, perhaps, useful to separate these geometric properties, to isolate them and study them one by one. This would amount to disregarding some properties while concentrating on others.

We must be careful, however, because some properties are interrelated, and the connections may not be noticeable at first glance. For example, distance and perpendicularity are related; a circle is the set of points at a fixed distance from a certain point, or it can be described as the set of all points which are the vertices of the right angle of a right triangle having a fixed hypotenuse. The problem of separating different kinds of properties is, therefore, not very simple.

We could solve the problem of separating the various properties by carefully analyzing the propositions that make up geometry; we could look at a few axioms and concentrate on the properties that could be derived only from these few axioms. In Section 2.5, we mentioned that our axioms of Groups 1 to 3 and Group 5 (excluding Group 4) would be a system of axioms for an n-dimensional affine geometry. We could learn about plane affine geometry by studying the properties that arise from these axioms when $n = 2$. We choose not to do this.

A quicker way to separate properties is to go back to our definition of Euclidean geometry. We said that Euclidean geometry was the study of those properties of figures that are not affected by change of position. In this geometry, there is no essential difference between two congruent figures. In order to isolate certain properties, we could allow more radical changes; for example, we might study the properties that are not affected by change of size. This geometry is called equiform and will be considered further in Chapter 7. In equiform geometry, there is no essential difference between similar figures. Parallelism, magnitude of angles, and ratios of segments are some of the properties that belong to equiform geometry. We can no longer consider the length of a segment or the area of a figure because they are altered when we change the size of the figures. Notice that if we allow ourselves more freedom in the way we change our figures fewer properties are preserved.

We now want to find a way to identify the properties of plane affine geometry (the geometry of the axioms of Groups 1 to 3 and Group 5) in a similar way. To do this, we shall describe a *stretching in a line*. If m is a fixed line and α is a fixed real number, then a stretching of length α relative to line m means that every point P of the space is moved to P', so that P' lies on the perpendicular from P to m and the distance from P' to m is α times the distance from P to m. If $\alpha > 0$, then P' is on the same side of m as P, and if $\alpha < 0$, then P' is on the opposite side. If α equals $\frac{1}{2}$ and F is the foot of the perpendicular from P to m, then P' has the position shown in Figure 3.1a. If α equals -1, then the image of P is P'', as shown in Figure 3.1a.

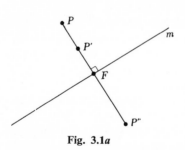

Fig. 3.1a

Now we can describe affine geometry. Affine geometry is the study of those properties of figures which are not affected by stretchings in lines. Let us look at two parallel lines p and q (Figure 3.1b). After a stretching of $\frac{1}{2}$ relative to line m, they have positions p' and q', and after a stretching of $\frac{1}{3}$ relative to the line n, they have positions p'' and q''. Notice that p'' is still parallel to q''. Parallelism is an affine property. However, a square may become a rectangle, or even a parallelogram; a circle may become an ellipse. Distances are not preserved, but the ratio of the lengths of two segments on the same line, or on parallel lines, is preserved. If three points are on a line, the images of these points are still on one line; we say that collinearity is preserved.

Some statements that have meaning in Euclidean geometry lose their meaning when we are in affine geometry. We cannot say, for instance,

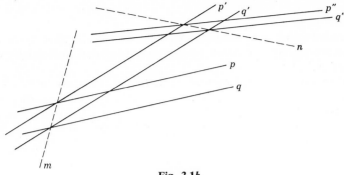

Fig. 3.1*b*

that two lines are perpendicular to each other. This is similar to the fact that the statement, "a line is vertical," loses its meaning when we move from physics to geometry.

The fact that perpendicularity has no meaning in affine geometry may bring up a question in your mind. If perpendicularity has no meaning, how can we talk about stretching in a line? We had to know what a perpendicular was in order to describe this type of change. To settle this difficulty we must remember that we have chosen not to abandon Euclidean geometry in our study. Sometimes it is useful to *pretend* that we know nothing about Eculidean geometry and then build a completely new system. It is not essential that we act this way all the time; in fact, this is sometimes the hard way to do things. Sometimes we can learn many useful things quickly by *remembering* Euclidean geometry and using its language to describe the new situation that we want to examine. It is this latter approach that we are using to talk about affine geometry.

In Euclid's treatment of geometry, affine and nonaffine properties are intermixed; some affine properties are sometimes proved by using properties that are not affine. Euclid, for instance, proves the existence of parallels by showing that two lines perpendicular to a third do not meet; such a proof would not be allowed in a formal development of affine geometry from a set of affine axioms.

Exercises

1. Draw a diagram to illustrate how a square can become a rectangle by a stretching in a line. Do the same to show how a square can become a parallelogram.
2. Draw a diagram to show that distance is not an affine property.

3. Prove that ratios of distances are preserved for segments on the same line or parallel lines.

4. Which of the following are affine properties: rhombus, trapezoid, parabola, circle, ellipse, ratio of lengths on two intersecting lines, and magnitude of angles? Why?

5. In Euclidean two-space, let every point $P = (x,y)$ be sent to $P' = (x',y')$ such that $x' = \alpha x$ and $y' = \beta y$. Show that this is an affinity (a composition of stretchings in lines).

6. Given any two ellipses, can one always be changed into the other by an affinity? Why?

3.2 PROJECTIONS

We have just seen that parallelism is an affine property but that perpendicularity is not. We know this because parallelism is preserved by stretchings in lines while perpendicularity is affected by these stretchings.

We now want to describe projective geometry in a similar way. To keep things simple, we shall be interested only in *plane* projective geometry and shall not discuss projective geometry of any dimension other than two. A surprising thing about plane projective geometry is that the easiest way to understand it is to look at Euclidean three-space.

To get an intuition of what we want to do, let us first think of Euclidean three-space as the physical space in which we live. We could say that projective geometry is the study of those properties of plane figures that

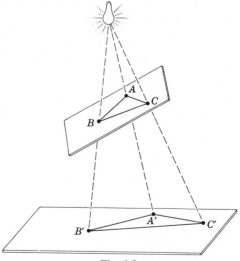

Fig. 3.2a

are preserved by their shadows. Imagine that a triangle *ABC* has been drawn with a black grease pencil on a clear plate of glass (Figure 3.2a) and that a light shines through this glass onto a board casting the shadow of the triangle *A'B'C'*. The property of being a triangle is preserved by shadows.

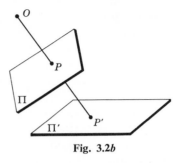

To make this notion more mathematical, we can now abstract from physical three-space and think of geometric three-space. Here the analog of casting shadows will be called *projections*. If Π and Π' are two planes in three-space (Figure 3.2b) and *O* is a fixed point not in either plane,

Fig. 3.2b

then the projection of a point *P* in plane Π from the center *O* is the point *P'* in Π' that is the intersection of the line through *O* and *P* with the plane Π'.

Since we can consider any plane figure as made up of points, it makes sense also to talk about the projection of a plane figure. Projective geometry is the study of those properties of plane figures that are preserved (not affected) by projections.

Let us take a closer look at projections. The first thing we should notice is that the points *O,P,P'* may appear in different orders on the line they determine. For example, if we consider another portion of the planes in the last example, we may have *P'* between *O* and *P* (Figure 3.2c). It is also easy to find situations in which *O* would be between *P* and *P'*.

As we mentioned before, we can think of a figure as being made up of points; the projection of the figure will be the projections of all its points.

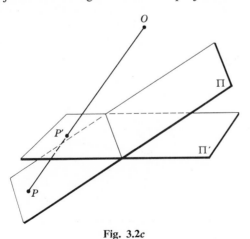

Fig. 3.2c

This applies in particular to a straight line; however, it would be an endless task to find the projection of every point on a line. If line m is in plane Π and we want the projection of m in plane Π' from center O (Figure 3.2d) instead of joining O to each point of m separately, we can consider the totality of all these joins (we shall use the short word "join" to mean "line joining"); they constitute a plane Λ and the projection of the line m onto Π' will be the intersection of the plane Λ with the plane Π'.

In order to avoid confusion between the lines on the planes Π and Π' and the lines joining the points on Π and Π' to the center of projection O, we shall refer to the lines through O as *rays*. We shall refer to the planes through O (the totality of rays through a line) as *flats*. We can say, then, that the projection of a point P onto the plane Π' is the meet (intersection) of that plane with the ray through P; and the projection of a line m onto Π' is the intersection of Π' with the flat containing m.

If we think about the properties of Euclidean geometry, we find that most of them are not preserved by projection, but let us begin with some that are preserved. If three points A,B,C are on the same line m in the plane Π and they are projected onto three points A',B',C' in Π', then the points A',B',C' are also collinear. This means that *collinearity is preserved* by projection.

Instead of saying that a point P lies on a line m, or that a line m passes through a point P, we shall often use the less specific expression, "the point P and the line m are incident." If P and m are incident and projected onto P' and m' in Π', then P' and m' are also incident. We say the *incidence is preserved.*

We come now to the properties that are *not* preserved. It is not hard to see that perpendicularity is not preserved by projections. A right triangle, for example, may go into a triangle that has no right angles. Magnitude of angles in general is not preserved, nor is the length of a segment.

In Chapter 2, we talked about betweenness being a Euclidean property. We might wonder if this is also a projective property. In Figure 3.2e, we

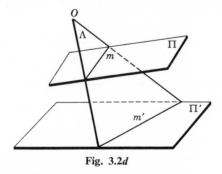

Fig. 3.2d

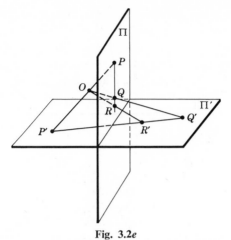

Fig. 3.2e

have three collinear points P,Q,R, in that order, in the plane Π. Because of the position of the center O, the projections P',Q',R' in Π', although collinear, have a different order; R' is between P' and Q'. This shows that betweenness is not a projective property.

Many Euclidean properties are lost under projections, but the situation is even worse that that. If a ray OP is parallel to Π', then there is no point P' that is the projection of P; a point may be lost in projection. Still worse, a whole line may be lost. If a line m in Π together with O determines a plane Λ parallel to Π' then the line has no projection (Figure 3.2f). It seems that the notions of point and line are not projective. It is hard to imagine how we can build a mathematical system called projective

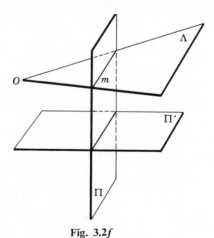

Fig. 3.2f

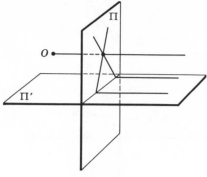

Fig. 3.2g

geometry if we do not even have lines and points. Fortunately, the difficulty can be overcome.

We notice immediately that these losses are exceptions. In a given projection, there is only one line (the intersection of Π with the plane through O which is parallel to Π′) that is lost, and the only points lost are those on that line. We have here an "operation," the "operation of projection," that in general leads to definite results but, in some cases, fails to do so. The situation is somewhat similar to several situations in arithmetic. There the operations of subtracting, dividing, and extracting square roots fail in some cases. In the set of positive integers $3 - 5$

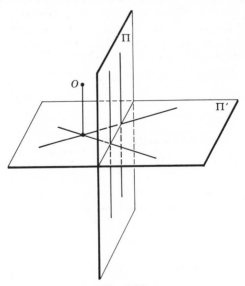

Fig. 3.2h

cannot be performed; $3 \div 5$ cannot be performed in the set of integers; $\sqrt{-2}$ cannot be performed in the real numbers. The remedy is to extend the set of numbers in each case—to build the integers, the rationals, and the complex numbers. In the next section, we shall try to remedy the difficulty we have met in geometry by an analogous procedure: we shall extend the idea of a point and line.

Before we introduce these extensions, we should mention another important property which is not projective. Because points are lost in projection, it is possible for two intersecting lines to project into two parallel lines; this happens if the point of intersection is lost (Figure 3.2g). In a similar way, a pair of parallel lines in Π may project into a pair of intersecting lines on Π', or we can think of projecting the lines in Π' onto the parallel lines in Π (Figure 3.2h). This shows that we must add parallelism to our list of nonprojective properties.

Exercises

1. Show that a circle in plane Π can project into a circle, an ellipse, a hyperbola, or a parabola in plane Π'. This indicates that, in projective geometry, we shall not be able to distinguish the different types of conics.
2. Which of the following properties are projective: triangle, median of a triangle, parallelogram, isosceles triangle, circle, conic, and diameter of a circle? Why?
3. If, instead of projecting by lines through 0, we project by parallel lines from figures in Π to Π', what properties are preserved? Which geometry do you think is characterized by these projections?

3.3 INTRODUCTION OF IDEAL ELEMENTS

Now we want to develop in detail the extensions of point and line mentioned in the last section. In arithmetic, we talk about operations like addition and subtraction; given two numbers, an operation determines a unique third number. We can use the term loosely and speak of operations in geometry; given two points there is a unique line containing both of them, and given two lines there is a unique point which is their intersection (or meet). As in arithmetic, some operations are not always possible. Using only the positive integers, subtraction is sometimes possible, sometimes not. In Euclidean geometry, finding the line joining two points is always possible, but finding the point in which two lines meet is sometimes not possible (the case of parallel lines).

In arithmetic, we make subtraction possible without exception by introducing new numbers: zero and the negative integers (they were called false numbers in the 17th century). We may say that we are extending the concept of number when we add new numbers to a system. Can we do a similar thing in geometry? Can we extend the concept of point and line so that the operation of finding meets is always possible?

Our discussion of projections in the last section gives us an idea of how this can be done. In projecting from one plane to another, two intersecting lines sometimes go into two parallel lines. The point of intersection is lost, but what is lost can be recovered by projecting back again. It seems that we can extend the set of points by projections. However, in projections some points are recovered while at the same time other points are lost. How can we introduce the necessary points without losing some other points? Let us look closer at the operation of projection.

A projection is made up of two steps. In projecting a point P of plane Π through a center O onto a plane Π' we (1) join P to the center of projection O, obtaining a ray OP, and (2) find the intersection P' of the line OP with the plane Π'. Notice that, if we lose a point, it occurs in the second step (if OP is parallel to Π'). We never lose anything in the first step; we can always find the line joining two points in space. Perhaps we can overcome the difficulty of losing points by using only the first step. Let us do it.

The first step assigns a *ray* to every point of Π. What does it do to the lines in Π? To project a line m in Π, we project all the points of m. Each point is assigned a ray through O, so to m we assign a *flat* (plane) through O; this flat consists of the totality of all the rays to the points on m. For different lines on Π, we get different flats and rays through O. If we want to speak of all the rays and flats through O we shall call it a *bundle* Ω.

Immediately, we notice one of the properties of the mapping (assigning) accomplished in step one. If a point P lies on a line m, then the corresponding ray OP is in the flat (plane) determined by point O and line m. We could say that this mapping *preserves incidence*.

On one hand, we have a plane with its points and lines, and on the other a bundle with its rays and flats. The first configuration has the advantage that we can easily draw representations of it on a blackboard or piece of paper. The second has the advantage that two rays always determine a flat and two flats always determine a ray. We want to combine the advantages of both.

Here is how we shall do it. We shall speak of the rays of a bundle Ω as *projective points*, of flats in Ω as *projective lines*, and of the bundle Ω as the *projective plane*. This change in terminology is similar to the change that we make in arithmetic. Originally, by number we meant only the positive integers; later, we used the term for the integers, the rationals, the irrationals, and even the complex numbers.

If we consider a bundle Ω and a plane Π which is not through the center of the bundle, some rays meet Π; we call them *actual (projective) points*. Some rays do not meet Π (those that are parallel to Π); we call them *ideal (projective) points*. Similarly, some flats of Ω meet Π; we call them *actual lines*. There is one flat which does not meet Π; we call it the *ideal line*. We can say that all ideal points are incident with the ideal line. We can also say that two actual lines that correspond to parallel lines meet in an ideal point (this means that if two flats meet Π in two parallel lines their common ray is parallel to Π).

It is very important to emphasize that the distinction between actual and ideal elements of the projective plane is not an intrinsic or absolute distinction. This distinction depends on the choice of the plane Π. If we consider a different plane Π' not through the center of the bundle, some points that had to be called actual relative to Π will be ideal relative to this new plane Π' and vice versa. Any projective line may be considered as the ideal line and its points may be considered as the ideal points; all we have to do is pick the appropriate plane Π relative to O.

In some discussions of projective geometry, surprising statements are made, for instance: "Two parallel lines meet at a point at infinity." After the discussion above about bundles has been totally understood and well digested, it is safe to make another change in terminology and start to call ideal elements "points at infinity" and "the line at infinity." This terminology may be helpful, but it may also give rise to doubts and misunderstandings. If that happens, it means that the theory has not been well understood and it is then advisable to go back to speaking of ideal and actual points and lines.

Exercises

Translate the following sentences into the language of rays, flats, and bundles:
(a) Given a line m and a point P not on it, there is one and only one line n through P such that n is parallel to m.
(b) Two lines parallel to a third are parallel to each other.
(c) Points P,Q,R are collinear.
(d) Lines m and n intersect in a point P.

3.4   INTRODUCTION OF IDEAL ELEMENTS IN COORDINATES

Because of the importance of ideal elements and because of the difficulty that some people have when they first meet these concepts, it seems like a good idea to approach the situation from a second point of view. We shall now take the point of view of plane analytic geometry.

In ordinary plane analytic geometry, a point P is represented by two coordinates, $P = (x,y)$. A line is given by an equation $ax + by + c = 0$, where a and b are not both zero.

We should notice that, although the equation of a line involves three constants a,b,c, only their ratios are important; if we divide by any number $k \neq 0$, the resulting equation $(a/k)x + (b/k)y + (c/k) = 0$ still represents the same line. If we try to simplify this representation of a line by agreeing to make one of the coefficients equal to 1, we get equations of the form $dx + ey + 1 = 0$, $x = ny + f$, or $y = mx + g$. Each of these equations fails to represent some lines. The first can never represent a line through the origin, the second fails to represent lines parallel to the x-axis, and the third misses those lines parallel to the y-axis. In other words, reducing the number of constants to two causes the *loss* of some lines represented. (It is possible to reduce the number of constants to two by using trigonometry, but this would lead us away from our subject.) Therefore, we keep the representation of lines by three numbers a,b,c.

Since we lose something by trying to reduce the line constants to two, maybe we can *gain* something if we represent points by three numbers. For any point $P = (x,y)$, we can always express x and y as ratios, $x = U/W$ and $y = V/W$ where $W \neq 0$. For example, the point $(3,5)$ can be written as $(\frac{6}{2}, \frac{10}{2})$. Thus, we can represent the ordered pair $(3,5)$ by the ordered triple $(6,10,2)$; it can also be represented by many other triples such as $(3,5,1)$ and $(-9,-15,-3)$. To be precise, we should say that the ordered pair (x,y) is represented by a *class* of ordered triples of real numbers; (U,V,W) and (R,S,T) are in the same class (represent the same point) if there exists a real number $k \neq 0$ such that $U = kR$, $V = kS$, and $W = kT$.

Let us see what happens to the equation of a line. Substituting $x = U/W$ and $y = V/W$ into the equation of a line and multiplying by W, we get $aU + bV + cW = 0$. This is certainly more symmetric than the original equation since it involves three numbers U,V,W characterizing a point and also three numbers a,b,c characterizing the line. The numbers (U,V,W) are called the *homogeneous coordinates* of a point. The advantage of characterizing a point by three numbers goes beyond the esthetic advantage of symmetry. As a matter of fact, the symmetry is not yet complete. The three numbers U,V,W are subject to the restriction that $W \neq 0$; the three numbers a,b,c are subject to the restriction that a and b do not vanish simultaneously. This tempts us to investigate what happens if we suspend these restrictions. Of course, we shall not want a,b,c or U,V,W to all be zero, but this is the only restriction that we shall make.

At present, we have no idea what geometric significance U,V,W have when $W = 0$. We shall call three ordered numbers (not all zero) an "analytic point." Similarly, we shall call any three ordered numbers a,b,c (not all zero) an "analytic line." If the equation $aU + bV + cW = 0$ is satisfied, we shall say that the point and line are incident.

When $W \neq 0$, there is an ordinary geometric point corresponding to the analytic point (U,V,W). When a and b do not vanish simultaneously, there is an ordinary geometric line corresponding to $[a,b,c]$ (we shall use square brackets to indicate the coefficients of a line). But there are analytic points, namely $(U,V,0)$, that do not correspond to ordinary geometric points; there are analytic lines $[a,b,c]$ with $a = b = 0$ that do not correspond to geometric lines. It is better to say that there is one such line because all triples $[0,0,c]$ for different values of c represent the same analytic line—only ratios are significant. Notice that all the exceptional points $(U,V,0)$ are incident with this exceptional line $[0,0,c]$.

If we actually identify those analytic points that represent geometric points with these geometric points, and do the same with the analytic lines, we see that analytic points and lines may be thought of as an extension of the original plane in the same way that ideal points and the ideal line were an extension of the plane Π. As a matter of fact, this is essentially the same extension.

In order to see this, we now think of our analytic plane as being in three-space perpendicular to one of the three coordinate axes. To be definite, let us let our plane Π be parallel to the x,y-plane and intersecting the z-axis one unit above the origin (Figure 3.4a). A vector with tail at the origin may be thought of as a ray from center O (it represents a point P in our plane). The vector is represented by three components $\{U,V,W\}$ or, in our particular cases, $\{U,V,1\}$.

Lines on our plane are represented by flats through O, and the flats (which are planes) can be represented by a vector which is perpendicular to the flat. So a line m on the plane Π is also represented by three components $\{a,b,c\}$. The relation $aU + bV + cW = 0$ is nothing but the dot product of the vectors $\{a,b,c\}$ and $\{U,V,W\}$. If the dot product of two nonzero vectors is zero, we know that this means that the vectors are perpendicular to each other. From the way we have chosen our vectors to represent the point and line, this is exactly what we would expect to

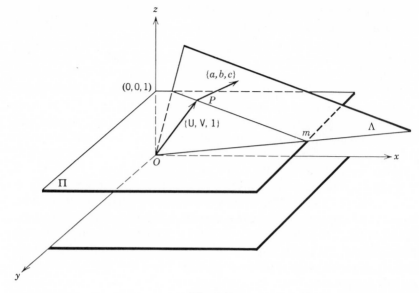

Fig. 3.4a

happen. So the homogeneous coordinates (U,V,W) of a point are nothing but the components (in the coordinate system introduced above) of a vector $\{U,V,W\}$, and similarly for $[a,b,c]$ which represents a line.

It should not be surprising now that analytic points $(U,V,0)$ that correspond to no geometric points have coordinates that are the components of a vector on a ray that is parallel to our plane. Thus $(U,V,0)$ is an ideal point. Similarly, the analytic line $[0,0,c]$ to which no geometric line corresponds is represented by a vector perpendicular to a flat which is parallel to our plane. We can identify analytic points with projective points (rays) and analytic lines with projective lines (flats). The points $(U,V,0)$ are the ideal points (or the points at infinity) and the line $[0,0,c]$ is the ideal line (or the line at infinity).

Exercises

1. Find the line through $(1,2,4)$ and $(-3,5,1)$.
2. Find the point of intersection between the lines having coefficients $[1,0,3]$ and $[-2,-1,4]$.
3. Find the ideal point of $3U + 4V = 5W$.
4. Find the line that contains $(2,1,-3)$ and the ideal point on the line $[1,1,-1]$.

5. Which of the following sets of points are collinear:
   (a) $(1,0,1)$, $(0,0,1)$, $(1,1,1)$.
   (b) $(1,1,1)$, $(1,2,0)$, $(-2,-5,1)$.
   (c) $(2,1,0)$, $(0,1,0)$, $(-1,0,0)$.
6. Find a necessary and sufficient condition for three lines $[a_1,b_1,c_1]$, $[a_2,b_2,c_2]$, and $[a_3,b_3,c_3]$ to be concurrent.

3.5 HARMONIC PAIRS

By introducing ideal elements, we removed the difficulty of losing points and losing a line in projections. Let us summarize what we have accomplished. At this point, we are able to describe plane projective geometry as the study of those properties of plane figures that are not affected by projections. This description makes sense if we think of projective points as the distinct rays through a fixed point O and the projective lines as the distinct flats through O. Another realization of projective points and lines that makes the operation of projection reasonable is to think of points as the distinct classes of ordered triples (U,V,W) of real numbers (not all zero) and lines as the distinct classes of ordered triples $[a,b,c]$ of real numbers (not all zero). A point $P = (U,V,W)$ is incident with the line $m = [a,b,c]$ if the ray representing P is contained in the flat representing m, or analytically if $aU + bV + cW = 0$. We shall not always explicitly use these realizations in the discussion that follows, but it is only because of these realizations that any discussion of projections is possible.

Many Euclidean properties do not belong to projective geometry. We have already mentioned that betweenness, perpendicularity, length, and parallelism are not projective properties. However, some Euclidean concepts can be found in a modified form in projective geometry. The concept of the midpoint of a segment is one example; in this section, we shall try to find out in what way it appears in projective geometry.

The property of being the midpoint of a segment is certainly not projective. If M is the midpoint of segment AB in Π (Figure 3.5a) we have $AM/MB = 1$. By a suitable choice of O and Π', we can get $A'M'/M'B'$ in Π' to be any nonzero real number we desire.

To find a generalization of midpoint which is projective, let us consider how we construct a midpoint. One way involves using compasses (that is, circles), and this, as we mentioned in Section 3.1, involves perpendicularity. Since neither circles nor perpendicularity is a projective concept, this does not seem to be the place to start looking for a generalization. Fortunately, there is another construction for a midpoint which involves only one nonprojective notion: parallelism.

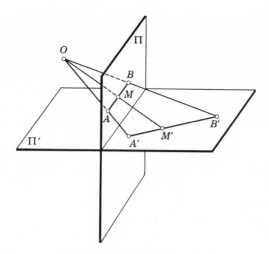

Fig. 3.5a

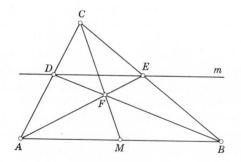

Fig. 3.5b

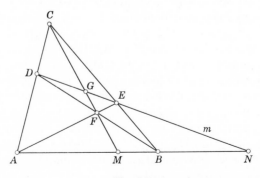

Fig. 3.5c

The midpoint M of a segment AB can be constructed as follows. Let A and B be two vertices of a triangle and choose any point C as the third vertex (Figure 3.5b). Draw any line m parallel to AB and not containing C. Let D and E be the intersections of this line with AC and CB. Let the lines DB and AE meet at point F, then line CF meets AB at the desired midpoint M. (The proof of this construction will be left as an exercise.)

The construction just described is not projective because it uses parallelism, but some aspects of it are projective; for example, the collinearity of A,D,C *is* projective. In order to generalize this construction to a completely projective one, let us project the figure into another plane and eliminate the parallelism. Let us choose the center and the plane so that AB and DE will become intersecting lines and also so that none of the points mentioned above are lost. The figure now has the form of Figure 3.5c. (We shall omit the primes on the names of the points and simply remember that we have projected the original figure.) The two lines AB and DE which were parallel now meet in a point N. We could say that the point N corresponds to the point at infinity on the original parallel lines. Notice that M is no longer the actual midpoint of AB; we shall say that M is the midpoint of AB relative to N. We could also say that the actual midpoint of AB in the original figure is the midpoint of AB relative to the point at infinity on AB.

If you have been observant you may have an objection to defining M as the midpoint of AB relative to N on AB. We can define something like this only if M is completely determined by $A,B,$ and N. In our construction, however, we also used the arbitrary point C and the line m containing $D,E,$ and N. We have a right to define M as the midpoint of AB relative to N only if we can show that the position of M does not depend on the choice of C and m. We shall prove this now.

In order to show that M is not dependent on the choice of C and m, we must take any two constructions of M and show that we get the same result from each construction. Let the first construction be as in Figure 3.5c and choose another auxiliary point C' and a new line m' (Figure 3.5d) and repeat the construction. Let the intersection of the line through F' and C' with the line through A and B be called M'. The question is whether M' is the same point as M. The answer is *yes*. To see this we project back into the original plane where m was parallel to AB and do this from the same center of projection. The point N goes back to infinity, so the line m' will go into a line parallel to AB, and therefore M' will go to the actual midpoint of the original segment AB. We now have both M and M' arising from the original midpoint of AB by the same projection. Since the operation of projecting points sends a point to only *one* point, the only way the original midpoint can go to both M and M' is if M is

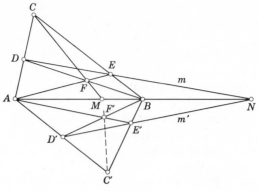

Fig. 3.5*d*

identical with *M'*. This shows that the construction of the midpoint of *AB* relative to *N* is independent of the choice of *C* and *m*.

We are now able to accept the definition of the midpoint *M* of a segment *AB* relative to *N* on *AB*. The construction used in this definition (Figure 3.5*c*) involves only the notion of collinearity (the triples *AMB*, *ADC*, *BEC*, *DEN*, *DFB*, *EFA*, and *CFM* are collinear). Because of this, we can say that the midpoint *M* of a segment *AB* relative to *N* on *AB* is a projective relationship on the four points *A*,*B*,*M*, and *N*; that is, it is preserved by projections, or we say that it is an invariant under projections.

If we would like to describe the construction that we have just used in words, we can do so by means of the concept of a *quadrifigure*. A quadrifigure is a plane figure consisting of four points (vertices), no three of which are collinear and taken in a definite order (as *D*,*C*,*E*,*F* in Figure 3.5*c*) and four sides (*DC*, *CE*, *EF*, *FD*) joining these points consecutively. A line joining two opposite vertices (two vertices not on the same side) is called a *diagonal line* of the quadrifigure (*DE* and *CF*) and a point in which two opposite sides meet is called a *diagonal point* (*A* and *B*). Using this terminology, the midpoint *M* of *AB* relative to *N* on *AB* is the point in which one diagonal line of a quadrifigure with diagonal points *A*,*B* meets the join of these points, if the other diagonal line meets this join at *N*.

From this formulation it becomes clear that, if *M* is the midpoint of *AB* relative to *N*, then *N* is the midpoint of *AB* relative to *M*. In other words, *M* and *N* play similar roles in the relationship that we are discussing. (No one should object to *M* lying between *A* and *B* whereas *N* does not—we know from Section 3.2 that betweenness is not a projective property.) The relationship is therefore a relationship on two pairs of points, *A*,*B* and *M*,*N*—we shall say that the pair *M*,*N* is harmonic to the pair A,B. Sometimes we say that N is the fourth harmonic of A,B,M (and M is the fourth harmonic of A,B,N).

The two pairs of points play different roles in our construction (for instance, three lines of our figure meet at A or B, and only two at M or N). Nevertheless, it is true that the roles of the two pairs are the same as far as the relationship of harmonicity is concerned. To prove this, we must show that B is the midpoint of MN relative to A. We can prove this by projecting Figure 3.5c into a new plane so that the point A goes to infinity. The resulting figure is something like Figure 3.5e in which the lines MN, FE, and DC are parallel because A went to infinity. It can be proved using Euclidean geometry that B is the midpoint of MN relative to a point at infinity. (This, too, is left as an exercise.) It then follows that, in Figure 3.5c, B is the midpoint of MN relative to A; so A,B is harmonic to M,N, and M,N is also harmonic to A,B.

Since sending point A to infinity led to an interesting result, we might wonder what we could observe by sending point C in Figure 3.5c to infinity (Figure 3.5f) but keeping the line AB and the points on it in place; we can do this by projecting into a plane which intersects the original one in the line AB. Lines AD, MF, and BE are now parallel and there are three pairs of similar triangles in the figure, ADN and BEN, AFM and AEB, ADB and MFB. The similar triangles give us the following proportions between the lengths of certain segments:

$$AN/BN = AD/BE, \qquad AB/AM = BE/MF,$$

and

$$MB/AB = MF/AD.$$

Multiplying them together and cancelling we get $(AN/BN)(MB/AM) = 1$. Since A,B,M,N are on the same line, we can consider these segments as directed; taking this into account, $MB = -BM$ and the equation can be written as $(AM/BM)/(AN/BN) = -1$. This tells us that, if four points A,B,M,N are harmonic, then the condition on their mutual distances is $(AM/BM)/(AN/BN) = -1$.

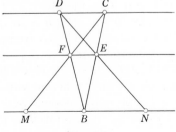

Fig. 3.5e

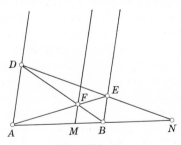

Fig. 3.5f

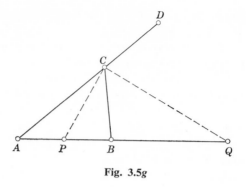

Fig. 3.5g

We should notice now that the condition for harmonicity (a projective concept) that we have just found is expressed in terms of distances and ratios that have no projective meaning. Situations of this kind occur often in geometry. We met a similar situation in affine geometry (Section 3.1) when we were defining a stretching in a line. In ordinary analytic geometry, we have another example: the expression for the distance between two points is given in terms of coordinates that have in themselves no geometrical meaning.

We shall call the expression $(AM/BM)/(AN/BN)$ the *cross ratio* (sometimes it is called the double ratio) of the four collinear points A,B,M,N. If the cross ratio of four points on a line is equal to -1, then it has an invariant projective meaning—the two pairs of points A,B and M,N are harmonic. Notice that although we cannot speak of the linear arrangement of collinear points (because betweenness is not projective), the cross ratio of four collinear points does depend upon the arrangement in which the points are *considered* (the order in which we substitute them into the formula for cross ratio).

The condition for harmonicity in terms of ratios of segments leads to another interesting observation. In Euclidean geometry, the bisector of an interior angle of a triangle divides the opposite side in the same ratio as the other two sides. For example, in Figure 3.5g, the bisector PC of the angle ACB divides the side AB internally so that $AP/PB = AC/BC$. The bisector CQ of the exterior angle DCB divides the side AB externally and $AQ/BQ = AC/BC$ in this triangle. Combining these two proportions, we get $AP/PB = AQ/BQ$ or $(AP/BP)/(AQ/BQ) = -1$. This tells us that the points A,B,P,Q are harmonic. Although we began with the concept of an angle bisector which is not a projective notion, we have arrived at the relationship of harmonicity once again, and this does have projective significance.

Exercises

1. Using Euclidean geometry, prove that the construction of the midpoint of a segment given in Figure 3.5b is valid.
2. In the midpoint construction using parallelism (Figure 3.5b), must line m enter triangle ABC, or could it be chosen external to the triangle? Why?
3. Using Euclidean geometry, prove that in Figure 3.5e, B is the midpoint of MN.
4. Using Euclidean geometry, prove that in Figure 3.5g, $AP/PB = AC/BC$ and $AQ/BQ = AC/BC$.
5. Let $A = (3,0,1)$, $B = (8,0,1)$, and $M = (7,0,1)$. Find N the fourth harmonic point with respect to A,B and M.
6. Using the cross ratio equal to -1 as the condition for harmonicity, show that if the pair M,N is harmonic with respect to A,B, then A,B is harmonic with respect to M,N.
7. In Figure 3.5c let the meet of CF and DE be G. Besides A,B,M,N there are two other sets of harmonic points in the figure. Find them.
8. If A,B,N,M are four harmonic points, their cross ratio is -1 (if the points are considered in the order listed). Four points can be considered in $4! = 24$ different ways. How many different cross ratios arise from four harmonic points if all possible arrangements are considered? What are they?
9. Prove that a necessary and sufficient condition for M and N to be harmonic with respect to A and B is that $XM \cdot XN = a^2$ if X is the midpoint of AB and $AB = 2a$.

3.6   CROSS RATIO

In the last section, we introduced the notion of the cross ratio of four collinear points. We have already seen its importance in the case of harmonic points; if the cross ratio of four points is -1, then it has an invariant projective meaning (that is, it is not affected by projections)—the points are harmonic. It does not follow from *this* that a cross ratio always has a projective meaning, but you should be wondering at this point whether it does have a general projective meaning. We shall now prove that it does; the cross ratio of four collinear points is a projective invariant.

Let A,B,M,N be four collinear points. If we project the line m containing these points into another plane, we get another line n containing the images A',B',M',N' of the four points. These two lines, m and n, together with the center of projective O will be in the same flat. In Figure 3.6a we look only at this flat. There are several triangles having their base on m and a vertex at O; they all have the same altitude (the distance from O to

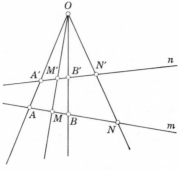

Fig. 3.6a

the line m), so that their areas are proportional to their bases. Because of this, we can write

$$\frac{AOM}{BOM}\bigg/\frac{AON}{BON} = \frac{AM}{BM}\bigg/\frac{AN}{BN}.$$

(We shall use AOM to represent the area of the triangle AOM.) On the other hand, the area of a triangle is equal to half of the product of two of its sides times the sine of the included angle, so we can also write

$$\frac{AOM}{BOM}\bigg/\frac{AON}{BON} = \frac{OA \cdot OM \sin \sphericalangle AOM}{OB \cdot OM \sin \sphericalangle BOM}\bigg/\frac{OA \cdot ON \sin \sphericalangle AON}{OB \cdot ON \sin \sphericalangle BON}.$$

Combining these two results, we get

$$\frac{AM}{BM}\bigg/\frac{AN}{BN} = \frac{\sin \sphericalangle AOM}{\sin \sphericalangle BOM}\bigg/\frac{\sin \sphericalangle AON}{\sin \sphericalangle BON}.$$

We could repeat this same reasoning with the points A',B',M',N'; since the angles are the same in both cases, we can conclude that

$$\frac{AM}{BM}\bigg/\frac{AN}{BN} = \frac{A'M'}{B'M'}\bigg/\frac{A'N'}{B'N'}.$$

This proves that cross ratio has a projective meaning; it is not affected by projections—it is a projective invariant.

Again you should notice that, although the length of a segment (or the distance between two points) and the ratio of two lengths have no projective meaning, the ratio of two such ratios (or the cross ratio) *is* projective. Cross ratio plays a role in projective geometry which is analogous to distance in Euclidean geometry.

In projective geometry, any two points can always be projected into any other two points. More than that, any three collinear points can be projected into any other three collinear points (this will be proved later in Section 3.8). Because of these possible transformations, it is impossible to assign a real number to two or three points in an invariant way. For *four* collinear points, the situation is different because of the fact that cross ratio is a projective invariant; four collinear points constitute the minimal configuration that has a projective significance and the cross ratio is an expression of this significance.

As a corollary of the reasoning above, we may speak of the *cross ratio of four concurrent lines*. We can define the cross ratio of four lines *a,b,m,n* concurrent at *P* to be

$$\frac{\sin \sphericalangle APM}{\sin \sphericalangle BPM} \bigg/ \frac{\sin \sphericalangle APN}{\sin \sphericalangle BPN}$$

where *A,B,M,N* are the meets of *a,b,m,n*, respectively, with any line *r* not containing *P* (Figure 3.6*b*).

If we are using the Euclidean plane with a usual Cartesian coordinate system, points are given by two coordinates. In general, the distances required to calculate the cross ratio of four collinear points *A,B,M,N* are a little complicated to compute. However, if *A,B,M,N* lie on the *x*-axis, then the distances can be computed from the abscissas x_1, x_2, x_3, x_4 of the four points; for example $AM = x_3 - x_1$, $BM = x_3 - x_2$, and so on; thus, the cross ratio of *A,B,M,N* is given by

$$\frac{x_1 - x_3}{x_2 - x_3} \bigg/ \frac{x_1 - x_4}{x_2 - x_4}.$$

The cross ratio of four concurrent lines can be calculated in a similar way by means of their slopes.

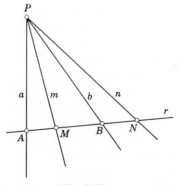

Fig. 3.6*b*

Exercises

1. Draw a diagram to illustrate how two given ponts can be projected into any two other points.

2. Prove that the cross ratio of four concurrent lines is invariant under projections.

3. Show how the cross ratio of four concurrent lines can be calculated by means of their slopes.

4. Four points can be considered in 24 different ways. Considering all these possible arrangements, how many different cross ratios can arise from four given points? Find a simple way in which these different cross ratios are related to each other.

5. Let A,B,M,N be collinear and let (AB,MN) represent the cross ratio of these points considered in the arrangement A,B,M,N. Prove that $(AB,MN) \times (AB,NM) = 1$ and that $(AB,MN) + (AM,BN) = 1$.

6. Show that if A,B,C,D,E are collinear, then

$$(AB,DE)(AB,EC)(AB,CD) = 1.$$

7. Find the cross ratio of the four points having abscissas $4,7,-1,0$.

8. If A,B,M have abscissas $1,3,2$, respectively, and $(AB,MN) = -5$, find N.

9. What conclusion can you draw about A,B,M,N if their cross ratio is 0? If it is 1? If it is infinite (assume that you are working in an extended real number system)? If their cross ratio is -1?

3.7 DUALITY

In the last section, we noticed that there is an analogy between the cross ratio of four collinear points and the cross ratio of four concurrent lines. You may have noticed also that points and lines play similar roles in a quadrifigure; the definition of diagonal point is analogous to that of diagonal line. Generalizing this, we arrive at the idea of *duality*. Given a figure consisting of points and lines, we may consider another figure called the *dual* of the first; this second figure consists of points and lines, but the lines of the second figure correspond to the points of the first, and the points of the second correspond to the lines of the first. For example, in Figure 3.7a, three concurrent lines are the dual of three collinear points.

Some figures are *self-dual*; that is, they are their own duals. For instance, a quadrifigure with its diagonal points and diagonal lines is self-dual. (Why?) But the figure consisting of only four harmonic points and the line containing them is not self-dual, nor the figure consisting of four concurrent lines which are harmonic (have a cross ratio of -1).

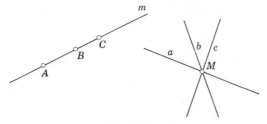

Fig. 3.7a

Instead of these figures, we could get a self-dual one by considering a figure consisting of a pair of points and a pair of lines. Let the points A,B be the diagonal points of a quadrifigure and the lines m,n be the diagonal lines of the same quadrifigure (Figure 3.7b). We now can speak of two harmonic pairs—one a pair of points, the other a pair of lines. If we want to, we may consider the line AB joining the diagonal points and then the meets M and N of AB with the diagonal lines—we then have two harmonic pairs of points A,B and M,N on AB. Similarly, we could consider the meet G of the diagonal lines and its joins a and b with the diagonal points—this gives us two harmonic pairs of lines a,b and m,n. The figure consisting of the two diagonal points and the two diagonal lines of the same quadrifigure *is* self-dual. We could say that this pair of points and pair of lines are harmonic, or that they have a cross ratio of -1. We could also generalize this and consider cross ratios of any pair of points and any pair of lines.

Since we have already met several examples of duality in projective geometry, it seems that we should consider, in connection with any proposition that arises, its *dual proposition*; that is, the one obtained from it by interchanging the words point and line, collinear and concurrent, meet and join, etc. It seems that if a proposition is correct, its dual will

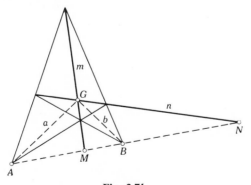

Fig. 3.7b

also be correct. This statement is called the *principle of duality*; but we have *not* proved it yet. Even so, it is useful as a guiding idea in developing projective geometry. (We shall prove it in Section 3.11.)

The principle of duality does not hold in Euclidean geometry and affine geometry. You may have noticed that the definition of cross ratio for lines is not dual to the definition of cross ratio for points. This happens because these definitions use concepts from Euclidean geometry, distances and sines. Although these forms of the definitions are not dual, the concepts are dual in projective geometry. Besides this, we can consider cross ratios in Euclidean geometry (even without the duality); in fact, cross ratio is a Euclidean invariant (it is not affected by translations, rotations, and reflections) as well as a projective invariant.

To make the concept of duality more useful, we shall make an adjustment in our terminology. We usually think of a line as composed of all the points on it—the dual of this is the totality of all the lines through a point—but we usually do not think of a point as *consisting* of all the lines passing through it. It would be logical to speak of the lines through a point as constituting that point, but it would sound strange; as a compromise, when we want to consider a point as the totality of all the lines through it, we shall speak of a *pencil* of lines through a point and call the point the *vertex* of the pencil.

Exercises

1. Find the duals of the following: the line connecting two points, a triangle, four points and their six joins, Figures 3.7c, 3.7d, and 3.7e.

2. Using homogeneous coordinates, we can also speak of duality. The point (r,s,t) is the dual of the line $[r,s,t]$. Find the duals of the origin $(0,0,1)$, a line $[a,b,1]$ not through the origin, and a point $(U,V,0)$ at infinity.

3. Show that cross ratio is a Euclidean invariant.

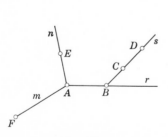

Fig. 3.7c

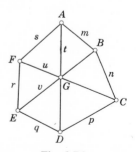

Fig. 3.7d

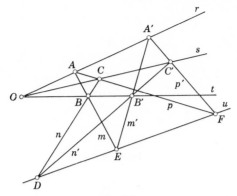

Fig. 3.7e

3.8 PERSPECTIVITY

In Section 3.6, we proved that the cross ratio of four collinear points is a projective invariant. The proof consisted in projecting the four points A,B,M,N on line m onto A',B',M',N' on line n in another plane and examining what happened in the flat containing lines m and n (Figure 3.6a). There is a subtle fact about the operation of projection which we should notice: it does *not* take place within the projective geometry we are building, but within Euclidean three-space. Plane projective geometry is concerned with figures formed by points and lines and the properties of these figures that are not affected by projections; the projections are a criterion from *outside* of projective geometry used to determine which properties belong to projective geometry.

Although projections are outside of projective geometry, we can consider an analogous operation or mapping *within* projective geometry. We can map four points A,B,M,N on a line m onto four points A',B',M',N' on line m' by using the meets of m' with the joins of A,B,M,N and a center S as the images (Figure 3.8a). Of course, we need not restrict ourselves to four points; any number of points can be mapped. This mapping is usually called a *perspectivity*. Since there is no essential difference between Figures 3.6a and 3.8a, we can conclude that cross ratios are preserved by perspectivities.

There are two questions that we shall now discuss: (1) are perspectivities the only mappings (within projective geometry) from one line to a different line that preserve cross ratios? (2) If not, what are the most general mappings that preserve cross ratios? Since cross ratio plays a role in projective geometry analogous to distance in Euclidean geometry, the

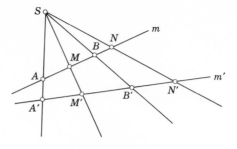

Fig. 3.8a

questions, in effect, are looking for the projective analog of the rigid motions.

To answer these questions, let us consider a mapping that results from the successive application of two perspectivities—we shall call it a *double perspectivity*. Points A,B,C on line m are mapped onto A',B',C' on m' from a point S, then A',B',C' are mapped onto A'',B'',C'' on m'' from a point T (Figure 3.8b). We could, so to say, forget about line m' and simply assign A,B,C to A'',B'',C''. This mapping is a double perspectivity. (Strictly speaking, we should distinguish between the mapping of the points A,B,C onto A'',B'',C'' and the particular construction, the double perspectivity, used to determine the mapping. The same mapping could possibly be achieved by many double perspectivities. However, we shall use the term "double perspectivity" for the mapping as well as the construction.) Since the cross ratio of four collinear points is not affected by each of the two perspectivities whose result is the double perspectivity, we can conclude that a double perspectivity is a cross ratio preserving mapping.

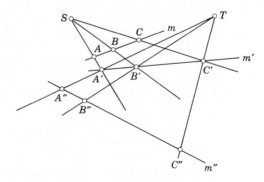

Fig. 3.8b

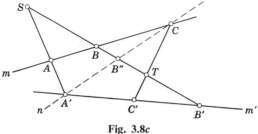

Fig. 3.8c

We are now on the way to an answer to question (1). Double perspectivities preserve cross ratios; if we can show that some double perspectivity is not a single perspectivity, then the answer to question (1) is negative. We shall do this now. Let A,B,C lie on line m and A',B',C' on m' in such a way that the joins of A and A', B and B', C and C' are not concurrent (Figure 3.8c). This mapping is *not* a perspectivity (why?) but it is a double perspectivity. To see that it is a double perspectivity, let the meet of AA' and BB' be S and the meet of BB' and CC' be T. Let the join of A' and C be n and the meet of n and BB' be B''. The first perspectivity from S assigns A,B,C on m to A',B'',C on n. The second perspectivity from T assigns A',B'',C on n to A',B',C' on m'. So this is a double perspectivity, and it is not a single perspectivity. Besides answering question (1), we have also proved here that there always exists a double perspectivity taking any three points of one line to any three points of another line. (If A,B,C and their images A',B',C' are all on one line, it is not always possible to achieve this mapping by a double perspectivity, but we are not concerned with mappings from one line to itself in this discussion.)

It remains now to answer question (2) and find the most general cross ratio preserving mapping. A double perspectivity gives a more general mapping than a single perspectivity. We might think that a triple perspectivity would be even more general. This is *not* the case. A double perspectivity *is* the most general cross ratio preserving mapping from one line to another line. Let us prove this.

We already know that three collinear points A,B,C and their images A',B',C' on another line determine a double perspectivity. If this mapping also takes point D to D', then the cross ratios $(AC/BC)/(AD/BD)$ and $(A'C'/B'C')/(A'D'/B'D')$ are equal because a double perspectivity preserves cross ratios. Let us assume that there is a more general cross ratio preserving mapping that also takes A,B,C to A',B',C'; let it take D to D'' so that A,B,C,D and A',B',C',D'' have the same cross ratios. We then know that

$$\frac{AC}{BC}\Big/\frac{AD}{BD} = \frac{A'C'}{B'C'}\Big/\frac{A'D''}{B'D''},$$

so that

$$\frac{A'C'}{B'C'} \bigg/ \frac{A'D'}{B'D'} = \frac{A'C'}{B'C'} \bigg/ \frac{A'D''}{B'D''} \,.$$

It now follows that

$$\frac{A'D'}{B'D'} = \frac{A'D''}{B'D''} \,,$$

$$\frac{A'D'}{B'D'} - 1 = \frac{A'D''}{B'D''} - 1,$$

$$\frac{A'D' - B'D'}{B'D'} = \frac{A'D'' - B'D''}{B'D''} \,,$$

$$\frac{A'B'}{B'D'} = \frac{A'B'}{B'D''} \,,$$

$$B'D' = B'D'';$$

that is, D'' is the same distance from B' as D', in fact, $D'' = D'$. This shows that a cross ratio preserving mapping is entirely determined by three points and their images. We can now answer question (2). Since a cross ratio preserving mapping is completely determined by three points and their images and a double perspectivity always exists taking A,B,C to A',B',C' so that cross ratios are preserved, a double perspectivity is the most general cross ratio preserving mapping.

Exercises

1. A perspectivity maps four collinear points onto four other collinear points. Describe the dual of a perspectivity and how it is constructed. Is the cross ratio of four concurrent lines preserved by this dual operations? Why?
2. Draw a diagram to illustrate two different double perspectivities (constructions) which determine the same mapping.
3. Draw a diagram to illustrate a double perspectivity which is equivalent (determines the same mapping as) to a single perspectivity.
4. Prove that a cross ratio preserving mapping which leaves three points of a line leaves every point of that line fixed.
5. Describe the dual of a double perspectivity.
6. Dualize Exercise 4.
7. Let three collinear points A,B,C on m be mapped onto three collinear points A',B',C' on m'. These points and their images determine a double

perspectivity. Show how to construct the image D' on m' under this double perspectivity of any point D on m.

8. Describe the dual construction to Exercise 7.

9. If A,B,C and their images A',B',C' are all collinear, in general, how many perspectivities are necessary to achieve this mapping? Explain why.

10. Prove the fundamental theorem of projective geometry: Given three collinear points A,B,C and their three collinear images A',B',C', they determine a unique mapping which can be achieved by a finite sequence of perspectivities.

11. Prove that a necessary and sufficient condition for a double perspectivity taking one line into a different line to be a single perspectivity is that the point of intersection of the two lines is mapped into itself.

12. Dualize Exercise 11. Prove it.

3.9   PROPOSITIONS OF DESARGUES AND PAPPUS

In Section 3.5, we began with the Euclidean concept of the midpoint M of a segment AB and found that it appears in a more general form as the midpoint M of a segment AB relative to N on the line through A and B. We said that A,B and M,N were harmonic pairs. Now we want to begin with the Euclidean concept of similar figures and see if this can be found in some more general form in projective geometry.

A basic theorem related to similarity states that, *if two parallel lines m and n intersect the sides of an angle O at A,B and A',B'* (Figure 3.9a), *then $OB/OA = OB'/OA'$.* The converse of this theorem is also true: *if two lines m and n intersect the sides of an angle O at A,B and A',B' and $OB/OA = OB'/OA'$, then m and n are parallel.* Since each pair OB and OA, OB' and OA', lies on a line, this theorem and its converse belong to affine geometry as well as to Euclidean geometry; in affine geometry the ratio of two segments on the same line is not affected by stretchings in lines (affinities).

We are talking about affine geometry because it is midway between Euclidean geometry and projective geometry. To move from Euclidean geometry to projective geometry, we must discard the notions of distance and parallelism; in affine geometry we have parallelism but no real distance.

There are two things that we should notice about the theorem that we have mentioned. It is possible to state the theorem in other ways in Euclidean geometry that are not possible in affine geometry, and the property of similarity with which it is concerned in Euclidean geometry does not appear in its totality in affine geometry. Let us discuss these two points. In Euclidean geometry, we could substitute $OB/OB' = OA/OA'$

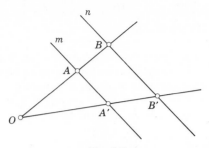

Fig. 3.9a

into the theorem and it would still be a true proposition; in affine geometry, we cannot do this because OB and OB' are not on the same line (or parallel lines) and the ratio OB/OB' is not preserved by all affinities. The second difference is in the property under consideration. The theorem is concerned with similarity in Euclidean geometry, but similarity is not an affine property. (Why?) What affine property are we concerned with? Triangles AOA' and BOB' are not only similar, but also similarly situated (the joins of corresponding vertices are concurrent). We say that triangles AOA' and BOB' are *homothetic*—similar and similarly situated. Homothety, a special kind of similarity, is affine. (Why?)

We now want to move all the way to projective geometry. To move from Euclidean geometry to affine, we had to restrict ratios to ratios of segments on the same line (or parallel lines). In projective geometry, we must eliminate ratios completely because distance, even as a ratio, is not projective. To do this, we consider three concurrent lines instead of two and two pairs of parallel lines AA' and BB', $A'A''$ and $B'B''$ (Figure 3.9b). Using the theorem twice, we obtain $OB/OA = OB'/OA'$ and $OB'/OA' = OB''/OA''$. We then conclude that $OB/OA = OB''/OA''$. The converse then tells us that AA'' and BB'' are parallel. We could state this result as an affine (and Euclidean) theorem.

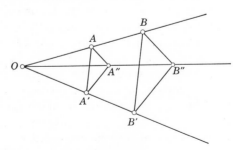

Fig. 3.9b

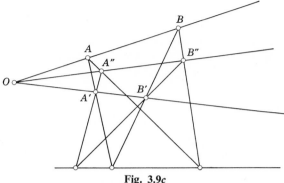

Fig. 3.9c

Theorem. *If the joins of corresponding vertices of two triangles are concurrent, and two pairs of corresponding sides are parallel, then the third sides are parallel.*

To generalize this theorem so that it holds in projective geometry, we must say that two lines meet at a point at infinity instead of saying that they are parallel. The theorem then reads as follows: If the joins of corresponding vertices of two triangles are concurrent and two pairs of corresponding sides meet at a point at infinity, then the third pair of sides meet at a point at infinity. Since, in projective geometry, the line at infinity is just like any other line, we arrive at the following projective theorem (Figure 3.9c).

Theorem (Desargues). *If the joins of the corresponding vertices of two triangles are concurrent, then the meets of the corresponding sides are collinear.*

There is another important theorem of projective geometry which we can derive from the same Euclidean theorem on ratios, if we eliminate the ratios in a different way. Consider two lines m and n meeting at O with six points, A,B,C on m and A',B',C' on n, so that AB' is parallel to

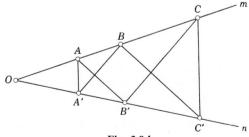

Fig. 3.9d

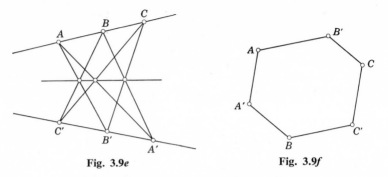

<table>
<tr><td>Fig. 3.9*e*</td><td>Fig. 3.9*f*</td></tr>
</table>

BC' and $A'B$ is parallel to $B'C$ (Figure 3.9*d*). We know that $OA/OB = OB'/OC'$ and $OB/OC = OA'/OB'$. Multiplying we get $OA/OC = OA'/OC'$ and we can conclude that AA' and CC' are parallel.

In projective geometry, AB' and BC', $A'B$ and $B'C$, and AA' and CC' meet at points on the line at infinity; that is, the meets are collinear. Thus, in projective geometry, we know that if the points A,B,C are on a line m and A',B',C' are on another line n, then the meets of AB' and BC', $A'B$ and $B'C$, and AA' and CC' are collinear (Figure 3.9*e*). The theorem is usually not stated this way because the six points can be thought of as the vertices of a hexagon $AB'CC'BA'$. The sides of the hexagon are AB' $B'C$, CC', $C'B$, BA', and $A'A$, and the three points that are collinear are the meets of AB' and $C'B$, BA' and $B'C$, and AA' and CC'. If we consider a hexagon (Figure 3.9*f*) with "sides which do not intersect each other" (we use quotes because this statement has no meaning in projective geometry), we see that the three collinear points are the meets of opposite sides. Using this terminology, we can state the theorem in its traditional form.

Theorem (Pappus). *If the alternate vertices of a hexagon lie on two straight lines, the meet of the opposite sides are collinear.*

Exercises

1. Prove that homothety is an affine invariant.
2. Draw several different cases of two triangles having the joins of the corresponding vertices concurrent and verify experimentally that the Desargues theorem holds.
3. Compare the converse and the dual of the Desargues theorem.
4. Prove the converse of Desargues.

5. What theorem of affine geometry can be obtained by projecting Figure 3.9*b* so that *O* goes to infinity?

6. Prove that in Euclidean three-space, if two triangles are in different planes and the joins of the corresponding vertices are concurrent, then the meets of the corresponding sides are collinear.

7. Use Exercise 6 and Euclidean geometry to prove the Desargues theorem.

8. State the dual of the Pappus theorem. Draw a figure to illustrate it. How is this figure related to the Pappus configuration?

3.10   CONICS

We have already found several generalizations of Euclidean concepts which appear in projective geometry. Harmonicity is a generalization of the midpoint of a segment (or an angle bisector); cross ratio generalizes distance, and it follows that double perspectivities are the analog of the rigid motions; the Desargues and Pappus theorems arise from similarity. We shall now look at the Euclidean concept of circle and find its analog in projective geometry.

Again we must begin with some basic Euclidean theorem, this time about circles. We choose the following: *If the vertices of two angles are on a circle and their sides meet on the circle cutting off the same arc, then the angles are equal.* For example, in Figure 3.10*a*, *APB* is equal to *AP'B*.

If we consider, instead, four lines *a,b,c,d* through *P*, and four lines *a',b',c',d'* through *P'* which meet the corresponding lines through *P* on the circle (Figure 3.10*b*), then the corresponding angles are equal. Since the cross ratio of four lines through a point can be expressed in terms of the sines of the angles (Section 3.6), then the cross ratio of the four lines through *P* is equal to that of the corresponding lines through *P'*. We

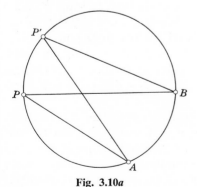

Fig. 3.10*a*

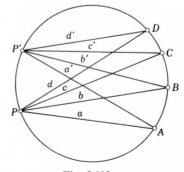

Fig. 3.10*b*

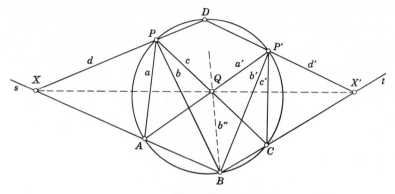

Fig. 3.10c

could consider more than four pairs of corresponding lines; we could talk about two pencils of lines with vertices at P and P', and we could map one pencil on the other by considering the corresponding lines (those that meet on the circle). From our discussion of four pairs of lines, we see that this is a cross ratio preserving mapping. We have talked about cross ratio preserving mappings before and we know that such a mapping can always be achieved by a double perspectivity. We are looking for the projective analog of a circle; perhaps we can find it if we describe a double perspectivity which gives us the same mapping as the circle did.

In Section 3.8, we showed how to construct a double perspectivity in which three points A,B,C on one line m are assigned to three points A',B',C' on another line m'. In our present discussion, we have the dual situation—three lines a,b,c of the pencil P must be assigned to the three lines a',b',c' of pencil P'. Let the corresponding lines meet at the points A,B,C on the circle (Figure 3.10c). If you refer back to Section 3.8, you can describe a construction by dualizing each step that appears there. Let s be the join of the meet of a and a' and the meet of b and b'. Let t be the join of the meet of b and b' and the meet of c and c'. Let Q be the meet of a' and c (Q is the dual of n in Section 3.8) and the join of Q and B be b''. The first perspectivity assigns a,b,c in pencil P to a',b'',c in pencil Q because these corresponding lines intersect on the line s. The second perspectivity uses line t and assigns a',b'',c in pencil Q to a',b',c' in pencil P'.

In order to map any other line d of pencil P onto a line d' in pencil P' by this double perspectivity, we find the meet X of d and s, draw the join of X and Q and let its meet with t be X'. $P'X'$ is then the line d'. Since the double perspectivity assigning a,b,c to the lines a',b',c' is a cross ratio preserving mapping (Exercise 1, Section 3.8), and the mapping established by the circle is cross ratio preserving, we can use reasoning similar to Section 3.8 and say the double perspectivity that we have constructed gives the same mapping as the circle and the meet D of d and d' lies on the circle.

The description of the construction given above is somewhat complicated. The resulting configuration, however, can be described easily. If the vertices of a hexagon $PCBAP'D$ lie on a circle, then the respective meets Q,X',X of the opposite sides PC and AP', CB and $P'D$, and BA and DP are collinear. You probably remember that we had a hexagon with this property in the Pappus theorem. The difference here is that the vertices of the hexagon lie on a circle instead of on two straight lines. We shall say that a hexagon is *Pascalian* if the meets of the opposite sides are collinear. Using this terminology, we arrive at the following theorem.

Theorem.   *A hexagon inscribed in a circle in Pascalian.*

We can also say that the Pascality of a hexagon is a necessary condition for its inscribability in a circle, but this condition is certainly not sufficient. We know from the Pappus theorem that a hexagon inscribed in an angle is Pascalian. A hexagon inscribed in an ellipse is also Pascalian because an ellipse may be considered as the projection of a circle and Pascality, being defined in terms of collinearity, is not affected by projections. We would suspect that this property of Pascality belongs to any hexagon inscribed in a conic. In terms of projective geometry, however, we do not know what a conic is. Our task now is to establish a projective definition of a conic and this will be the projective analog of a circle that we are looking for. We shall use the property of Pascality in this definition.

We shall define a *conic* as a locus such that any hexagon inscribed in it is Pascalian. (An alternate definition is that a conic is a locus of the meets of corresponding lines of two pencils which are mapped onto each other by a double perspectivity.)

A definition cannot be proved, of course; often it may be justified. To justify this definition of a conic in terms of Pascality, we must answer several questions. We know how to construct, given five points, any number of sixth points each of which, together with the given five points, constitute the vertices of a Pascalian hexagon. If, after constructing a sixth point, we would use another set of five points from the six we now have, would we get the same locus? If we would take the six points in a different order, we would have a different hexagon (it would have the same vertices but different sides); would this hexagon be Pascalian? To answer these questions, we need a new method which will be introduced in the next chapter. In the meantime, we shall accept this definition of a conic as if we had settled these difficulties.

Let us see what duality means when we speak of conics. Our theorem says that a hexagon inscribed in a circle is Pascalian. We could give more details and say that, if the six vertices of a hexagon are points of a circle, then the meets of the opposite sides are collinear. Dualizing this, we get the theorem of Brianchon: If the six sides of a hexagon are lines of a circle then the joins of the opposite vertices are concurrent. Of course, we do not know whether this dual theorem is true, since we do not have the principle of duality yet. Further, what are these "lines of a circle"? A reasonable guess would be lines tangent to a circle. Brianchon's theorem would then read: *If the six sides of a hexagon are tangent to a circle, then the joins of the opposite vertices are concurrent.* If this guess is correct, we should be able to dualize the mapping of Figure 3.10c and find that it is a a cross ratio preserving mapping. Let us check this first. If we are right, then we can talk about a proof of Brianchon's theorem.

Instead of two pencils of lines with vertices at P and P' on a circle, in the dual we have two lines (sets of collinear points) m and m' tangent to a circle (Figure 3.10d). A point X_1 on m corresponds to Y_1 on m' if the join of X_1 and Y_1 is tangent to the circle (the dual of the correspondence of the lines which meet on the circle). If we have dualized correctly, then this correspondence is a cross ratio preserving mapping.

If we have four points X_1, X_2, X_3, X_4 on line m and their images Y_1, Y_2, Y_3, Y_4 on m', we would have to show that the two cross ratios are equal. We can calculate the various differences in these expressions by

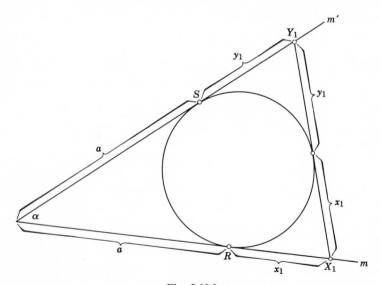

Fig. 3.10*d*

using the distance of the points from the points of contact, R and S, on the circle. For example, $X_1 - X_3 = x_1 - x_3$ where x_1 is the distance from R to X_1, and similarly for x_3. So we must show that

$$\frac{x_1 - x_3}{x_2 - x_3} \Big/ \frac{x_1 - x_4}{x_2 - x_4} = \frac{y_1 - y_3}{y_2 - y_3} \Big/ \frac{y_1 - y_4}{y_2 - y_4}.$$

If we remember that the two tangents from a point outside a circle are of equal length, we can express the relationship between the sides of the triangle in Figure 3.10d by

$$(x_1 + y_1)^2 = (a + x_1)^2 + (a + y_1)^2 - 2(a + x_1)(a + y_1)\beta,$$

where β is the cosine of α, the angle between m and m'. This relationship can be written $Ax_1y_1 + By_1 - Cx_1 - D = 0$ where $A = (1 + \beta)$, $B = a(\beta - 1)$, $C = a(1 - \beta)$ and $D = a^2(1 - \beta)$, or

$$y_1 = \frac{Cx_1}{Ax_1} + \frac{D}{B}.$$

We should note that A,B,C,D are constants, that is, the same for all lines $X_1 Y_1$, but x_1 and y_1 are variables. Now we use this expression to find $y_1 - y_3$.

$$y_1 - y_3 = \frac{Cx_1 + D}{Ax_1 + B} - \frac{Cx_3 + D}{Ax_3 + B}$$

$$= \frac{(CB - DA)(x_1 - x_3)}{(Ax_1 + B)(Ax_3 + B)}.$$

Using similar expressions for the other difference, we can show that the two cross ratios are equal. It follows that the mapping that we are considering is cross ratio preserving.

Now we can prove the theorem of Brianchon. Since we have been able to dualize the correspondence between two pencils of lines so that it was a cross ratio preserving mapping, we can also dualize the construction of the double perspectivity in Figure 3.10c and in doing this we arrive at the theorem of Brianchon.

Exercises

1. Using Euclidean geometry and a regular hexagon, prove that a hexagon inscribed in a circle is Pascalian.

2. Using Euclidean geometry and a regular hexagon, prove Brianchon's theorem.

3. Using a hexagon with the same vertices as Exercise 1, but considered in different order (so that the sides are different), prove the theorem of Exercise 1.

4. Using a hexagon with the same sides as Exercise 2, but considered in different order (so that the vertices are different), prove the theorem of Brianchon.

5. Complete the proof of the Brianchon theorem given in this section. Draw the appropriate figure.

6. Given five points, construct a sixth point so that it and the five given points are the vertices of a Pascalian hexagon.

3.11   POLE AND POLAR

In adapting the concept of circle to projective geometry, we started with a property of circle (the equality of inscribed angles cutting the same arc) that did not involve the idea of the center. Now we want to find the projective counterpart of the center. We first think of the center in terms of distance: a circle is a locus of points equidistant from a fixed point, the center. There is another property of the center that lends itself better to projective generalization: the property of the center being the midpoint of all the chords passing through it. The center of a circle shares this property with the center of an ellipse and the center of a hyperbola. Since the midpoint of a segment can be considered as a ratio of segments on the same line, this is an affine property. If we start with this property, the job of generalizing the center is half finished.

Before we begin the generalization, we should notice that it is inconvenient to have to consider *all* the chords through a point. In a circle, it is easy to see that if a point P is the midpoint of two chords passing through it, then P is the center of the circle. Because of this, we need only consider two chords in the following discussion.

We now are ready to generalize the notion of center. In Section 3.5 we found that, in projective geometry, the midpoint of a segment has been defined as the midpoint of a segment relative to a point on the line containing the segment. If we consider two chords AB and CD of a conic, we can speak of their intersection X as their midpoint relative to two points R and S on the lines containing the chords (Figure 3.11a). This means that A,B and X,R, and C,D and X,S are two sets of harmonic pairs.

The points R and S determine a line m, so we could call X the center of the conic relative to m. *The center of a conic relative to a line m* (not a tangent to the conic) *is the common midpoint of two chords relative to the meets of the lines containing these chords and the line m.* If m is a tangent, then the center of the conic relative to m is the point of tangency. Just as any point on a line can be considered the midpoint of a segment on that

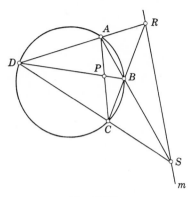

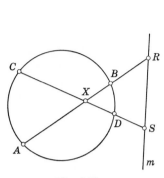

Fig. 3.11*a*   Fig. 3.11*b*

line relative to some point on that line, so too *any* point is the center of a conic relative to *some* line.

Given a conic and a point *P* not on the conic, it is not difficult to construct the line *m* relative to which *P* is a center. We simply construct a quadrifigure *ABCD* (Figure 3.11*b*) with vertices on the conic and *P* the meet of the diagonals *AC* and *DB*. The join of the diagonal points *RS* is then the desired line *m*. A proof of this construction will be asked for in the exercises at the end of this section.

The center of a conic relative to a line is usually called a *pole* and the line is called its *polar*.

To justify the above definition, it is necessary to prove that the line obtained by the construction is completely determined by the conic and the point, and does not depend on the quadrifigure used. We could prove this analogous to the method that we used in Section 3.5 where we were dealing with the midpoint of a segment relative to a point. There we projected the figure so that the one point went to infinity and the other point became the actual midpoint of the figure. Here we could project the figure so that the center becomes the actual center and the line goes to infinity. However, it is not necessary to always return to this Euclidean model; in this case, we can prove the uniqueness of the construction from within projective geometry.

The theorem that we must prove could be stated as follows.

Theorem. *If the meets of the diagonal lines of two quadrifigures inscribed in a conic coincide, then the joins of the diagonal points coincide also.*

Proof. Given two quadrifigures q_1 and q_2 inscribed in a conic with diagonal lines all containing *P*, we can always find a third quadrifigure q_3 which shares one diagonal with q_1 and another with q_2. We shall show that

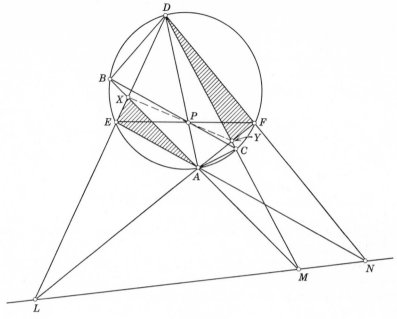

Fig. 3.11c

M, a diagonal point of q_1, is collinear with diagonal points L and N of q_3. The proof that the other diagonal point of q_1 is collinear with L and N and the proofs for the diagonal points of q_2 are similar. This would lead to the conclusion that the joins of the diagonal points of q_1 and q_2 coincide.

Let q_1 have vertices $ACDB$ and let q_3 have vertices $AFDE$ (Figure 3.11c). All three diagonals AD, BC, and EF contain P. M is the meet of BA and DC, L the meet of DE and AF, and N the meet of EA and DF. Using the Pascality of the inscribed hexagon $ABCDEF$, we find that X, P, Y are collinear, where X is the meet of AB and DE and Y is the meet of CD and FA. It follows that the joins of the corresponding vertices of triangles AEX and DFY are concurrent at P and thus, Desargues' theorem applies, telling us that L, M, N are collinear.

Now that we have justified our definition of the center of a conic relative to a line (or pole and polar of a conic), there are some other facts that we should observe. Four points, such as $ABCD$ in Figure 3.11b, determine not one, but three quadrifigures, depending on the order in which we take them. If we consider the quadrifigure $ABCD$, taking the points in that order, then the diagonal points are R and S and the meet of the diagonal lines is P. If we take them in the order $ACDB$ (the opposite sides are AC and DB, and CD and AB), then the diagonal points are P and S and the meet of the diagonal lines is R. If we take the vertices in the order $ADBC$, the diagonal points are R and P and the meet of the diagonal lines is S. So if this quadrifigure is inscribed in a conic, P and RS, R and PS, and S and RP are poles and corresponding polars. The triangle PRS with sides the polars of the opposite vertices is called an *autopolar triangle*. Using the autopolar triangle that we have just found, it is easy to prove the following theorem (it will be left as an exercise).

Theorem. *If a line p passes through M the pole of m, then m passes through P the pole of p.*

This theorem leads us to two important results. First of all, you should be wondering at this point if it is possible to find the pole when we are given a conic and a polar. The theorem gives us a method. Given a conic and a line m (Figure 3.11d), we choose any two points R and S on m and find their respective polars r and s by the quadrifigure construction. The meet M of s and r is then the pole of line m.

The second result that follows from this theorem is a proof of the principle of duality. First, we restate the previous theorem as follows: If P and p, and M and m are poles and corresponding polars, and p and M are incident, then m and P are incident. In view of this formulation, if we are given any configuration (call it F) consisting of points and lines, and a conic, we can assign to F a configuration F' (called the *polar configuration* of F with respect to the conic) consisting of points and lines by assigning each point to its polar and each line to its pole. The important thing about this mapping is that we know from the restated theorem that incidence is preserved. (Mappings that assign lines to points and points to lines in a 1-1 manner and preserve incidence are called *correlations*.

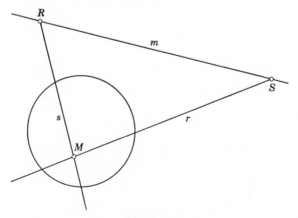

Fig. 3.11d

The mapping assigning points to their polars and lines to their poles relative to some conic is a correlation.) It is this mapping that can be used to prove the principle of duality.

Suppose that we have a true theorem in projective geometry. It has a hypothesis H which asserts some incidences and a conclusion C about the same structure. Let H' be a hypothesis dual to H. Let F' be the configuration for which H' holds. Map F' onto its polar configuration F with respect to some conic. Since incidence is preserved by this mapping, F will satisfy a hypothesis dual to H', that is, H. The theorem itself tells us that the conclusion C holds for F, but then C' the dual of C must hold for F'. Thus, for each true theorem in projective geometry, the dual theorem is true also.

Exercises

1. In Euclidean geometry, prove that if a point P is the midpoint of two chords of a circle, then P is the center of the circle.
2. Using Exercise 1 of this section and Exercise 6 of Section 3.1, prove that if P is the midpoint of two chords of an ellipse, then P is the center of the ellipse.
3. Show that, in Euclidean geometry, the actual center (the center relative to the line at infinity) of an ellipse is the meet of the diagonals of any parallelogram inscribed in the ellipse.
4. Prove that the construction given in Figure 3.11b does make P the center of the conic relative to line m according to the definition.
5. In the construction given in Figure 3.11b, P need not be within the conic (this has no projective meaning). Draw a diagram illustrating the construction if P is outside the conic.
6. Using Euclidean geometry, prove that the polar of a point inside a circle (not the center) is perpendicular to the line containing the diameter through that point.
7. In Figure 3.11c, prove that the meet of DB and AC is collinear with L and N.
8. Prove the theorem stated in this section: If a line p passes through M the pole of m, then m passes through P the pole of p.
9. Prove that the coordinate axes and the line at infinity form an autopolar triangle with respect to a circle with the center at the origin.
10. Prove that, if a line m is drawn through a point P and meets the polar of P in the point Q and the conic in the two points R and S, then P,Q and R,S are harmonic pairs.
11. Give an intuitive discussion of why the polar of a point on a conic should be defined as the tangent at that point.

12. Prove that, if two tangents can be drawn to a conic from a point P, then the join of the points of contact is the polar of P with respect to the conic.

3.12   THE ANALOG OF PERPENDICULARITY

We have considered several concepts of Euclidean geometry and, for each one, we have found a projective concept that has the Euclidean concept as a special case. Now we want to look at the Euclidean notion of perpendicularity and attempt to find the projective concept for which it is the special case.

Perpendicularity applies to lines, and lines belong to pencils. In a pencil of lines, we could assign each line to the line in that pencil that is perpendicular to it. This is a mapping, but unlike the mappings of lines that we have already considered (mappings which assign lines of one pencil to lines of a different pencil) this is a self-mapping—the pencil is mapped onto itself. There is no reason, however, why we should not ask the same question that we found important in the other cases: is this mapping cross ratio preserving? The answer is that *it is*. In fact, angles are preserved by this mapping (the angle between two lines is equal to the angle between the two lines perpendicular to them) and, since the cross ratio of lines is expressed in terms of angles, it too is preserved.

There are infinitely many pencils of lines in the projective plane that we are considering, but we need not treat them separately. If we consider the line at infinity and a point on it, exactly one line from each pencil will go through it (all these lines are parallel to each other). Since all of the lines that meet at one point at infinity are perpendicular to another set of lines (one from each pencil) which are also concurrent at some other point at infinity (because they are all parallel to each other), instead of mapping the lines of pencils onto themselves, we can map the points at infinity onto themselves. This mapping is also cross ratio preserving. (Why?)

We are looking for the analog of perpendicularity, and we have been led to a cross ratio perserving mapping of the points at infinity onto themselves. Remembering once again that, in projective geometry, the line at infinity (the set of all points at infinity) is just like any other line, we shall consider cross ratio preserving self-mappings of any line.

On the line that we are studying, we can introduce coordinates if we specify points by their distances from a fixed point. This is, of course, not projective—but we know that the cross ratio of these distances has a projective meaning. Let four points have coordinates x, x_1, x_2, x_3 and be mapped onto x', x_1', x_2', x_3' respectively. The fact that cross ratios are preserved means that

$$\frac{x' - x_1'}{x' - x_2'} \bigg/ \frac{x_3' - x_1'}{x_3' - x_2'} = \frac{x - x_1}{x - x_2} \bigg/ \frac{x_3 - x_1}{x_3 - x_2}.$$

In order to study this cross ratio preserving self-mapping, we shall have to concentrate on one point and its image. We can accomplish this if we keep x_1, x_2, x_3 fixed, then under a particular mapping x_1', x_2', x_3' are also fixed. The equation above then expresses a relationship between the variable points x and x'. To isolate these variables further, we could write the above relation as

$$\frac{x' - x_1'}{x' - x_2'} = K \frac{x - x_1}{x - x_2}$$

where K is a certain combination of known constants.

Before we investigate the special properties of the perpendicular mapping, let us discuss a question that could not arise when we mapped the points of one line onto a different line. In the case of self-mappings, we can ask if there are any points that correspond to themselves. If there is such a point, $x = x'$, we shall call it a *fixed point*. The last equation gives us an answer for the mapping under consideration; setting $x = x'$, it becomes a quadratic equation in x. If that equation has two real roots, then the mapping has two fixed points; if it has no real roots, then it has no fixed points.

If a mapping has two fixed points, x_1 and x_2, we can use them to simplify our study of perpendicularity. The equation that characterizes the mapping can then be written as follows:

$$\frac{x' - x_1}{x' - x_2} = K \frac{x - x_1}{x - x_2}.$$

If the mapping also has the properties of the perpendicular mapping, we would expect it to be possible to interchange x and x' without affecting this equation. This is because we speak of two lines being mutually perpendicular; if m is perpendicular to m', then m' is perpendicular to m. Interchanging x and x', we get

$$\frac{x - x_1}{x - x_2} = K \frac{x' - x_1}{x' - x_2};$$

this is equivalent to the former equation only if $K = 1$ or $K = -1$. (Why are there no other possibilities?) If $K = 1$, every point is mapped onto itself, and this is not what we are looking for. If $K = -1$, it means that the cross ratio of x_1, x_2, x, x' is -1 because

$$\frac{x - x_1}{x - x_2} \Big/ \frac{x' - x_1}{x' - x_2} = -1.$$

Or we could say that x_1, x_2, x, x' are harmonic. The transformed point x' is the fourth harmonic of the two fixed points and the point x. Therefore, the mapping is determined easily if we know the two fixed points. Unfortunately, this cannot be the perpendicular mapping that we are looking for because perpendicularity has no fixed points (no line is perpendicular to itself in Euclidean geometry). Because of this, it is not possible to use the fixed point simplification in our study of perpendicularity.

We are looking for a reciprocal (x and x' can be interchanged) cross ratio preserving self-mapping that has no fixed points. It does not seem to be a simple job. Perhaps there is a clue to the solution in the algebraic criterion for fixed points. If a mapping has no fixed points, this means that a certain quadratic equation has no real roots. However, if a quadratic equation with real coefficients has no real roots, it must have two complex roots which are conjugates of each other. This suggests the idea of introducing complex numbers into projective geometry. Perhaps we can find an analog of perpendicularity if we represent points and lines by complex numbers and interpret all the formulas that we have developed as applying to complex numbers. It is not unreasonable to attempt this because operations with complex numbers obey the same rules as operations with real numbers. (The only difficulty that would arise is with expressions that have a denominator that is the sum of squares. In the real case, they are automatically not equal to zero if the quantities squared are not all zero. In the complex case, we shall have to exercise some caution with such expressions.)

We are not going to completely develop projective geometry using complex numbers. However, we shall apply this idea to our present problem to show how useful it is.

If we allow the use of complex numbers, we can interpret the perpendicular mapping to mean that there are no fixed points with *real* coordinates, but of course there will be two fixed points represented by conjugate complex numbers. We know that the cross ratio of four points on a line can be computed using the cross ratio of four lines of a pencil which meet the given line at the four points. In turn, the cross ratio of the lines can be computed by their slopes (Exercise 3, Section 3.6). If the slopes of the four lines are m, m', m_1, m_2 with m_1 and m_2 belonging to the lines that contain the two complex fixed points, the perpendicular map sends m to

m' and is given by

$$\frac{m - m_1}{m - m_2} \bigg/ \frac{m' - m_1}{m' - m_2} = -1.$$

We can use this formula to verify that we have developed this analog of perpendicularity correctly. Since m_1 and m_2 represent fixed lines in this formula, they must be complex conjugates. We can further simplify this equation by changing the system of coordinates so that m_1 and m_2 are i and $-i$. The formula then becomes

$$\frac{m - i}{m + i} \bigg/ \frac{m' - i}{m' + i} = -1$$

or

$$\frac{m - i}{m + i} + \frac{m' - i}{m' + i} = 0.$$

Combining the terms of this formula, we arrive at $2(mm' + 1) = 0$ or $mm' = -1$ which is the usual condition for perpendicularity in terms of slopes.

Exercises

1. Do some mappings of a line onto itself have only one fixed point? If so, give an example; if not, why not?
2. Explain in full why m_1 and m_2, the slopes of the fixed lines in the formula developed in this section, must be complex conjugates and how they can be changed to i and $-i$.

4 Two Representations of Projective Geometry

In Chapter 3 we talked about two representations of projective geometry, the projective bundle and homogeneous coordinates. In this chapter, we shall deal with two more representations: vectors and projective coordinates.

You may be wondering why we bother to discuss four different representations of the same geometry. Objectively, one representation is as good as another; subjectively, there are reasons to consider more than one. For example, some problems can be solved easier in one representation than in another. Another reason is that each new representation that we see helps build our intuition about projective geometry. Intuition about a mathematical system may not be mathematics, but it is indispensable if we want to work efficiently within the mathematical system.

4.1 INTRODUCTION OF VECTORS

The notion of vector is based on parallelism, so it may seem that vectors have no place in projective geometry. However, you may remember that in Section 3.4 vectors already had an indirect use in projective geometry; we used them to prove that the geometry of homogeneous coordinates is the same as the geometry of rays and flats. Since vectors make it possible to derive propositions by computation, it seems worthwhile to investigate a more direct use of vectors.

The method that we used in Chapter 3 is what we want. A ray can be represented by any nonzero vector in that ray having its tail at O, the vertex of the bundle. Any nonzero vector in that ray may be used; if vector A represents a ray, then any multiple αA (with α different from zero) will represent the same ray. A flat will be represented by any nonzero vector perpendicular to that flat. Again, any multiple αa of a vector a representing a flat will represent the same flat. To distinguish between the two roles of vectors, we shall use capital *italic* letters for

103

rays (points) and lower case *italic* letters for flats (lines). Strictly speaking, we should use different symbols for a point, the ray representing that point, and the vector representing that ray. However, we shall not do this; the single letter A will stand for a vector in a ray, that ray, and the point represented by that ray. Similarly, a will stand for a vector perpendicular to a flat, that flat, and the line represented by that flat. Although A and a are vectors, we shall use *italic* rather than **bold** letters in order to remind ourselves that they represent a point and a line.

If we want to derive propositions using vectors, we shall need a vector representation of the line joining two points A and B, or we could say the flat determined by two rays A and B. A flat is represented by a vector perpendicular to it. Since the cross product $A \times B$ is perpendicular to the vectors A and B, it is also perpendicular to the rays containing A and B and so to the flat determined by them. It follows that $A \times B$ is one vector representing the line joining points A and B.

Similarly, the meet of two lines a and b can be represented by $a \times b$. This is because the vector $a \times b$ is perpendicular to both vector a and vector b and so is parallel to both flats a and b; this means that vector $a \times b$ is parallel to the intersection of flats a and b and, therefore, it is equivalent to a vector that lies in the ray which is their intersection.

What about incidence? This was already mentioned in Section 3.4. If a point A and a line a are incident, then $A \cdot a = 0$. This condition is derived from the fact that point A incident with line a means that the ray A lies in the flat a, or that the vector A is perpendicular to the vector a.

We are now able to express three concepts of projective geometry in terms of vector operations: $A \times B$, the join of the points A and B; $a \times b$, the meet of lines a and b; and $A \cdot a = 0$, the incidence of point A and line a. All of the other relations of projective geometry can be expressed in terms of these three. For example, if three points A,B,C are collinear, then we can say that C is incident with the join of A and B, or $A \times B \cdot C = 0$, or $(ABC) = 0$ (see Section 1.9). Of course, we could also say that A is incident with the join of B and C, but this will not change anything because we are allowed to permute the terms in a triple scalar product. (We need not be concerned about a sign change since this product is zero.) Similarly, the concurrence of three lines a,b,c is expressed by $(abc) = 0$.

Since the two vector operations of dot and cross product have a meaning in projective geometry, you should be wondering if a linear combination of vectors has any use in projective geometry.

One use would be to represent any projective point in terms of three non-collinear points; that is, if A,B,C are noncollinear points ($A \times B \cdot C \neq 0$), then any point X can be expressed as $X = \alpha A + \beta B + \gamma C$ for some real numbers α,β,γ because any vector in three-space can be written as a linear combination of three linearly independent vectors. We could think of α,β,γ as the coordinates of X relative to vectors A,B,C.

There is another use of linear combinations in projective geometry. If A and B are independent vectors, then $\alpha A + \beta B$ (where α,β are arbitrary real numbers) represents all the vectors (rays) in the plane (flat) determined by these vectors. In other words, any point on the line joining points A and B can be represented in the form $\alpha A + \beta B$. This means that we have two different ways of representing the line through A and B; one is the cross product $A \times B$ (this represents the line itself), and the other is the linear combination $\alpha A + \beta B$ (this represents all of the points on the line).

Similarly, if a and b are two different lines, then $\alpha a + \beta b$ represents all the lines passing through their point of intersection. Thus, we also have a choice of the representative of the meet of the lines a and b; $a \times b$ represents the point of intersection of a and b, and $\alpha a + \beta b$ represents the pencil of lines through the point of intersection (see Section 3.7).

Exercises

1. Show that $A \times B \cdot C \neq 0$ implies that A,B,C are not collinear.
2. Explain why $\alpha a + \beta b$ (where a and b are distinct fixed lines and α,β are variable real numbers) represents all the lines passing through the point of intersection of a and b.
3. If we express any point X in projective geometry as $X = \alpha A + \beta B + \gamma C$ with $(ABC) \neq 0$ and call α,β,γ the coordinates of X, is this a unique representation of X? Explain your answer.

4.2 APPLICATIONS OF VECTORS

We shall not try to build all of projective geometry using vectors. Instead, we shall look at a few of the concepts developed in the last chapter: harmonic points, cross ratio, the theorems of Desargues and Pappus, and conics. These notions will illustrate some of the advantages of using vectors. Vectors will allow us to free harmonic points and cross ratio from the Euclidean concept of distance; the theorems of Desargues and Pappus can be proved very elegantly using vectors; and finally, vectors will make it possible to answer some questions that are still open about the definition of a conic (Section 3.10).

Harmonic Points

We already know that a pair of points A,B and a pair of lines m,n are harmonic if $(AM/BM)/(AN/BN) = -1$ where M and N are the respective meets of m and n with the line joining A and B (Section 3.7). Here, the projective concept of harmonicity is described in terms of the Euclidean concept of distance. Using vectors, it is possible to describe harmonicity without using distance.

Let $DCEF$ be a quadrifigure (Figure 4.2a) with diagonal points A,B and diagonal lines m,n. (This means that A,B,m,n are harmonic.) We can now think of these letters as denoting vectors. We shall show that a necessary condition for harmonicity is $(A \cdot m/A \cdot n)/(B \cdot m/B \cdot n) = -1$ [or $(A \cdot m/B \cdot m)/(A \cdot n/B \cdot n) = -1$].

Since D,C,E,F are vectors in three-space, we know that they are linearly dependent; there exist reals $\delta,\gamma,\varepsilon,\varphi$ not all zero such that $\delta D + \gamma C + \varepsilon E + \varphi F = O$. In projective geometry, any multiple of a vector has the same significance as the vector itself, so δD represents the same point as D, and similarly for the other vectors. Because of this, we can simplify the notation and denote by D,C,E,F what we have just denoted by $\delta D, \gamma C, \varepsilon E$, and φF. The relation above then can be written as $D + C + E + F = O$. We say that we have absorbed the coefficient into the vector.

It follows from the last equation that $D + C = -E - F$. If we notice that $D + C$ is a point on the join of D and C, while $-E - F$ is a point on the join of E and F, then the only possible point that can be $D + C$ is the diagonal point A, $A = D + C$. Similarly, $B = C + E$.

The diagonal lines m and n can also be expressed in terms of the vertices: $m = C \times F$ and $n = D \times E$.

Using the above information, we can compute $A \cdot m$ in terms of the vertices: $A \cdot m = (C + D) \cdot C \times F = C \cdot C \times F + D \cdot C \times F = (DCF)$. Similarly, $A \cdot n = (CDE)$, $B \cdot m = (ECF)$, and $B \cdot n = (CDE)$.

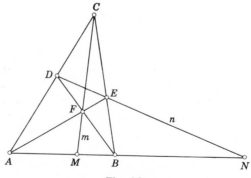

Fig. 4.2a

In order to prove that $(A \cdot m/A \cdot n)/(B \cdot m/B \cdot n) = -1$, we must show that $(A \cdot m)(B \cdot n) + (A \cdot n)(B \cdot m) = 0$. This is now a straightforward computation:

$$
\begin{aligned}
(A \cdot m)(B \cdot n) + (A \cdot n)(B \cdot m) &= (DCF)(CDE) + (CDE)(ECF) \\
&= (CDE)[(D + E) \cdot C \times F] \\
&= -(CDE)[(C + F) \cdot C \times F] = 0,
\end{aligned}
$$

and the proof is complete.

Cross Ratio

We have just found that $(A \cdot m/A \cdot n)/(B \cdot m/B \cdot n) = -1$ is the condition for the harmonicity of A,B,m,n, while in the last chapter the condition was that the cross ratio of A,B,m,n was -1. This seems to indicate that $(A \cdot m/A \cdot n)/(B \cdot m/B \cdot n)$ is the cross ratio of A,B,m,n in the general case. We shall now prove this.

Consider four collinear points A,B,M,N; their cross ratio is $(AM/AN)/(BM/BN)$, where AM,AN,BM,BN represent the distances between these points. Let H be a point not on the line AB and consider the four triangles with bases AM,AN,BM,BN and with common vertex H. The areas of these triangles are proportional to their bases (since they have the same altitude); so we can replace the segments in the cross ratio above by the areas as we did once before (Section 3.6). Now we introduce the point p (the common tail of the vectors corresponding to the four collinear points) and consider the four tetrahedra with the triangles as bases and with common vertex p. The volumes of these tetrahedra are proportional to their bases, so we may replace the distances AM,AN,BM,BN in the cross ratio by these volumes. We know that six times the volume of a tetrahedron is equal to the triple scalar product of three adjacent edges considered as vectors (Section 1.9), so we may write the cross ratio that we are studying as

$$
\frac{A \cdot H \times M}{A \cdot H \times N} \bigg/ \frac{B \cdot H \times M}{B \cdot H \times N} = \frac{A \cdot m}{A \cdot n} \bigg/ \frac{B \cdot m}{B \cdot n}
$$

where m and n are the lines represented by $H \times M$ and $H \times N$. This last expression is therefore the cross ratio of A,B,m,n as we conjectured.

Theorem of Desargues

Let A,B,C and A',B',C' be the vertices of two triangles with the joins $A \times A'$, $B \times B'$, $C \times C'$ all passing through a point P. We want to use vectors to prove that the meets of the corresponding sides X,Y,Z are collinear (Figure 4.2b).

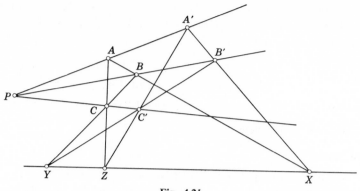

Fig. 4.2b

The fact that P,A,A' are collinear tells us that the vectors representing them are coplanar, so there exist reals α,β,γ not all zero such that $\alpha P + \beta A + \gamma A' = O$. Absorbing the numerical factors into the vector symbols as we did earlier, we can write this relation as $P + A + A' = O$. Similarly, the collinearity of P,B,B' and P,C,C' can be expressed by $P + B + B' = O$ and $P + C + C' = O$. From the first two of these relations, it follows that $A - B = A' - B'$. Now $A - B$ is a point on the join of A and B, while $A' - B'$ is a point on the join of A' and B'; since this is the same point it must be the meet X of the corresponding sides $A \times B$ and $A' \times B'$. We can now write $X = A - B$. Similarly, $Y = B - C$ and $Z = C - A$ are the meets of the other pairs of corresponding sides. Adding together these last three relations, we find that $X + Y + Z = O$; this tells us that the meets of the corresponding sides are collinear. (This proof was found by K. B. Leisenring.)

Theorem of Pappus

Now we consider the Pappus configuration (Figure 4.2c); hexagon $ABCDEF$ has alternate vertices lying on two straight lines. We must

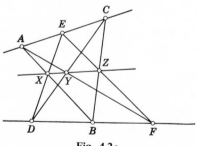

Fig. 4.2c

prove, using vectors, that the meets of the opposite sides X, Y, Z are collinear. It is not possible here to achieve the same simplicity as in the last proof because several points appear each in several relations. We can go halfway, however, and express the statement that X, Y, Z are on sides $A \times B$, $C \times D$, and $E \times F$, respectively, by writing $X = \alpha A + \beta B$, $Y = \gamma C + \delta D$, and $Z = \varepsilon E + \varphi F$ for some real numbers $\alpha, \beta, \gamma, \delta, \varepsilon, \varphi$. The statement that these points are also on $D \times E$, $F \times A$, and $B \times C$ can be expressed by $(XDE) = 0$, $(YFA) = 0$, and $(ZBC) = 0$.

Substituting the first sets of relations into the second, we get $\alpha(ADE) + \beta(BDE) = 0$, $\gamma(CFA) + \delta(DFA) = 0$, and $\varepsilon(EBC) + \varphi(FBC) = 0$. What we must show is that X, Y, Z are collinear, that is, that $(XYZ) = 0$. Using the first set of relations above,

$$(XYZ) = \alpha\gamma\varepsilon(ACE) + \alpha\gamma\varphi(ACF) + \alpha\delta\varepsilon(ADE) + \alpha\delta\varphi(ADF)$$
$$+ \beta\gamma\varepsilon(BEC) + \beta\gamma\varphi(BCF) + \beta\delta\varepsilon(BDE) + \beta\delta\varphi(BDF).$$

The second and fourth terms add up to zero from what we have shown above, and similarly for the third and seventh terms, and the fifth and sixth terms. What remains is

$$\alpha\gamma\varepsilon(ACE) + \beta\delta\varphi(BDF).$$

Thus far, we have not taken into consideration the collinearity of A, C, E and B, D, F. These collinearities tell us that $(ACE) = 0$ and $(BDF) = 0$, therefore, the whole expression for (XYZ) vanishes and X, Y, Z are collinear.

Conics

The preceding discussion can be used to obtain another important result. We can now settle the questions raised in connection with the definition of a conic in Section 3.10. The vanishing of $\alpha\gamma\varepsilon(ACE) + \beta\delta\varphi(BDF)$ means that the meets of the opposite sides of hexagon $ABCDEF$ are collinear—the hexagon is Pascalian. Using this, we want to find a condition for Pascality which is symmetric in each of the six terms. We have already shown that

$$\alpha(ADE) + \beta(BDE) = 0, \qquad \gamma(CFA) + \delta(DFA) = 0,$$

and

$$\varepsilon(EBC) + \varphi(FBC) = 0$$

arise from the fact that X, Y, Z are the meets of the opposite sides of the hexagon. Taking the second term of each of these expressions to the right-hand side and multiplying all three together, we get

$$\alpha\gamma\varepsilon(ADE)(CFA)(EBC) = -\beta\delta\varphi(BDE)(DFA)(FBC).$$

Combining this with $\alpha\gamma\varepsilon(ACE) + \beta\delta\varphi(BDF) = 0$, the condition becomes

$$\frac{(ACE)}{(ADE)(CFA)(EBC)} = \frac{(BDF)}{(BDE)(DFA)(FBC)},$$

or

$$\frac{(AEC)(BDE)}{(AFC)(BDF)} = \frac{(ADE)(EBC)}{(ADF)(FBC)}.$$

This is a necessary and sufficient condition for the six points $ABCDEF$ to form a Pascalian hexagon. This last condition is symmetric in each point. To see this, we notice that if the relation is true for six points taken in the arrangement $ABCDEF$, it remains true if we interchange E and F. Since any permutation can be achieved by successive changes of two neighboring symbols, we have proved that: *If six points form a Pascalian hexagon taken in a given order, they form a Pascalian hexagon taken in any order.* Briefly, the Pascality of six points is independent of order. This settles one question raised in Section 3.10.

The other question to be answered is: Given five points A,B,C,D,E, if we construct a sixth point F such that A,B,C,D,E,F are the vertices of a Pascalian hexagon, and then use A,B,C,D,F to find another sixth point G which is Pascalian with A,B,C,D,F, does G form a Pascalian hexagon with A,B,C,D,E? The answer is yes, and the proof is as follows.

Since A,B,C,D,E,F are Pascalian, they satisfy the condition

$$\frac{(AEC)(BDE)}{(AFC)(BDF)} = \frac{(ADE)(EBC)}{(ADF)(FBC)}.$$

We can rewrite this as

$$\frac{(ACE)(BDE)}{(ADE)(BCE)} = \frac{(ACF)(BDF)}{(ADF)(BCF)}.$$

Since A,B,C,D,F,G are Pascalian, we also have

$$\frac{(ACF)(BDF)}{(ADF)(BCF)} = \frac{(ACG)(BDG)}{(ADG)(BCG)}.$$

Combining these last two conditions, we now have

$$\frac{(ACE)(BDE)}{(ADE)(BCE)} = \frac{(ACG)(BDG)}{(ADG)(BCG)};$$

in other words, G forms a Pascalian hexagon with A,B,C,D,E, the five original points.

Now, if we consider a locus of points that forms Pascalian hexagons with five given points, we see that this locus has the property that any six points of it form a Pascalian hexagon. This justifies our definition of a conic in Section 3.10: *a conic is a locus of points such that any six of them form a Pascalian hexagon.*

The above discussion involving seven points A,B,C,D,E,F,G can be summarized by the following.

Seven-Point Theorem. *If two of the seven hexagons formed by six points out of a given set of seven points are Pascalian, then the remaining hexagons formed by six points out of the seven are Pascalian.*

We can also make use of the above discussion to find a vector equation of a conic. If A,B,C,D,E are five fixed points and X is a variable sixth point, then the relation

$$\frac{(ACX)(BDX)}{(ACE)(BDE)} - \frac{(ADX)(BCX)}{(ADE)(BCE)} = 0$$

assures us that A,B,C,D,E,X are the vertices of a Pascalian hexagon, so we may regard this relation as the vector equation of a conic.

Exercises

1. Prove that $(A \cdot m/A \cdot n)/(B \cdot m/B \cdot n) = -1$ is a sufficient condition for the harmonicity of A,B,m,n.
2. Explain in full why $(AEC)(BDE)/(AFC)(BDF) = (ADE)(EBC)/(ADF)(FBC)$ is a necessary and sufficient condition for the Pascality of hexagon $ABCDEF$.
3. Prove that any permutation of six symbols can be achieved by successive changes of two neighboring symbols.
4. Formulate a four-point theorem for collinearity. Prove it using vectors.
5. Formulate a five-point theorem for cocircularity (Cocircularity is the property that four points lie on the same circle).
6. Prove that the general equation of a conic in homogeneous coordinates is the general quadratic in three variables.

4.3 PROJECTIVE COORDINATES

We have already discussed two types of coordinates in projective geometry. In Section 3.4 we moved from the ordinary coordinates of Euclidean geometry to the homogeneous coordinates of projective geometry. In Section 4.1 we showed that, given three points A,B,C not on a line, we could express any point X as a linear combination $X = \alpha A + \beta B + \gamma C$ for some real numbers α,β,γ and then think of α,β,γ as the coordinates of X relative to A,B,C. Both of these types of coordinates have a disadvantage: they have no clear geometric meaning and we are not able to determine the position of points relative to some fixed configuration (analogous to the two coordinate axes in Euclidean geometry). What we want to find in this section is a clear-cut system in which the position of every point of the projective plane can be given with respect to a fixed configuration by numbers that have a definite geometrical meaning.

Let us try to use something similar to two coordinate axes and choose two distinct fixed lines a and b. Given these and an arbitrary point, we know that this does not lead to any numbers because the simplest numerical invariant in projective geometry, the cross ratio, involves four elements. Let us add a fixed point E (not on either of the lines) to the lines a and b. The arbitrary point X, together with E,a,b determine a cross ratio $(X \cdot a/ X \cdot b)/(E \cdot a/E \cdot b) = v$. We now have a number v that gives us some information about the point X. Unfortunately, this information is not enough since all the points on the line joining X to the meet of a and b would give the same cross ratio. If we introduce a third line c (not containing E, and not concurrent with a and b) we can form two new cross ratios:

$$\lambda = (X \cdot b/X \cdot c)/(E \cdot b/E \cdot c) \qquad \text{and} \qquad \mu = (X \cdot c/X \cdot a)/(E \cdot c/E \cdot a).$$

Each of these together with v permits us to locate X.

There are some difficulties in locating points by means of the cross ratios that we have just described. If X is on the line b, then v loses its meaning, and a similar thing happens if X is on a or c. If X is one of the points of intersection of a,b,c, then two of the cross ratios lose their meaning. Because of this, it is not desirable to use the cross ratios as they are.

Instead, let us consider the ratios

$$X_1 = X \cdot a/E \cdot a, \qquad X_2 = X \cdot b/E \cdot b, \qquad \text{and} \qquad X_3 = X \cdot c/E \cdot c.$$

If we choose E so that it is not on any of the lines a,b,c, these ratios always exist. When the cross ratios exist, they can be given in terms of X_1,X_2,X_3; for example, $v = X_1/X_2$. There is an additional advantage in using the quantities X_1,X_2,X_3 rather then the cross ratios; they are in the nature of generalized Cartesian coordinates. This advantage offsets the slight disadvantage that only their ratios have projective significance. Notice that they share this disadvantage with the other two coordinate systems mentioned at the beginning of this section.

Besides using X_1,X_2,X_3 to locate the position of X relative to a,b,c,E, it is also possible to develop a formula that gives X in terms of the coordinates and the fixed elements. To do this, we must once again think of the points and lines as vectors.

We shall use the equation developed in Exercise 9 of Section 1.9. Letting **a,b,c,d** in Exercise 9 be A,B,C,X, we get

$$(ABC)X = (BCX)A + (CAX)B + (ABX)C.$$

Let $A = b \times c$, $B = c \times a$, $C = a \times b$ where a,b,c are the three fixed lines that are not concurrent. We want to substitute these products into the above formula in order to find an equation for X in terms of X_1, X_2, X_3.

Let us calculate the first coefficient on the right-hand side. (BCX) means $B \times C \cdot X$, and $B \times C = (c \times a) \times (a \times b)$. Using the formula for the triple vector product (Section 1.9), we get

$$B \times C = (c \cdot a \times b)a - (a \cdot a \times b)c = (abc)a,$$

so $(BCX) = (abc)a \cdot X$. Similarly, $(CAX) = (abc)b \cdot X$, and $(ABX) = (abc)c \cdot X$; the left-hand coefficient $(ABC) = A \times B \cdot C = (abc)c \cdot C = (abc)^2$. We now make these substitutions in the formula from Exercise 9 of Section 1.9 and cancel (abc), this gives

$$(abc)X = (a \cdot X)A + (b \cdot X)B + (c \cdot X)C.$$

Using the definitions of X_1, X_2, X_3, this becomes

$$(abc)X = (E \cdot a)X_1 A + (E \cdot b)X_2 B + (E \cdot c)X_3 C.$$

This is the explicit expression for a point in terms of its coordinates which we were looking for.

Using the notion of duality, we could establish a coordinate system for lines in terms of three fixed noncollinear points and a line not containing any of these points. In order to relate these new line coordinates to the point coordinates that we have just found, we let the fixed points A,B,C be the vertices of the triangle formed by the lines a,b,c and let e be a line not containing A,B,C. The line coordinates x_1, x_2, x_3 of a line x are then

$$x_1 = x \cdot A / e \cdot A, \qquad x_2 = x \cdot B / e \cdot B, \qquad \text{and} \qquad x_3 = x \cdot C / e \cdot C.$$

The expression for the line x in terms of its coordinates is

$$(ABC)x = (e \cdot A)x_1 a + (e \cdot B)x_2 b + (e \cdot C)x_3 c.$$

Since we now have expressions for x and X in terms of their coordinates, we can look for a condition for the incidence of x and X in terms of coordinates. The vector condition is $x \cdot X = 0$ and, substituting the expressions above for x and X and observing that $a \cdot A = b \cdot B = c \cdot C$ while all products of the form $a \cdot B$ are zero, we get

$$(E \cdot a)(e \cdot A)X_1 x_1 + (E \cdot b)(e \cdot B)X_2 x_2 + (E \cdot c)(e \cdot C)X_3 x_3 = 0.$$

Since e has not been specified other than a line not containing A,B,C, we can take

$$e = a/E \cdot a + b/E \cdot b + c/E \cdot c,$$

then $(E \cdot a)(e \cdot A) = (E \cdot b)(e \cdot B) = (E \cdot c)(e \cdot C)$ and the condition for incidence becomes $X_1x_1 + X_2x_2 + X_3x_3 = 0$.

Thus far, we have not used the fact that, in projective geometry, any vector may be replaced by its numerical multiple without changing the geometric meaning. If we replace a,b,c by their numerical multiples chosen so as to make

$$a \cdot E = b \cdot E = c \cdot E = 1,$$

then the expression for point coordinates becomes

$$X_1 = a \cdot X, \qquad X_2 = b \cdot X, \qquad \text{and} \qquad X_3 = c \cdot X.$$

Since we have chosen e so as to make $(a \cdot E)(A \cdot e) = (b \cdot E)(B \cdot e) = (c \cdot E)(C \cdot e)$, we now have

$$A \cdot e = B \cdot e = C \cdot e$$

and, since only ratios of coordinates are important, we may set

$$x_1 = A \cdot x, \qquad x_2 = B \cdot x, \qquad \text{and} \qquad x_3 = C \cdot x.$$

The triangle with sides a,b,c and vertices A,B,C together with the point E and the line e play the same role in analytic projective geometry as the coordinate axes and the unit length play in Euclidean analytic geometry.

The triangle ABC is often called the *fundamental triangle*. However, there is nothing fundamental about it, any triangle can be made to play the same role. As in other geometries, it is useful and important to be able to pass from one reference system to another. Therefore, we want to derive formulas for the transformations of projective coordinates so that we can change from coordinates based on A,B,C,a,b,c,E,e to coordinates based on another fundamental triangle $A'B'C'$ with sides a',b',c' together with the point E' and line e'.

Since we are considering two reference systems, X has two representations $X_1A + X_2B + X_3C = X_1'A' + X_2'B' + X_3'C'$. Since the vectors A',B',C' are linearly independent, each of the vectors A,B,C may be expressed as their linear combinations

$$A = \alpha_1 A' + \beta_1 B' + \gamma_1 C',$$
$$B = \alpha_2 A' + \beta_2 B' + \gamma_2 C',$$
$$C = \alpha_3 A' + \beta_3 B' + \gamma_3 C'.$$

Substituting these values into the last equality and equating the coefficients of A', B', C' we obtain

$$\rho X_1' = \alpha_1 X_1 + \alpha_2 X_2 + \alpha_3 X_3,$$
$$\rho X_2' = \beta_1 X_1 + \beta_2 X_2 + \beta_3 X_3,$$
$$\rho X_3' = \gamma_1 X_1 + \gamma_2 X_2 + \gamma_3 X_3.$$

These are the formulas for transforming coordinates X_1, X_2, X_3 in the first reference system to coordinates X_1', X_2', X_3' in the second reference system. The number ρ which is arbitrary appears in the formula because only the ratios of the coordinates are significant.

Exercises

1. Explain why homogeneous coordinates do not permit us to describe the position of a point relative to some fixed configuration. Do the same thing for the linear combination representation of a point described at the beginning of this section.
2. Draw a diagram and explain how three fixed lines a, b, c and a fixed point E together with the cross ratios v and λ defined in this section can be used to locate the position of a point X.
3. In what sense are the projective coordinates X_1, X_2, X_3, which we developed in this section, a generalization of Cartesian coordinates?
4. Prove that if $e = a/E \cdot a + b/E \cdot b + c/E \cdot c$, then e does not contain $a \times b$, $b \times c$, and $c \times a$.
5. Show that the join of the points X and Y can be represented in terms of their coordinates X_1, X_2, X_3 and Y_1, Y_2, Y_3 by

$$\begin{vmatrix} A & B & C \\ X_1 & X_2 & X_3 \\ Y_1 & Y_2 & Y_3 \end{vmatrix}$$

and find the corresponding expression for the meet of two lines x and y.
6. Find a condition in terms of coordinates for the collinearity of three points and the concurrence of three lines.
7. Prove that if we consider c as the line at infinity, a and b perpendicular to each other, and $E = (1,1,1)$, then $(X_1/X_3, X_2/X_3)$ are the ordinary Cartesian coordinates of X.
8. Derive the formulas for transforming line coordinates from one reference system to another.
9. Show that, if we consider two reference systems A, B, C, E and A', B', C', E', we can write a point X as $X_1 A + X_2 B + X_3 C = X_1' A' + X_2' B' + X_3' C'$ where X_1, X_2, X_3 and X_1', X_2', X_3' are the coordinates of X with respect to the two systems.

5 Inversive Geometry

5.1 INVERSIONS

In studying Euclidean, affine, and projective geometry, we noticed that there was a relationship between the changes that are permitted in a geometry and the properties that are not affected by these changes. In projective geometry, for instance, if we consider double perspectivities, cross ratios are not affected by these changes. In inversive geometry, a fundamental property will be that points lie on the same circle. Unlike the other geometries, we shall not begin with the permissible transformations (changes) but with this fundamental property. Beginning with the property that we want to preserve, we shall soon find the changes that are allowed in this geometry.

Again we shall assume that Euclidean geometry is known; we shall allow ourselves to use anything we want from it. In this chapter, we shall be developing inversive geometry in a plane, so it will be two-dimensional Euclidean geometry that we shall be using for the major part of the discussion.

In Euclidean geometry, a circle can always be constructed through three noncollinear points, thus, if *three* points lie on a circle, this is not an interesting relationship. In the case of *four* noncollinear points, they may or may not be on the same circle, so this is a relationship worth considering. If four points lie on a circle, we shall say that they are *cocircular*.

In elementary geometry, the following theorem is proved: *A necessary and sufficient condition for four points* (*no three of which are collinear*) *to lie on a circle is that* $OA \cdot OA' = OB \cdot OB'$ *where O is the meet of the segments AA' and BB'* (Figure 5.1a). In this theorem, $OA \cdot OA'$ means the product of the directed lengths of the segments OA and OA'. If AA' is parallel to BB', it is understood that we shall rename the points so that the segments do intersect.

Let us see if we can use this elementary theorem to find a transformation that preserves cocircularity. Let A, A', O be three fixed collinear points and let X, X' be two variable points collinear with O but not collinear with A and A'. If $OX \cdot OX' = OA \cdot OA' = \rho$, then X, X' is a pair of points

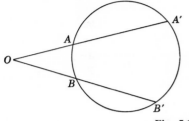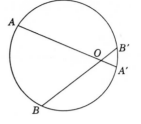

Fig. 5.1*a*

cocircular with A,A'. We could also read the relationship this way: If $OX \cdot OX' = OA \cdot OA' = \rho$, then every point X (except those on the line through A and A') is assigned to a point X' which, together with X, is cocircular with A and A'. This second description makes it clear that we are dealing with a transformation of the plane (except for the line through A and A'); every point X is assigned to a unique point X'.

Since this transformation looks so much like the theorem about co-circularity, we now hope that it preserves this basic property. To show this, we would have to take any four cocircular points X,Y,U,V and any three collinear points A,A',O (but of course not collinear with any of X,Y,U,V), find X',Y',U',V' such that they have the proper collinearities and $OX \cdot OX' = OY \cdot OY' = OU \cdot OU' = OV \cdot OV' = OA \cdot OA'$, and then prove that X',Y',U',V' are cocircular. It is possible to prove this (in Exercise 3), but it will be much easier to discuss this in the next section when we have a precise definition of inversion and can deal with this change analytically. Now we shall show that, in many cases, this transformation does preserve cocircularity.

We shall make one restriction: O must be the intersection of XY and UV (Figure 5.1*b*). Since X,Y,U,V are cocircular, we know that

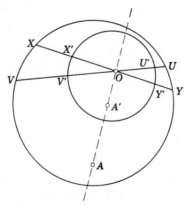

Fig. 5.1*b*

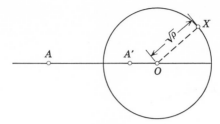

Fig. 5.1c

$OX \cdot OY = OU \cdot OV$ or $OX/OU = OV/OY$. From the conditions of the transformation $OX \cdot OX'/OU \cdot OU' = OV \cdot OV'/OY \cdot OY'$. Using the cancellation property of real numbers, we get $OX'/OU' = OV'/OY'$ or $OX' \cdot OY' = OU' \cdot OV'$, and X',Y',U',V' are cocircular.

Now we are ready for a question: Can a point be transformed into itself? This will depend on the sign of ρ. If ρ is negative (that means that O is between A and A'), it is impossible. If ρ is positive, we simply have to choose X at a distance $\sqrt{\rho}$ from O to have $OX \cdot OX = \rho$. Since the set of points at a distance $\sqrt{\rho}$ from O lie on a circle, all these invariant points are on a circle called the *circle of inversion* (Figure 5.1c).

The class of changes that does permit of invariant points is precisely those changes which characterize inversive geometry. Since they always determine a circle of inversion, we speak of *inversion in a circle* and use this circle to give a more precise definition of inversion which will transform almost the whole plane (before, we could not get the image of points on the line through A and A'; now, the only exception will be O).

Definition. *An inversion in a circle with center at O and radius R takes every point P of the plane (except O) to the point P' such that P,P',O are collinear, P' is on the same side of O as P, and $OP \cdot OP' = R^2$.*

Inversive geometry can now be defined as the study of those properties of figures that are preserved by inversions. Any transformation that results from a consecutive application of a finite number of inversions will be called an *inversive transformation*. Inversive properties are those properties that are not affected by inversive transformations.

Exercises

1. Prove that a necessary and sufficient condition for four points A,A',B,B' to be on a circle is that $OA \cdot OA' = OB \cdot OB'$ where O is the intersection of AA' and BB'.

2. If A, A', O are three fixed collinear points and X, X' are two variable points collinear with O but not with A and A', show that the relationship $OX \cdot OX' = OA \cdot OA'$ assigns the point X' to X uniquely.

3. Prove that the transformation described in Exercise 2 preserves cocircularity if O is not on the circle being transformed (Figure 5.1d).

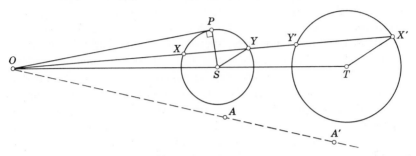

Fig. 5.1d

4. Show that inversion in a circle takes a point inside of the circle outside, a point outside goes inside, and a point on the circumference is invariant.

5. Show that the image P' of a point P outside of the circle of inversion can be constructed as follows. Draw a tangent PT (T the point of contact) from P to the circle of inversion; draw the line OP, O the center of inversion; and drop a perpendicular TP' from T to OP; P' is the image of P (Figure 5.1e).

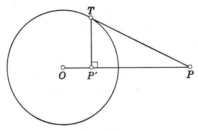

Fig. 5.1e

6. Prove that a point P and its image under inversion P' are harmonic conjugates with respect to the points in which the line through PP' meets the circle of inversion.

7. Prove that any two points and their images under inversion are cocircular.

8. Show that a line through the center of inversion is transformed into itself by inversion in that circle.

9. Show that inversion does not preserve the order of collinear points.

10. What can you say about the image of a straight line completely outside of the circle of inversion? A circle through the center of the circle of inversion? The circle of inversion itself?

5.2 INVERSIONS IN ANALYTIC FORM

In inversive geometry as in other geometries, it is sometimes convenient to use an analytic approach. Rectangular coordinates, however, are not the best analytic tool—polar coordinates are; this is not surprising since circles are so much a part of this geometry. We can think of polar coordinates as complex numbers; that is, if a point has rectangular coordinates (x,y), we can name the same point with the complex number $z = x + iy$ or $z = r(\cos \theta + i \sin \theta)$ where $r = \sqrt{x^2 + y^2}$ and $\theta = $ arc tan (y/x) (Figure 5.2a). This trigonometric form of the complex numbers can be shortened to $z = re^{i\theta}$ if we consider the power series expansions of sine, cosine, and e (they hold for complex numbers as well as for real numbers). If you are not familiar with the study of complex variables, you can think of $e^{i\theta}$ as a short way to write $\cos \theta + i \sin \theta$. From your knowledge of trigonometry, everything we say shall still be valid.

As we develop inversive geometry, we shall have to use the conjugate of complex numbers. If $z = x + iy$, the conjugate of z is $x - iy$ and we write $\bar{z} = x - iy$. In the other form, if $z = re^{i\theta} = r(\cos \theta + i \sin \theta)$, then

$$\bar{z} = r(\cos \theta - i \sin \theta) = r[\cos (-\theta) + i \sin (-\theta)] = re^{-i\theta}.$$

Geometrically, $\bar{z}$ is the reflection of z in the real axis (Figure 5.2b).

Using complex numbers, we want to find a formula for the inverse of a point with respect to any circle, say a circle with center at point a and having radius R. To do this, we shall first consider the simplest case, a unit circle about the origin, then any circle about the origin, and finally any circle at all.

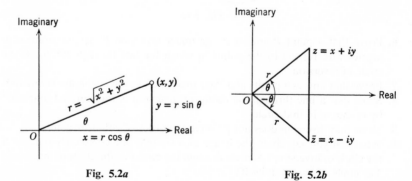

Fig. 5.2a   Fig. 5.2b

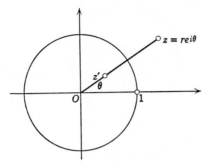

Fig. 5.2c

The inverse of a point $z = re^{i\theta}$ with respect to the unit circle about the origin will be a point on the line from z to the origin, so θ is unchanged. The inverse of z, which we shall call z', must be at a distance s from the origin so that $sr = 1$ (Figure 5.2c). The only possibility is that $s = 1/r$ and then $z' = (1/r)e^{i\theta}$. We can write $(1/r)e^{i\theta} = 1/re^{-i\theta} = 1/\bar{z}$; thus, $z' = 1/\bar{z}$.

If, instead of a unit circle, we wish to use a circle of radius R about the origin, we can use the same reasoning, except that this time $sr = R^2$, so $z' = (R^2/r)e^{i\theta} = R^2/\bar{z}$.

Now we can consider the most general case, the inverse of a point z with respect to a circle of radius R about the point a. Since we are carrying out this transformation in a Euclidean plane, we can take advantage of the permissible changes in Euclidean geometry. The Euclidean properties of length, collinearity, and betweenness (which are used in the definition of inversion) are not affected by changes of position; in particular, they are not affected by translations. Since we already know about inversions with respect to circles about the origin, we can translate our problem to the origin, find the solution, then translate back to the original position (Figure 5.2d).

The entire problem can be translated to the origin by subtracting a from each point; the center of the circle of inversion goes to $a - a = O$, and z goes to $z - a$. The inverse of $z - a$ with respect to a circle of radius R about the origin is $(z - a)' = R^2/\overline{z - a} = R^2/(\bar{z} - \bar{a})$. This is the same point that we would have if we had found z' in the original position and then applied the translation, so $(z - a)' = z' - a$. Finally, $z' - a = R^2/(\bar{z} - \bar{a})$, and $z' = a + R^2/(\bar{z} - \bar{a})$ is the desired formula.

We are now in a position to check whether or not inversions preserve cocircularity. You have probably noticed already that, if a circle goes through the center of inversion, its image is an unbounded figure, and thus cannot be a circle. In spite of this, we can still hope that inversions will

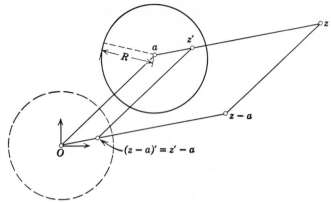

Fig. 5.2d

preserve cocircularity in many cases, and possibly all cases, if we modify our language a little.

In ordinary analytic geometry, the equation of a circle has the form $\alpha x^2 + \alpha y^2 + 2\beta x + 2\gamma y + \delta = 0$ where $\alpha \neq 0$. (If $\alpha = 0$, then this is a straight line.) It is easy to show that if $z = x + iy$, then $x = (z + \bar{z})/2$, $y = (z - \bar{z})/2i$, $x^2 + y^2 = z\bar{z}$, $2x = z + \bar{z}$, and $2y = i(\bar{z} - z)$. The equation of a circle then becomes $\alpha z\bar{z} + \beta(z + \bar{z}) + i\gamma(\bar{z} - z) + \delta = 0$ or $\alpha z\bar{z} + \bar{\varepsilon}z + \varepsilon\bar{z} + \delta = 0$ if we let $\varepsilon = \beta + i\gamma$. Let us see what happens to this equation after inversion in a unit circle about the origin. z goes to $1/\bar{z}$ and $\bar{z}$ goes to $1/\bar{\bar{z}} = 1/z$. The equation becomes

$$\alpha(1/z\bar{z}) + \bar{\varepsilon}(1/\bar{z}) + \varepsilon(1/z) + \delta = 0, \qquad \text{or} \qquad \alpha + \bar{\varepsilon}z + \varepsilon\bar{z} + \delta z\bar{z} = 0.$$

Notice that the resulting equation is of the same type as the original. If δ is not zero, this is still a circle, but if $\delta = 0$, it is a straight line. Thus, under inversions, some circles go to circles, but also some circles go to straight lines and vice versa. The property of being a straight line or a circle are not inversive properties, or we could say that the distinction between straight lines and circles is not a valid *inversive* distinction. The situation is similar to that in Euclidean geometry where the distinction between vertical and horizontal lines is not a valid *Euclidean* distinction, or in projective geometry where the distinction between intersecting and parallel lines is not a valid *projective* distinction.

We began our study of inversive geometry with the desire to preserve cocircularity. It now appears that we have completely lost the notion of circles. We can save the situation if we agree on a slight change of language. The only problem is that we cannot distinguish straight lines from circles. If we agree to use the word "circle" to include both the circles of Euclidean geometry and the straight lines of Euclidean geometry, then we can say that circles go to circles under inversions.

Exercises

1. Show that $\overline{z + w} = \bar{z} + \bar{w}$, $\overline{z - w} = \bar{z} - \bar{w}$, $\overline{zw} = \bar{z} \cdot \bar{w}$, $\overline{(z/w)} = \bar{z}/\bar{w}$, and $\bar{\bar{z}} = z$.

2. Prove that the transformation that takes each point z to $z - a$ is a translation.

3. Find the inverse of the point $(2, -2)$ with respect to a circle of radius 10 about the point $(-1,2)$.

4. Develop a formula for rectangular coordinates that will give the inverse of any point with respect to any circle.

5. If $z = x + iy$, show that $x = (z + \bar{z})/2$, $y = (z - \bar{z})/2i$, $x^2 + y^2 = z\bar{z}$, $2x = z + \bar{z}$, and $2y = i(\bar{z} - z)$.

6. We saw that circles may go to circles or to straight lines under inversions in a unit circle about the origin. Why are we sure that the same thing will happen under inversion in any circle?

7. Find analytically the image of each of the following under inversion in the unit circle about the origin: the line $y = 5$, the circle $(x - \frac{1}{4})^2 + y^2 \to \frac{1}{16}$, the circle of radius $\frac{1}{2}$ about the origin, the line $y = x$, and the line $y = -1$.

5.3 RELATIONSHIP BETWEEN EUCLIDEAN AND INVERSIVE GEOMETRIES

In the first part of this book, we described Euclidean geometry as the study of those properties of figures which are invariant under changes of position. Translations, rotations, and reflections in lines are all examples of such changes; in fact, it can be proved that every Euclidean transformation (also called a distance preserving transformation, an isometry, and sometimes a rigid motion, although some authors do not consider reflections to be rigid motions) can be accomplished by the successive application of a finite number of translations, rotations, and reflections. We shall not attempt to prove this here but shall accept it as a known Euclidean fact.*

If we look a little closer at translations, rotations, and reflections, we shall see that there is a relationship between these transformations. A combination of two reflections in parallel lines is actually a translation in a direction perpendicular to the two lines and equal in length to twice

---

* H. S. M. Coxeter, *Introduction to Geometry*, John Wiley and Sons, New York, 1961, pp. 39–46; and Howard Eves, *A Survey of Geometry*, Volume One, Allyn and Bacon, Boston, 1963, pp. 134–7.

the distance between them. Conversely, we could begin with any translation and find a sequence of two reflections in parallel lines which is equivalent to it. Similarly, a combination of two reflections in intersecting lines is equivalent to a rotation about their point of intersection and through an angle which is twice the magnitude of one of the angles between them (depending on which line is used first). In other words, every Euclidean transformation could be accomplished by the successive application of a finite number of reflections.

In this section, we shall consider the relationship between Euclidean and inversive transformations. Since inversion in circles involves the use of the conjugate of complex numbers (which are reflections in the real axis), we suspect that there is a close relationship between reflections and inversions.

There is an intuitive way to illustrate the relationship. Consider a circle with center O and through a point T (Figure 5.3a). As OT gets larger, the inverse P' of a point P outside the circle and on the line through O and T approaches P_0, the reflection of P in the tangent to the circle at T. We can see this if we consider the definition of inversion. P' is on the line through P and O and $OP \cdot OP' = OT^2$ or

$$(OT + TP)(OT - P'T) = OT^2$$
$$(OT - P'T) = OT^2/(OT + TP)$$
$$P'T = OT - OT^2/(OT + TP)$$
$$P'T = OT \cdot TP/(OT + TP)$$
$$P'T = TP/(1 + (TP/OT)).$$

If we keep T and P fixed and let OT increase indefinitely, $P'T$ approaches TP. Of course, this is not a geometric proof since it makes use of the notion of a limit, but it should convince us that there is a very close relationship between inversions in circles and reflections in straight lines.

A geometric proof of the relationship is obtained by considering the successive applications of three inversions in unit circles. Let the first

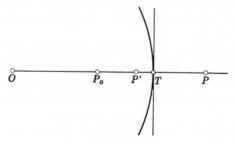

Fig. 5.3a

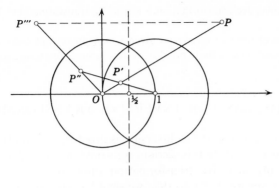

Fig. 5.3b

inversion be in a unit circle about the origin; P goes to P' (Figure 5.3b) and, in coordinates, we have z going to $z' = 1/\bar{z}$. Let the second inversion be in a unit circle about the point 1; P' goes to P'', or z' goes to $z'' = 1 + 1/(\bar{z'} - 1) = \bar{z'}/(\bar{z'} - 1)$. Finally, we invert P'' in a unit circle about the origin getting P''', or $z''' = 1/\bar{z''} = (\bar{\bar{z'}} - 1)/\bar{\bar{z'}} = (z' - 1)/z' = 1 - \bar{z}$. Thus, after three inversions, we have z going to $1 - \bar{z}$. If we translate this into rectangular coordinates, (x,y) goes to $(1 - x,y)$ and what we have accomplished is actually a reflection in the line perpendicular to the x-axis and through the point $(\frac{1}{2},0)$. Since any line in the Euclidean plane can be changed into this line, what we have just shown is that every reflection in a line can be expressed by a composition of three inversions.

Since a translation can be accomplished by two reflections in parallel lines, it could also be accomplished by six inversions. Similarly, every rotation is equivalent to the composition of six inversions. It now follows that every Euclidean transformation is an inversive transformation. Since we arrived at our definition of inversion in Section 5.1 by a desire to preserve cocircularity (and the rigid motions do preserve it), this result should not be surprising.

Exercises

1. Prove that every translation can be expressed as the composition of two reflections in parallel lines.

2. Prove that every rotation can be expressed as a composition of two reflections in intersecting lines.

3. Is every inversive transformation a Euclidean transformation? Why, or why not?

4. Read one of the two references given which prove that every rigid motion is a composition of a finite number of translations, rotations, and reflections.

5.4   FORMULAS FOR INVERSIVE TRANSFORMATIONS

We already know that one inversion is given by a formula of the form $z' = a + R^2/(\bar{z} - \bar{a})$. In this section, we would like to find a formula that represents any inversive transformation (any composition of a finite number of inversions). To do this, we shall have to use some of the facts that we have already established about the rigid motions.

We shall make use of the idea that a translation can always be given by six inversions, and that in complex numbers $z' = z + a$ represents a translation (see Exercise 2 of 5.2). A rotation can also be given by six inversions; in complex numbers, $z' = e^{i\theta}z$ is a rotation about the origin since this leaves the distance from the origin unchanged while it changes the angle between the real axis and the line from z to the origin.

In addition, we shall use the transformation $z' = 1/z$ (which has no special name). It can be obtained by an inversion in a unit circle about the origin followed by a reflection in the real axis (that is, taking the conjugate of the complex number). Since a reflection is three inversions, the transformation $z' = 1/z$ is a composition of four inversions.

We shall also make use of a transformation called a *stretching*. If we consider two consecutive inversions in two concentric circles about the origin, we have $z' = R^2/\bar{z}$ and $z'' = S^2/\bar{z'}$. Combining these two formulas, we get $z'' = (S^2/R^2)z$, which changes the distance of a point from the origin but leaves the line from the point to the origin unchanged. We shall call this transformation a stretching in the origin (even if $S^2 < R^2$, which makes it a shrinking). We could write a stretching in the origin in the form $z' = \rho z$ where ρ is any real number greater than zero.

With all this background, we are now ready to develop the general formulas for inversive transformations.

Theorem. *Every equation of the form $z' = (az + b)/(cz + d)$, where a,b,c,d are complex numbers and $bc - ad \neq 0$ represents an even number of inversions. Conversely, every composition of an even number of inversions can be represented by an equation of this form.*

Proof. Let $u = cz + d$ and assume, temporarily, that $c \neq 0$. If $c = \gamma e^{i\theta}$, γ represents a stretching in the origin and $e^{i\theta}$ represents a rotation about the origin. Adding d represents a translation. This means that $u = cz + d$ could be accomplished by fourteen inversions.

Let $v = 1/u$, which we know is the result of four inversions. Finally, let $z' = (b - ad/c)v + a/c$. This transformation is of the same form as the first one; $b - ad/c \neq 0$ so it is an inversive transformation; it is the result of fourteen inversions.

Composing these three transformations (an even number of inversions), we get

$$z' = (b - ad/c)v + a/c$$

$$= (b - ad/c)[1/(cz + d)] + a/c$$

$$= (az + b)/(cz + d).$$

If $c = 0$, neither a nor d is zero because $bc - ad \neq 0$. The formula then reduces to $(a/d)z + b/d$, which we know is an even number of inversions.

What we have just shown is that $z' = (az + b)/(cz + d)$ with $bc - ad \neq 0$ (called a *fractional linear transformation*) is a composition of an even number of inversions.

Conversely, every composition of an even number of inversions has this form. You can verify this by composing $u = a + R^2/(\bar{z} - \bar{a})$ and $z' = b + S^2/(\bar{u} - \bar{b})$, simplifying the result (you get a fractional linear transformation), and showing that the composition of two fractional linear transformations is always a fractional linear transformation. |

Theorem.   *Every equation of the form* $z' = (a\bar{z} + b)/(c\bar{z} + d)$ *where* a,b,c,d *are complex numbers and* $bc - ad \neq 0$ *represents an odd number of inversions. Conversely, every composition of an odd number of inversions can be represented by an equation of this form.*

Proof.   To see that $z' = (a\bar{z} + b)/(c\bar{z} + d)$ is an odd number of inversions, we repeat the same sequence of transformations as in the previous theorem except that we first send z to $\bar{z}$ (three inversions).

To prove the converse, assume that we are given an odd number of inversions. If we first take the conjugate $\bar{w}$ of the point w to be transformed (three inversions), and then apply the odd number of inversions, we get an even number of inversions, or w goes to $(aw + b)/(cw + d)$ where $bc - ad \neq 0$. But $(aw + b)/(cw + d) = (a\bar{\bar{w}} + b)/(c\bar{\bar{w}} + d)$ and we took the conjugate of w before we applied the odd number of inversions, so the odd number of inversions has the form $z' = (a\bar{z} + b)/(c\bar{z} + d)$ where $bc - ad \neq 0.$ |

Exercises

1. Prove that a stretching in the origin sends every triangle into a similar triangle.

2. Show that a stretching in the origin sends circles to circles.

3. Show that the composition of $u = a + R^2/(\bar{z} - \bar{a})$ and $z' = b + S^2/(\bar{u} - \bar{b})$ is a fractional linear transformation. (Do not forget to verify that the condition on the constants holds.)

4. Show that the fractional linear transformations are closed under composition.

5. Show that the transformation $z' = z$ is an inversive transformation.

6. If $z' = (az + b)/(cz + d)$ where $bc - ad \neq 0$, what transformation will send z' back to z? Does it always exist?

7. Prove that the fractional linear transformations form a group under composition.

8. Is the group of fractional linear transformations under composition a commutative group?

5.5 COMPLETING THE INVERSIVE PLANE

In inversion, no point corresponds to the center of the circle of inversion, so we could say that the plane as we have been dealing with it is incomplete. The situation is similar to what we had in projective geometry —a point is lost. We want to remedy the situation the way we did in projective geometry, that is, by introducing ideal elements. It turns out that, in this case, it is enough to introduce only *one* such element, an ideal point which we shall denote by Ω.

In an inversion, as the point P approaches the center of inversion, its image P' recedes indefinitely. This is the reason why the point Ω is sometimes called the point at infinity. However, giving a name to something that does not exist is not a very satisfactory way to introduce it into a mathematical system. It is possible to introduce the point Ω in two different ways—one analytic, the other by a special kind of projection called a sterographic projection.

The analytic way is very similar to the corresponding procedure in projective geometry. There we introduced homogeneous coordinates by writing $x = u/w$, $y = v/w$ and using the ordered triple (u,v,w) to represent projective points. Here we identify the complex number z with the ratio

z_1/z_2 and use the ordered pair (z_1, z_2) to represent inversive points. Of course, many ordered pairs (z_1, z_2) will represent the same point since multiplying each member of the ordered pair by any complex number (not equal to zero) leaves the ratio unchanged. As long as $z_2 \neq 0$, we do not get anything new, but if we allow $z_2 = 0$ we get one new point $(z_1, 0)$ or $(1, 0)$. This is the point that we shall call Ω.

The fractional linear transformation obtained by substituting $z = z_1/z_2$ becomes $z_1'/z_2' = (az_1 + bz_2)/(cz_1 + dz_2)$. We could write this in two parts: $\rho z_1' = az_1 + bz_2$ and $\rho z_2' = cz_1 + dz_2$ where $\rho \neq 0$. If $cz_1 + dz_2 = 0$, then the point (z_1, z_2) is sent to Ω. If $a \neq 0$ and $c \neq 0$, Ω is sent to an ordinary point by the inversive transformation. We could do a similar thing for an odd number of inversions.

To illustrate the above, we could consider inversion in a unit circle about the origin, $z' = 1/\bar{z} = (0\bar{z} + 1)/(1\bar{z} + 0)$. In this form, the origin 0 has no image. Now we can write $\rho z_1' = 0\bar{z}_1 + 1\bar{z}_2$ and $\rho z_2' = 1\bar{z}_1 + 0\bar{z}_2$. The origin can be represented by the ordered pair $(0,1)$; it goes to $(1/\rho, 0) = (1, 0)$, the point Ω.

The other way to introduce Ω is to use a stereographic projection. Let the inversive plane Π that we are interested in be a part of three-dimensional Euclidean space. Assume that on Π there is a circle of radius R about a point O and we want to talk about inversion in this circle. Let there be a sphere of radius R with center at O; Π will be an equatorial plane of this sphere (Figure 5.5a). Let N be an extremity of the diameter of the sphere which is perpendicular to Π. Let each point P on Π be assigned to the point P^* on the sphere, where P^* is the intersection of the line through P and N with the sphere. Every point P of the plane Π corresponds to a unique point P^* on the sphere. Every figure on the plane has a corresponding figure on the surface of the sphere, and every transformation of the plane Π corresponds to a transformation on the surface of the sphere.

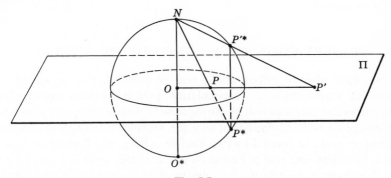

Fig. 5.5a

If we begin with a point P^* on the surface of the sphere, we can find a point P in the plane that corresponds to it by reversing the procedure, that is, unless $P^* = N$. The point N corresponds to no ordinary point of Π. We shall say that N corresponds to a point Ω, then if we carry out inversion by means of the images on the sphere, there will be no exceptions. On the sphere the inverse of a point P^* can be found by considering the intersection of the sphere with the line through P^* and perpendicular to Π. Point O on Π corresponds to O^* on the sphere, the inverse of O^* is N, which corresponds to Ω; thus Ω is the image of O under inversion in the circle with radius R and center at O. Even if we consider inversion in some other circle, Ω turns out to be the inverse of the center of that circle also.

Exercises

1. Analytically, find the image of a circle through the origin after inversion in a unit circle about the origin. Show that $\Omega = (1,0)$ lies on the image of the circle.

2. Prove analytically that, under inversion in any circle, the center of that circle goes to $(1,0) = \Omega$.

3. Prove analytically that Ω is on every straight line.

4. Prove that, if we project P stereographically from N to the point P^* on the surface of the sphere and the project P^* back to the original plane from O^*, the result is equivalent to inversion in the equator.

5. Show that, on the sphere, the inverse of P^* is the intersection of the perpendicular from P^* to Π and the sphere.

6. What is the image of a circle on Π (not through O) when it is projected onto the sphere? What is the image of a circle on Π which passes through O? What is the image of a line through O? A line not through O?

7. Let the sphere about O and the plane Π be given as in this section. Consider an inversion in a circle other than the equator. Why is the image of the center of inversion Ω?

5.6   PRESERVATION OF MAGNITUDE OF ANGLES

We have already talked about one property that is preserved by inversive transformations—cocircularity (which includes collinearity, since lines and circles cannot be distinguished). Another property preserved by inversions is the magnitude of an angle. Of course, an angle in inversive geometry could be formed by two Euclidean lines, two Euclidean circles, or a Euclidean line and a Euclidean circle. If the angle is formed by a Euclidean circle, we measure it by means of the tangent to the circle at the vertex of the angle. It will be sufficient to prove that the magnitude of angles is preserved in the second case (the angle between two Euclidean circles) since we could easily add these circles in the other two cases. We shall assume that the center of inversion does not lie on either of the circles (the other case will be left as an exercise).

Let two circles be given which intersect at Q (Figure 5.6a). Join Q to the center of inversion O. The angle α between the two circles is the sum of the angles α_1 and α_2 between the circles and the line OQ. It is sufficient to show that the magnitude of these angles is preserved. We shall do this for α_1.

α_1 is equal to β_1, which is the angle between the tangent at Q and the chord PQ. β_1 is equal in magnitude to any inscribed angle subtending the chord PQ, as $\measuredangle PRQ$. Let P',Q',R' be the respective images of P,Q,R after inversion in O. Points P',Q',R' lie on a circle which is the image of the circle through P,Q,R, so P',Q',R' still form an inscribed angle. We shall show that $\measuredangle Q'R'P' = \measuredangle PRQ$, which will complete the proof because the image of α_1 will be related to $\measuredangle Q'R'P'$ in the same way that α_1 was related to $\measuredangle PRQ$.

Since an exterior angle of a triangle is equal to the sum of the two non-adjacent interior angles $\measuredangle PRQ = \measuredangle OQR - \measuredangle OPR$. By the definition of inversion, $OP \cdot OP' = OR \cdot OR'$ or $OP/OR' = OR/OP'$. This tells us that triangles OPR and $OR'P'$ are similar and $\measuredangle OPR = \measuredangle OR'P'$. Similarly, $\measuredangle OQR = \measuredangle OR'Q'$. Therefore,

$$\measuredangle PRQ = \measuredangle OQR - \measuredangle OPR = \measuredangle OR'P' - \measuredangle OR'Q' = \measuredangle Q'R'P'.$$

We have just shown that an inversion preserves the magnitude of angles. At the same time, we saw that it changes the sense of an angle.

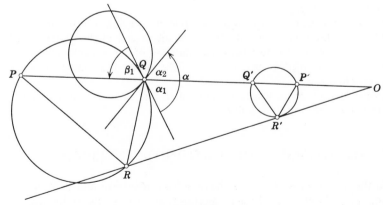

Fig. 5.6a

The magnitude of an angle is preserved by any number of consecutive inversions, that is, by any inversive transformation. The sense will be changed by any odd number of inversions, and will be preserved by an even number of inversions.

We should notice, in particular, that a right angle will always go to a right angle under inversions; thus, we say that perpendicularity or orthogonality is preserved.

Inversive transformations are not the most general transformations that preserve the magnitude of angles. If a function $z' = f(z)$ in the complex numbers has a derivative defined by

$$\lim_{h \to 0} \frac{f(z + h) - f(z)}{h},$$

which is independent of the way h approaches zero, then this is an analytic function and it is called a conformal transformation because it can be shown to preserve the magnitude of angles. This is the most general type of angle preserving transformation. The corresponding geometry is called *conformal geometry*.

Exercises

1. Show that the magnitude of an angle is preserved under inversion even if the center of inversion is on one of the circles which make up the angle.

2. Show that orthogonal circles (their tangents at the point of intersection are perpendicular) invert into orthogonal circles.

3. Prove that tangent circles not through the center of inversion invert into tangent circles. What happens to tangent circles when the center of inversion is the point of tangency?

4. Show that a circle orthogonal to the circle of inversion inverts into itself.

5. If two circles are orthogonal, show that the inverse of the center of either circle with respect to the other is the midpoint of their common chord.

6. Use inversion to prove that the sum of the angles of a triangle is equal to two right angles.

7. Prove that all circles which are tangent to one circle and orthogonal to a second will be tangent to a third.

5.7   AN INVERSIVE DEFINITION OF INVERSION

In the preceding sections, we have defined inversion and then inversive geometry as the study of those properties that are not affected by inversion.

We know that the property of being a straight line, the property of a point being the center of a circle, and the concept of distance are not inversive properties. Nevertheless, inversion has been defined in terms of these properties. In order to have a consistent theory, we must check to see if the concept of inversion itself is an inversive concept. The fact that we cannot accept our present definition as inversive does not mean that the concept is not acceptable. We can show that the concept of inversion is acceptable if we can give another definition of inversion which includes our present definition but which uses only inversive concepts.

The concept of being a circle (in the generalized sense which includes straight lines) and the concept of a point belonging to a circle are certainly inversive concepts. These are the ideas that we shall use for our new definition of inversion. We shall make the assumption that there is one and only one circle through three distinct points. If the points are collinear in the Euclidean sense, then the circle is, of course, a straight line in the Euclidean sense. In Section 5.1, we talked about cocircularity and our desire to preserve this property. It turns out that this relation on four points (that they are cocircular) can be used as a basis for our new definition.

Definition. *Let P,P',Q,Q' be any four cocircular points. The inverse of any fifth point R with respect to P,P',Q,Q' is the point R' which is the other intersection of the unique circle through P,P',R and the unique circle through Q,Q',R (Figure 5.7a).*

If it should happen that the two circles have only the point R in common, then $R' = R$. If the two circles coincide, we can choose an arbitrary point S not on that circle, determine S', the inverse corresponding to it, and then use S and S' instead of Q and Q' to determine R'.

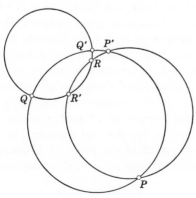

Fig. 5.7a

This definition of inversion is not equivalent to the one that we have been using, because it allows many more transformations than did our original definition; however, every inversion in a circle is one of these transformations. This is sufficient to guarantee that our original definition of inversion is inversive.

Exercise

Using Euclidean geometry, show that if O is the intersection of PP' and QQ' and $OP \cdot OP' > 0$, then the inverse R' of R, as defined above, is the same as inversion in a circle with center at O and having radius $\sqrt{OP \cdot OP'}$.

5.8   COCIRCULARITY IN COMPLEX FORM

We have already pointed out the fundamental importance of co-circularity in inversive geometry. In this section, we would like to find an analytic way to represent this relation.

In projective geometry, one of the important concepts was that of the cross ratio of four points. If the four points are on the x-axis, the cross ratio can be computed from their abscissas x_1, x_2, x_3, x_4, and has the form

$$\frac{x_1 - x_3}{x_2 - x_3} \bigg/ \frac{x_1 - x_4}{x_2 - x_4}.$$

At first, this does not seem to have anything to do with inversive geometry (although one instance of cross ratio in inversive geometry was mentioned in Exercise 6 of Section 5.1). However, if we recall that, in projective geometry, the fractional linear transformation $y = (Ax + B)/(Cx + D)$ (all the constants and variables are real numbers in projective geometry) has the property of preserving cross ratio (Section 3.10), we shall find a connection. This formula is identical in form with that for the even inversive transformations, although in inversive geometry we are using complex numbers. Formally, these transformations are identical, but the geometrical content is different because we are using different number systems. However, the properties of the operations on the complex numbers are the same as for the real numbers, so we can conclude immediately (without repeating the proof of Chapter 3) that the even fractional linear transformations preserve the cross ratio

$$\frac{z_1 - z_3}{z_2 - z_3} \bigg/ \frac{z_1 - z_4}{z_2 - z_4}$$

of any four inversive points z_1, z_2, z_3, z_4.

Now we are close to finding a condition for cocircularity. If four points z_1, z_2, z_3, z_4 are cocircular, it is always possible to transform the circle into a straight line by an even fractional linear transformation and, in fact, we can send the circle to the real axis. After transformation, the images z_1', z_2', z_3', z_4' are real numbers so

$$\frac{z_1' - z_3'}{z_2' - z_3'} \bigg/ \frac{z_1' - z_4'}{z_2' - z_4'} = \frac{z_1 - z_3}{z_2 - z_3} \bigg/ \frac{z_1 - z_4}{z_2 - z_4}$$

is a real number. This shows that a necessary condition for the cocircularity of z_1, z_2, z_3, z_4 is that their cross ratio be a real number. Conversely, we can show that this condition is also sufficient for cocircularity. We can state this result as a theorem.

Theorem. *Four distinct points z_1, z_2, z_3, z_4 are cocircular, if, and only if,*

$$\frac{z_1 - z_3}{z_2 - z_3} \bigg/ \frac{z_1 - z_4}{z_2 - z_4}$$

is a real number.

Exercises

1. Verify that the even fractional linear transformations are cross ratio preserving. Do not forget to consider the case where one of the points is Ω.
2. Prove that any three distinct points (and thus any circle) can be transformed into any other three distinct points by an even fractional linear transformation.
3. Show that, if the cross ratio of any four distinct points is a real number, then the points are cocircular.
4. If four points are not cocircular, there is a different circle determined by any three of them. There are four such circles. Between each pair of circles there is an angle (because they have a point in common). There are six such angles. Using the four points in all possible arrangements, there are six different cross ratios that can be formed. What is the relation between the six cross ratios and the six angles?

5.9 PENCILS OF CIRCLES

There are many problems that can be solved quite easily if we keep in mind some of the things that we have already proved. We have shown that angles are preserved under inversive transformations (in particular, orthogonality is preserved), and we have shown that any circle can be transformed into a straight line by an inversive transformation (Exercise 2 of Section 5.8).

Assume that we have a circle K and we want to find the family of circles orthogonal to K. There is an inversive transformation θ that takes K to a straight line m. The circles orthogonal to m are those with their centers on m (because m is perpendicular to their tangents at the point of intersection). Inversion preserves orthogonality, so we can send m back to K by θ^{-1} (see Exercise 6 of Section 5.4) and the images of the circles after applying θ^{-1} will be the circles orthogonal to K.

Another easy problem to solve is to find all the circles orthogonal to two given circles. Let K_1 and K_2 be the two given circles. If K_1 and K_2 have two points P and Q in common, we can apply a transformation taking Q to Ω. This transforms the circles into Euclidean straight lines (why?) m_1 and m_2 having the point P', the image of P, in common. Circles orthogonal to both m_1 and m_2 must have their centers on both lines, therefore their centers are all at P'. The inverse of the transformation takes these circles into the family (or pencil) of circles orthogonal to K_1 and K_2. Since no two concentric circles have a point in common, no two circles of this pencil have a point in common.

It is interesting to notice that any line through P' is orthogonal to all the circles of the pencil that we have just found. After applying the inverse transformation, these lines become circles through P and Q. Thus, we have two pencils, one consisting of all those circles through P and Q and the other consisting of all the circles orthogonal to these circles (Figure 5.9a).

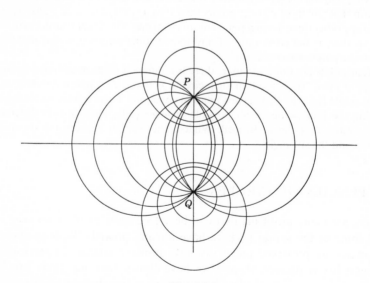

Fig. 5.9a

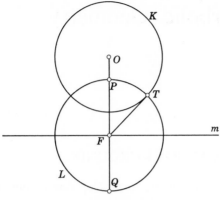

Fig. 5.9*b*

If the two given circles K_1 and K_2 do not have a point in common, we can still find a pencil of circles orthogonal to both of them. Let θ take K_1 to the straight line m and K_2 to a circle K (Figure 5.9*b*). If O is the center of the circle K, the line OF, which is perpendicular to m, will be transformed into an orthogonal circle by θ^{-1}. To find another orthogonal circle, we can consider the tangent FT to K from F. There is a circle L with center at F and passing through T (the point of contact). L is orthogonal to line m and to circle K. Let L intersect OF at P and Q. Under θ^{-1}, OF and L will become circles intersecting at two points. We know how to find all the circles orthogonal to them by the first case. The inverse images of K and m are two of the circles of this pencil. Thus, again we have two pencils of circles: in one pencil, all the circles pass through two fixed points; in the other pencil, no two circles have a point in common.

There is one other case. K_1 and K_2 may have just one point P in common. If we transform this point to Ω, the images of K_1 and K_2 will be two parallel lines (why?). The only circles orthogonal to both of them will be straight lines perpendicular to both. If we apply the inverse of the transformation, we get two pencils of circles. All of the circles of each pencil touch each other at a point P and every circle of one family is orthogonal to every circle of the other.

Exercise

Prove that, if the equations of two circles are $(x - h_1)^2 + (y - k_1)^2 = r_1{}^2$ and $(x - h_2)^2 + (y - k_2)^2 = r_2{}^2$, then a necessary and sufficient condition for orthogonality of the two circles is that $(h_1 - h_2)^2 + (k_1 - k_2)^2 = r_1{}^2 + r_2{}^2$.

6 Hyperbolic Geometry

6.1 HISTORICAL BACKGROUND

In this chapter we are going to develop one of the geometries that is traditionally called non-Euclidean: hyperbolic geometry. (Elliptic geometry is also called non-Euclidean.) Before we begin, a few historical remarks may help motivate our development.

Euclid's great achievement was to organize geometry. He built it as a deductive system based on a few axioms. To Euclid, axioms (or postulates) were self-evident or unmistakably true propositions. It seemed, at that time, that there was no question about the self-evidence of propositions such as "all right angles are equal to one another." All of Euclid's axioms* were self-evident in this sense—all, except one. In order to prove that the alternate interior angles formed by two parallel lines and a transversal are equal, Euclid had to assume a very complicated axiom: *If a straight line falling on two straight lines makes the interior angles on the same side together less than two right angles, the two straight lines, if produced infinitely, meet on that side on which the angles are together less than two right angles.* Even Euclid could not have been very satisfied with this axiom.

This axiom, Euclid's fifth, may be unfamiliar to you. This is because it usually does not appear in textbooks in this form today. In the 18th century, the geometer Playfair realized that a different proposition could be substituted for Euclid's fifth axiom: *Through a point not on a line there is not more than one line parallel to the given line.* This is what we referred to in Section 2.4 as the uniqueness part of Euclid's parallel postulate. Sometimes this part is called Playfair's axiom. Most texts use the entire Euclidean postulate in place of Euclid's original fifth axiom even though the existence part can be proved as a theorem using only the first four Euclidean axioms.

This substitution for Euclid's fifth axiom is a good illustration of the dissatisfaction that mathematicians had with the original axiom. They

---

* For a list of Euclid's axioms, see T. L. Heath, *The Thirteen Books of Euclid's Elements*, Three Volumes, Second Edition, Cambridge University Press, New York, 1926; Dover, New York, 1956

found many other propositions which are equivalent to Euclid's fifth axiom; that is, assuming the rest of Euclidean geometry, the fifth axiom could be used to prove each one of these propositions, and each one of these propositions could be used to prove Euclid's fifth axiom. The following are some of the propositions that are equivalent to Euclid's fifth axiom.

Proposition 1. Through a point not on a line there is, at most, one line parallel to the given line.

Proposition 2. The sum of the measures of the angles of any triangle is equal to π.

Proposition 3. There exist two similar non-congruent triangles.

Proposition 4. A circle exists through any three non-collinear points.

Proposition 5. There is no upper limit to the area of a triangle.

The fact that these propositions are all equivalent to the fifth axiom is surprising since their content is quite varied. There are many more propositions that could also be added to this list. Mathematicians believed that all of these were true propositions, but they did not have the self-evidence of the first four axioms, nor could they be proved from self-evident propositions. Sometimes a mathematician thought that he had proved one of these statements from self-evident statements, but either he had made a mistake in his reasoning or he had used some statement which was not considered self-evident by other mathematicians and which really belongs in this list.

At the beginning of the 19th century, things had developed to the point where mathematicians began to realize that it was not possible to replace Euclid's fifth axiom by a simple self-evident statement. On the contrary, it seemed possible to conceive of a geometry in which Euclid's first four axioms were true, but where his fifth was false. If the fifth axiom is not true, then of course neither are any of the statements equivalent to it.

The names of some of the men who realized this were Taurinus, Schweikert, Gauss, Bolya, and Lobachevski. Of these, the last two published their results. But in the second half of the 18th century, there was another man who seems to have been the first to make a statement that contains the germ of non-Euclidean geometry. He was Lambert, and we are going to develop his idea; at first it was ignored when it was suggested because it seemed ridiculous. We are going to construct a geometry which satisfies Euclid's first four axioms, but in which the fifth axiom is not true—hyperbolic geometry. Instead of checking Euclid's fifth axiom, we shall check to see that we have a counterexample to the uniqueness part of Euclid's parallel postulate.

The clue as to how to begin is given by the fact that, if the uniqueness part of Euclid's parallel postulate is true, then the sum of the measures of the angles of any triangle is π. Let us first convince ourselves of this.

Theorem. *Proposition 1 implies Proposition 2.*

Proof. Let triangle ABC be given (Figure 6.1a). Consider a line DC such that $\angle DCB = \angle CBA$. If the line DC meets the line AB at some point F, we have a triangle CBF and the exterior angle CBA is equal to one of the nonadjacent interior angles. This is impossible (the opposite can be proved without using Euclid's fifth axiom) so the line CD does not intersect AB. Similarly for a line CE through C and forming $\angle ECA = \angle CAB$. The line CE does not intersect AB. Proposition 1 then tells us that line CE must be the same as line DC because there is only one line through C which is parallel to AB. $\angle ECD$ is then a straight angle and has measure π, so Proposition 2 is true. |

Notice that, in this proof, we used Proposition 1 and several other facts from Euclidean geometry. All of these other facts can be proved without using any statement equivalent to Euclid's fifth axiom. Although this theorem is somewhat elementary, it is proved here to illustrate how we prove that one proposition implies another, and also because it will motivate our whole development of hyperbolic geometry. Since Proposition 1 implies Proposition 2, it follows that, if Proposition 2 is not true, then Proposition 1 is not true either. If we want a geometry in which the uniqueness part of Euclid's parallel postulate will not be true, then the sum of the angles of any triangle cannot be π.

One place where this occurs is on the surface of a sphere. We can talk about triangles on the surface of a sphere—the sides are arcs of great circles (circles cut out from the surface of the sphere by a plane which passes through the center of the sphere). On a sphere, the sum of the angles of a triangle need not be π. For example, if we call one great circle the equator and then take two meridians (great circles through the point analogous to the north pole) at right angles to each other, we have a triangle with three right angles, or angle sum $\frac{3}{2}\pi$.

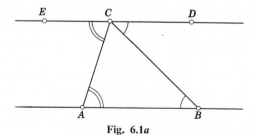

Fig. 6.1a

At first we might think that a geometry on the surface of the sphere is what we want. Unfortunately, in this geometry, any two great circles (lines) intersect, so there are no parallels at all. This will not do since the existence of parallels can be proved using only the first four axioms of Euclid. So our first attempt has failed, but in spite of the failure, we should feel encouraged because the situation on the sphere confirms the idea that there is a connection between the theory of parallels and the sum of the angles of a triangle. In the Euclidean plane, the sum is π, and the parallel to a line through a point not on the line is unique. On a sphere the sum is greater than π, and there are no parallels. Perhaps we shall find the lack of uniqueness if we can find a geometry in which the sum of the angles of a triangle is less than π.

The following theorem will give us a hint as to where to look for such a geometry. The proof will be left as an exercise.

Theorem.   *The difference between the sum of the angles S of a spherical triangle and π is equal to the area of the triangle A divided by the square of the radius R of the sphere, $S - \pi = A/R^2$.*

Let us try to modify this theorem for a situation in which the sum of the angles of a triangle is less than π. In this case, A/R^2 is a negative number. Area is usually considered to be a positive quantity, so this can only occur if the denominator R^2 is less than zero. This could happen if R is a pure imaginary number. This brings us back to Lambert. He said that a geometry on a sphere of imaginary radius will be the place where the uniqueness of parallels fails.

In the 18th century imaginary numbers were used, but the basis of the theory was shaky. It is no wonder that the remark of Lambert was not developed further—it must have sounded like a joke. Today the situation is different. The complex numbers are a completely respectable mathematical system. Without sacrificing rigor, we can follow Lambert's suggestion. Our plan will be to look at the geometry on the surface of a real sphere and then modify what happens there to the case of a sphere of imaginary radius. In the next section, we shall summarize all the facts about spherical geometry that we shall use to give us ideas for our new geometry.

Exercises

1. Prove the equivalence of Euclid's fifth axiom to each of the propositions listed in this section.
2. Prove that the difference between the sum of the angles S of a spherical

triangle and π is equal to the area of the triangle A divided by the square of the radius R of the sphere, $S - \pi = A/R^2$.

3. Show that the spherical excess, $S - \pi$, has the property of additivity (see Section 2.5); that is, if we split a spherical triangle in two, the sum of the spherical excesses of the parts is equal to the spherical excess of the whole.

6.2   SPHERICAL GEOMETRY

The geometry on the surface of a sphere is developed as part of Euclidean three-space, but spherical geometry is different from plane Euclidean geometry. There are no parallel lines. The sum of the angles of a triangle is greater than π. In many other ways, however, it is analogous to Euclidean geometry on a plane. Great circles on the sphere are the counterparts of Euclidean straight lines. The length of the arc of the great circle between two points (where the arc is not greater than half of the circumference) is the distance between two points. Angles on a sphere are formed by two great circles and are measured by the angle between the tangents to the circles at the point of intersection (or the angle between the two planes which cut out the great circles, or by the perpendiculars to these planes).

There is another way in which spherical geometry is different from Euclidean geometry. Two great circles meet in not only one, but two different points. If we wanted to keep spherical geometry as close to Euclidean geometry as possible, we can overcome this difficulty. Either we can simply identify all diametrically opposite points and consider them as one point, or we could get the same result if we used less than half of the sphere. In our development of hyperbolic geometry which follows, we shall pattern each step on spherical geometry, and when we want to guarantee that two lines meet in at most one point, we shall follow the latter course of restricting ourselves to less than half of the sphere.

The formulas of analytic spherical geometry are easy to develop if we make use of the vector geometry that we know. Let us consider a sphere of radius R about O, where O is the origin of the coordinate system. How can we identify a point that is on the surface of the sphere? We can think of a point P on the surface of the sphere as a vector with its tail at the center of the sphere. The length of this vector must be R; thus, $P = (x,y,z)$ where $x^2 + y^2 + z^2 = R^2$ (that is, the dot product of the vector with itself must be equal to the square of the radius).

Next, we want to be able to tell if a certain point P is on a given line, or great circle. The great circle is cut out by a plane through the origin. If $\mathbf{v}$ is a vector perpendicular to this plane, and P is a point on the great circle, then $P \cdot \mathbf{v} = 0$. So if $P = (x,y,z)$ and $\mathbf{v}$ has coordinates A,B,C, then $Ax + By + Cz = 0$ means that P is on the great circle.

In order to make sure that two great circles intersect in at most one point, we could make a restriction on the ordered triples which we use to represent the points on the sphere. Besides requiring that $x^2 + y^2 + z^2 = R^2$, we could also demand that $z > 0$. This would mean that we are talking about less than half of the sphere and then any two great circles would intersect in at most one point.

We have said that the distance between two points is the length of the arc of the great circle between them. How could we calculate this distance in coordinate form? If d is the distance between P and P', then the angle between P and P' considered as vectors with tails at the origin is d/R. Using the dot product, $P \cdot P' = R^2 \cos (d/R)$ or $\cos (d/R) = P \cdot P'/R^2$ or $d = R \operatorname{arc} \cos (P \cdot P'/R^2)$. Translating this to coordinate form, if $P = (x,y,z)$ and $P' = (x',y',z')$ then $\cos (d/R) = (xx' + yy' + zz')/R^2$.

Finally, we would like to know how to find the angle between two great circles in coordinate form. Let the vectors V and V' be perpendicular to the two planes which cut out the great circles. The angle between these two vectors is the same as the angle between the planes. If the angle between the planes is θ, then $\cos \theta = V \cdot V'/|V||V'|$ (see Section 2.9). If V has coordinates A,B,C and V' has coordinates A',B',C', then

$$\cos \theta = \frac{(AA' + BB' + CC')}{\sqrt{A^2 + B^2 + C^2}\sqrt{A'^2 + B'^2 + C'^2}}.$$

Exercises

1. Find y if $(-2,y,5)$ is a point on a sphere of radius 6.
2. Find the distance between $(1,5,3)$ and $(3,-1,5)$ on a sphere.
3. Find the angle between the two great circles which have perpendicular vectors $\{2,1,-3\}$ and $\{-1,0,4\}$. Find the point $(z > 0)$ of intersection of these two circles if the sphere has radius 5.
4. Find a formula for the distance from a point $P = (x,y,z)$ on a sphere of radius R to a great circle having perpendicular vector $\{A,B,C\}$.
5. What is the locus of all the points on a sphere of radius R that are at a distance d from a great circle cut by a plane with perpendicular vector $\{A,B,C\}$?

6.3 HYPERBOLIC POINTS AND LINES

A point on a real sphere of radius R has coordinates (x,y,z) where x,y,z are real numbers satisfying the equation $x^2 + y^2 + z^2 = R^2$ when the origin is the center of the sphere. We want to decide what will represent a point in hyperbolic geometry—a geometry on a sphere of imaginary radius.

Let the radius of the imaginary sphere be $i\rho$ where ρ is a fixed positive real number. In all that follows, we shall assume that such a ρ has been chosen. If we try to form the analog of the condition on the real sphere, we get $x^2 + y^2 + z^2 = (i\rho)^2$ or $x^2 + y^2 + z^2 + \rho^2 = 0$. There are no triples x,y,z of real numbers which will satisfy this equation. We could let x,y,z be complex numbers, but that seems to make things overly complicated. A simple way to find triples which will satisfy the equation is to let $z = i\zeta$, where ζ is real. In fact, we might as well require that ζ be a positive real number so that we are dealing with less than half of this imaginary sphere. We hope that this will eliminate the possibility of lines intersecting in more than one point, but we shall have to check that when we know what lines are.

At this point, we shall agree that the points of our new geometry are triples of real numbers (x,y,ζ), where $\zeta > 0$ and $x^2 + y^2 + \rho^2 = \zeta^2$. (We shall use the Greek letters ρ and ζ to remind us that these are actually the coefficients of pure imaginary numbers.)

What about lines? Hyperbolic lines are the analogs of great circles in spherical geometry. In spherical geometry, a great circle is determined by a plane through the center (the origin). If we know that the vector $\{A,B,C\}$ is perpendicular to a plane through the origin, then the great circle cut out by that plane is the locus of all the points satisfying the equation $Ax + By + Cz = 0$ and lying on the sphere; that is, satisfying $x^2 + y^2 + z^2 = R^2$. On our sphere of imaginary radius, we can define lines in a similar way. A line is the locus of all the points (x,y,ζ), where $\zeta > 0$ and $z = i\zeta$, satisfying $Ax + By + Cz = 0$ and $x^2 + y^2 + \rho^2 = \zeta^2$. Since $z = i\zeta$, we have $Ax + By + iC\zeta = 0$. The only triples of real numbers A,B,C which make sense here have $C = 0$. This seems like too much to demand; we would like the possibility of more lines. Instead, we could let $C = i\gamma$ where γ is real, then $Ax + By = \gamma\zeta$ could be called the equation of a hyperbolic line.

Although we are using our intuition and trying to define points and lines analogous to the situation on a real sphere, we cannot be so naive as to think that everything will work out the same. On a real sphere, every vector $\{A,B,C\}$ will represent a great circle—there is one exception if we require that $z > 0$, $\{0,0,C\}$ with $C \neq 0$. Every plane except the one perpendicular to $\{0,0,C\}$ will cut a great circle from the piece of the sphere that we are using. On the sphere of imaginary radius, we have no guarantee that every triple of real numbers A,B,γ will define a locus of points on the sphere. In order for a locus to exist, it must be possible to satisfy $Ax + By = \gamma\zeta$ and $x^2 + y^2 + \rho^2 = \zeta^2$ simultaneously. If for example $A = 0$, $B = 1$, $\gamma = 2$, and the radius of the sphere is i, there are no real triples x,y,ζ satisfying $0x + 1y = 2\zeta$ and $x^2 + y^2 + 1^2 = \zeta^2$. In other words, not every triple A,B,γ will represent a line in our new geometry. The problem of discovering a necessary and sufficient condition on A,B,γ for the existence of a simultaneous solution of $Ax + By = \gamma\zeta$ and $x^2 + y^2 + \rho^2 = \zeta^2$ is very difficult, and we shall not try to rediscover it ourselves. Instead, we shall state the condition as a theorem and prove that it is, indeed, necessary and sufficient.

Theorem. *A necessary and sufficient condition for the existence of a solution* (x,y,ζ) *where* x,y,ζ *are real,* $\zeta > 0$, *of the system of equations* $x^2 + y^2 + \rho^2 = \zeta^2$ *and* $Ax + By = \gamma\zeta$, *where* ρ,A,B,γ *are real, is that* $A^2 + B^2 > \gamma^2$.

Proof. First, we shall show that $A^2 + B^2 > \gamma^2$ is a *necessary* condition. Assume that a simultaneous solution exists. Consider the identity $(Ax + By)^2 + (Bx - Ay)^2 = (A^2 + B^2)(x^2 + y^2)$. (You might want to verify this.) Substituting $x^2 + y^2 = \zeta^2 - \rho^2$ into the right-hand side, we get

$$(Ax + By)^2 + (Bx - Ay)^2 + \rho^2(A^2 + B^2) = (A^2 + B^2)\zeta^2.$$

Now, substituting $Ax + By = \gamma\zeta$ on the left-hand side, we get

$$(Bx - Ay)^2 + \rho^2(A^2 + B^2) = (A^2 + B^2 - \gamma^2)\zeta^2.$$

Since the left-hand side is positive, we must have $A^2 + B^2 > \gamma^2$.

Assume now that $A^2 + B^2 > \gamma^2$. We shall show that this is *sufficient* to guarantee a solution of the system of equations. In this case, for all $\zeta > 0$ the right-hand side of the last equation, $(A^2 + B^2 - \gamma^2)\zeta^2$ is positive. However, if ζ is small, it could happen that

$$\rho^2(A^2 + B^2) > (A^2 + B^2 - \gamma)\zeta^2$$

and then there are no real x and y that will satisfy the equation. But we can always find ζ such that $\zeta^2 > \rho^2(A^2 + B^2)/(A^2 + B^2 - \gamma^2)$; for these ζ, we have $(Bx - Ay)^2 > 0$ and so $Bx - Ay$ is real, say $Bx - Ay = \delta$. Now we have two linear equations in x and y for any

$$\zeta > \sqrt{\rho^2(A^2 + B^2)/(A^2 + B^2 - \gamma^2)};$$

they are $Ax + By = \gamma\zeta$ and $Bx - Ay = \delta$. There is always a real solution x,y of such a system. |

In summary, we have decided that the points in our new geometry on the sphere of imaginary radius $i\rho$, $\rho > 0$, are triples of real numbers (x,y,ζ) where $\zeta > 0$ and $x^2 + y^2 + \rho^2 = \zeta^2$. The lines in this geometry are the loci of all points satisfying the equations of the form $Ax + By = \gamma\zeta$ where A,B,γ are real and $A^2 + B^2 > \gamma^2$.

Exercises

1. If the hyperbolic lines $2x + 3y = 0$ and $x - y = \zeta$ intertect in a point, what is the radius of the imaginary sphere?
2. Find the point of intersection of $x + y = \zeta$ and $-x + 2y = \zeta$ on a sphere of radius $(2/3)i$.
3. Assume that the point (x,y,ζ) satisfies the equations $A_1 x + B_1 y = \gamma_1\zeta$ and $A_2 x + B_2 y = \gamma_2\zeta$ where these are different lines. If (x,y,ζ) is on a sphere of radius $i\rho$, can there be more than one such point?
4. Find the equation of the hyperbolic line containing $(0,0,2)$ and $(1,0,\sqrt{5})$. Find the equation of the line containing $(1,2,\sqrt{30})$ and $(5,-1,\sqrt{51})$.
5. Given two points (x_1,y_1,ζ_1) and (x_2,y_2,ζ_2) on a sphere of imaginary radius, Find a formula to determine the coefficients of the equation of the line through these two points.

6.4   A COUNTEREXAMPLE TO EUCLID'S PARALLEL POSTULATE

At this point, we know what represents points and lines in our new geometry. We can also check to see if a certain point is on a line, or whether two lines intersect. Before we go any further, we should check to see if Euclid's parallel postulate holds. If it does, we are on the wrong track and shall have to start over.

Fortunately, the parallel postulate fails. We can prove this by giving one particular example of a line, a point not on the line, and more than one line through the point which does not intersect the given line.

Let us assume that $\rho = 1$; our sphere has imaginary radius i. Let the given line be $y = 0$; here we have $A = 0$, $B = 1$, and $\gamma = 0$, thus, $A^2 + B^2 > \gamma^2$, and this is a line. Let the point be $P = (0,1,\sqrt{2})$; $0^2 + 1^2 + 1^2 = (\sqrt{2})^2$ so this does represent a point in our geometry, and it is not on the line $y = 0$. All of the lines $Ax + By = \gamma\zeta$ through P are satisfied by P, so $A0 + B1 = \gamma\sqrt{2}$, or $B^2 = 2\gamma^2$ for all lines through P.

Now we want to know how to recognize whether or not these lines intersect $y = 0$. The points on $y = 0$ have the form $(x,0,\zeta)$ where $x^2 + 1^2 = \zeta^2$, because $0x + 1 \cdot 0 = 0\zeta$. If one of these points is also on a line through P,

$$Ax + B0 = \gamma\zeta$$
$$Ax = \gamma\zeta$$
$$A^2x^2 = \gamma^2\zeta^2$$
$$A^2x^2 = \gamma^2(x^2 + 1^2)$$
$$(A^2 - \gamma^2)x^2 = \gamma^21^2$$

and so $A^2 > \gamma^2$. Thus, $A^2 > \gamma^2$ is a necessary and sufficient condition for the intersection of a line through P with $y = 0$. In other words, if $A^2 \leq \gamma^2$ there is no intersection. For example, $1x + 2\sqrt{2}y = 2\zeta$ contains P (because $1 \cdot 0 + 2\sqrt{2} \cdot 1 = 2\sqrt{2}$) but does not intersect $y = 0$ because $1^2 \leq 2^2$. Similarly, $-1x + 2\sqrt{2}y = 2\zeta$ does not intersect $y = 0$, nor does $1x + \sqrt{2}y = 1\zeta$ and they are both through P. Thus, Euclid's parallel postulate is false in this geometry. This is encouraging.

Exercise

Instead of using a particular sphere of imaginary radius i, let the sphere have radius $i\rho$. Let P be the point $(0,1,\zeta)$ and show that there are many lines through P which do not intersect $y = 0$.

6.5 HYPERBOLIC TRANSFORMATIONS

We have already mentioned transformations several times in previous chapters. Euclidean geometry is the study of those properties that are invariant under the rigid motions. Projective geometry studies those properties that are not affected by projections. Inversive geometry studies the properties of figures that are unchanged by inversive transformations. If hyperbolic geometry is really a geometry, it too must study properties that are invariant under a certain set of transformations. For example, whatever these transformations are, they must leave the condition $x^2 + y^2 + \rho^2 = \zeta^2$ on points invariant and also the condition $A^2 + B^2 > \gamma^2$ on the coefficients of the equation of a line. If it should happen that the transformations that characterize hyperbolic geometry do not leave these conditions on points and lines invariant, then the things that we have been using to represent points and lines have no geometrical significance.

There is another reason for studying transformations. Often, they can be used to simplify problems. In analytic Euclidean geometry, conics are traditionally studied by transforming them to a position in which they are symmetric with respect to the origin or an axis. In this position, it is easy to distinguish the various conics and to study their properties. In some other position, it might be very difficult to do this. In inversive geometry, we saw several problems that could easily be solved by judiciously transforming one of the points to Ω. In our present study of hyperbolic geometry, we shall have occasion to do a similar thing.

Thus, we have two reasons for wanting to know what transformations characterize hyperbolic geometry: (1) to be able to distinguish properties that have geometrical significance, and (2) to simplify problems. We can find the transformations by continuing our analogy with the real sphere. On a real sphere, the transformations that send figures into congruent figures are the rotations of the sphere. It can be proved that every such transformation can be achieved by a finite sequence of rotations, each one of which leaves one coordinate fixed. This means that every transformation of the sphere can be accomplished by the following three sets of transformations.

(1) $x' = x \cos \theta_1 - y \sin \theta_1$ $y' = x \sin \theta_1 + y \cos \theta_1$

(2) $x' = x \cos \theta_2 - z \sin \theta_2$ $z' = x \sin \theta_2 + z \cos \theta_2$

(3) $y' = y \cos \theta_3 - z \sin \theta_3$ $z' = x \sin \theta_3 + z \cos \theta_3$

If Lambert was correct, the hyperbolic transformations can be obtained by forming the analogs of these three sets. Hyperbolic points have two real coordinates x,y and a third which arises from a pure imaginary number $z = i\zeta$. The first set of transformations leaves z unchanged, and thus no alteration is necessary. One set of hyperbolic transformations is

$$x' = x \cos \theta_1 - y \sin \theta_1 \qquad y' = x \sin \theta_1 + y \cos \theta_1.$$

The second set involves z and, if we substitute $i\zeta$, we get

$$x' = x \cos \theta_2 - i\zeta \sin \theta_2 \qquad i\zeta' = x \sin \theta_2 + i\zeta \cos \theta_2,$$

or we could rewrite the second one as $\zeta' = -ix \sin \theta_2 + \zeta \cos \theta_2$. Since ζ' is real, this only makes sense if $-ix \sin \theta_2$ is real, or if $\sin \theta_2$ is a pure imaginary. If we remember that

$$\sin \theta = \theta - \theta^3/3! + \theta^5/5! - \cdots$$
$$\cos \theta = 1 - \theta^2/2! + \theta^4/4! - \cdots$$

we see that $\sin \theta_2$ is a pure imaginary and $\cos \theta_2$ is real if θ_2 is a pure imaginary number. Our transformations are not rotations in the usual sense, but only analogs of rotations; our "angle of rotation" can be a pure imaginary number.

To simplify notation, we shall set $\cos \theta_2 = \sigma$ and $-i \sin \theta_2 = \tau$ where σ and τ are real numbers. Since $\cos^2 \theta + \sin^2 \theta = 1$ is true for complex values of θ, $\sigma^2 - \tau^2 = 1$. Our second set of transformations can now be written as

$$x' = x\sigma + \zeta\tau \qquad \zeta' = x\tau + \zeta\sigma$$

where σ and τ are real numbers satisfying $\sigma^2 - \tau^2 = 1$. The third set of transformations can be written in a similar way.

Exercises

1. Prove that the condition on points, $x^2 + y^2 + \rho^2 = \zeta^2$, is invariant under the transformations of our geometry. In other words, if a point $P = (x,y,\zeta)$ satisfies $x^2 + y^2 + \rho^2 = \zeta^2$ and is transformed to $P' = (x',y',\zeta')$, then $x'^2 + y'^2 + \rho^2 = \zeta'^2$.

2. Find the inverse of each of the sets of hyperbolic transformations; that is, the transformation that takes x' to x, y' to y, and ζ' to ζ.

3. Show that the condition on the coefficients of a line, $A^2 + B^2 > \gamma^2$ is invariant under the transformations.

4. Given a point P on a real sphere, prove that it can be sent to another point P' by a finite sequence of rotations, each of which leaves one coordinate fixed. Prove that a line (great circle) m can be sent to m' by a similar sequence of rotations. Show that a spherical triangle ABC can be sent to a congruent spherical triangle $A'B'C'$. Can any of these changes be accomplished by less than three rotations each of which leaves a coordinate fixed?

6.6   A HYPERBOLIC "COORDINATE SYSTEM"

Just as in analytic Euclidean geometry, many questions in hyperbolic geometry can be answered quite easily if we transform the figure in question to a convenient position. In Euclidean geometry, we often send a particular point to the origin, or a line to one of the axes, in order to achieve this.

In hyperbolic geometry, the analog of the origin is the point $(0,0,\rho)$; this is a point on the sphere of imaginary radius since $0^2 + 0^2 + \rho^2 = \rho^2$. The analog of the axes look the same as in Euclidean geometry: $y = 0$ and $x = 0$, or $0x + 1y = 0\zeta$ and $1x + 0y = 0\zeta$. We shall now show that we can transform any given point to $(0,0,\rho)$, and that there is a sequence of transformations that takes any given line to the "x-axis."

Let the given point be $P = (x,y,\zeta)$. Using $x' = x \cos \theta - y \sin \theta$ and $y' = x \sin \theta + y \cos \theta$ and, choosing θ so that $x \sin \theta + y \cos \theta = 0$ $[\theta = \text{arc cot } (-x/y)]$, we can transform P to $P' = (x',0,\zeta)$. Now we use the second set of transformations $x'' = x'\sigma + \zeta\tau$ and $\zeta' = x'\tau + \zeta\sigma$. We can let $\sigma = \zeta/\rho$ and $\tau = -x'/\rho$ because $\sigma^2 - \tau^2 = \zeta^2/\rho^2 - x'^2/\rho^2 = 1$ from $x'^2 + \rho^2 = \zeta^2$. Under this second transformation, P' goes to $P'' = (0,0,-x'^2/\rho + \zeta^2/\rho)$. But, since the transformations leave the condition on points unchanged and the third coordinate is positive, we must have $P'' = (0,0,\rho)$. We shall call this point the "origin."

To show that any line can be transformed to the "x-axis," we must begin with any line $Ax + By = \gamma\zeta$ and change it to $y = 0$. To do this, we use the inverses of the first and third sets of transformations:

$$x = x' \cos \theta + y' \sin \theta \qquad y = -x' \sin \theta + y' \cos \theta$$

and

$$y = \sigma y' - \tau \zeta' \qquad \zeta = -\tau y' + \sigma \zeta'$$

or, in our case,

$$y' = \sigma y'' - \tau \zeta. \qquad \zeta = -\tau y'' + \sigma \zeta'.$$

Substituting the first set for x and y in the equation $Ax + By = \gamma\zeta$, we get $(A \cos \theta - B \sin \theta)x' + (A \sin \theta + B \cos \theta)y' = \gamma\zeta$. We can choose θ so that $A \cos \theta - B \sin \theta = 0$, then the equation has the form $B'y' = \gamma\zeta$. Using the other set of transformations, we get $(B'\sigma + \gamma\tau)y'' = (B'\tau + \gamma\sigma)\zeta'$. We can let $\sigma = B'/\sqrt{B'^2 - \gamma^2}$ and $\tau = -\gamma/\sqrt{B'^2 - \gamma^2}$ because $\sigma^2 - \tau^2 = 1$ and $B'^2 > \gamma^2$. The equation now is equivalent to $y = 0$.

Exercises

1. Find a necessary and sufficient condition for the intersection of two lines $A_1 x + B_1 y = \gamma_1 \zeta$ and $A_2 x + B_2 y = \gamma_2 \zeta$.
2. Prove that any line can be transformed to the "y-axis."
3. Show that, given any line $Ax + By = \gamma\zeta$ and any point (x,y,ζ) not on the line, the line can be transformed to the "x-axis" and, at the same time, the point can be transformed to a point on the "y-axis", $(0,y_0,\zeta_0)$.

6.7   DISTANCE AND ANGLE

In the geometry on a real sphere, we saw that the distance d between two points (x,y,z) and (x',y',z') could be written as

$$\cos (d/R) = (xx' + yy' + zz')/R^2,$$

where R is the radius of the sphere. The angle θ between two great circles $Ax + By + Cz = 0$, and $A'x + B'y + C'z = 0$ is given by

$$\cos \theta = \frac{(AA' + BB' + CC')}{\sqrt{A^2 + B^2 + C^2}\sqrt{A'^2 + B'^2 + C'^2}}.$$

Using these two formulas, we can define the distance between two points and the angle between two lines in hyperbolic geometry. If (x,y,ζ) and (x',y',ζ') are two points on a sphere with imaginary radius $i\rho$, then the distance δ between the two points is defined by

$$\cos (\delta/i\rho) = (xx' + yy' - \zeta\zeta')/(-\rho^2)$$
$$= (\zeta\zeta' - xx' - yy')/\rho^2.$$

If $Ax + By = \gamma\zeta$ and $A'x + B'y = \gamma'\zeta$ are two lines, then the angle θ between them can be defined as

$$\cos \theta = \frac{AA' + BB' - \gamma\gamma'}{\sqrt{A^2 + B^2 - \gamma^2}\sqrt{A'^2 + B'^2 - \gamma'^2}}.$$

It is easy enough to form these two analogs, but now we must ask a question. Do distance and angle defined as above make proper sense? First, if they have any geometrical significance at all, they must be invariant under the three sets of transformations. They are invariant; we leave this for you to check.

Besides this invariance of distance, we would like distance to be a real number. It seems reasonable to expect this, because we are trying to build a geometry that differs from Euclidean geometry only in the parallel postulate, and there are many properties of distance that do not seem to depend on parallelism.

From the power series expansion of $\cos \theta$, δ is real, if and only if, $\cos (\delta/i\rho) \geq 1$. To show that $(\zeta\zeta' - xx' - yy')/\rho^2 \geq 1$, we transform the two given points so that the first point goes to $(0,0,\rho)$ and the second goes to (x'',y'',ζ''). Since the expression that we are interested in is invariant under the transformations, we can use these two new points to see whether or not it is positive. Now $\cos (\delta/i\rho) = \rho\zeta''/\rho^2 = \zeta''/\rho$. Since $\zeta'' \geq \rho$ and they are both positive, $\cos (\delta/i\rho) \geq 1$ and δ is a real number. Since $\cos \theta = \cos (-\theta)$, there are two values of δ determined by this formula. We shall use $\delta \geq 0$.

As far as angle measure is concerned, we cannot expect that it will be the same as in Euclidean geometry because, from our list of equivalents to Euclid's fifth axiom, we know that the notion of magnitude of angle is closely related to the theory of parallels. Because of the condition on lines, $A^2 + B^2 - \gamma^2 > 0$ and $A'^2 + B'^2 - \gamma'^2 > 0$; it follows that the denominator of the expression for $\cos \theta$ is real. To see into the kind of "angles" we get by this formula, we can transform the second line into the "x-axis" $0x + 1y = 0\zeta$, and we shall assume that the other line is $Ax + By = \gamma\zeta$. The angle between the lines is given by $\cos\theta = B/\sqrt{A^2 + B^2 - \gamma^2}$. If θ is real, we must have $\cos^2\theta \leq 1$. From the formula, $\cos^2\theta = B^2/(A^2 + B^2 - \gamma^2)$ and this is less than one if $A^2 > \gamma^2$. Notice that this is the same condition that we found in Section 6.4 for the existence of a point of intersection between a line and $y = 0$. If two lines intersect on a sphere of any radius $i\rho$, then $A^2 > \gamma^2$, so two intersecting lines form a real angle. If $A^2 = \gamma^2$, then $\cos\theta = 1$ and $\theta = 0$ or π. If $A^2 < \gamma^2$, then $\cos^2\theta > 1$ and, from the power series expansion, we see that θ must be imaginary. We can still call this an "angle" if we wish.

Exercises

1. Prove that the formula for the distance between two points is invariant under the transformations.
2. Prove that the formula for the angle between two lines in an invariant.
3. On a sphere of radius $i\rho$ find a condition on a line $Ax + By = \gamma\zeta$ to guarantee that it intersects $x = 0$.

6.8 PARALLELS AND DIVERGENTS

We are now in a position to talk about the different cases that arise when we consider two lines in hyperbolic geometry. In the Euclidean plane, two lines either intersect or are parallel; in other words, they form an angle θ with $0 < \theta < \pi$, or in the parallel case, we say $\theta = 0$ or π. In hyperbolic geometry, we can see what happens to any two lines by looking at the line $Ax + By = \gamma\zeta$ and the "x-axis" as we did in the last section. Let us assume that the line $Ax + By = \gamma\zeta$ contains a point $P_0 = (0, y_0, \zeta_0)$ where $y_0 \neq 0$. P_0 is a point on the "y-axis" (Figure 6.8a). If $A^2 > \gamma^2$ the line intersects the "x-axis" and they form a real angle. If $A^2 = \gamma^2$, there is no intersection, and the angle formed is 0 or π. There are two such lines, $Ax + By = A\zeta$ and $-Ax + By = A\zeta$; we shall say that these lines are *parallel* to the "x-axis." If $A^2 < \gamma^2$, the line does not meet the "x-axis" (there are infinitely many such lines), and the "angle" formed is imaginary. In this case, we shall call the line and the "x-axis" *divergent*. (They are sometimes called hyperparallels.)

In plane Euclidean geometry, a parallel to the "x-axis" is perpendicular to the "y-axis." In hyperbolic geometry, a parallel to the "x-axis" through a

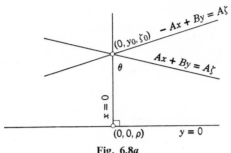

Fig. 6.8a

point $P_0 = (0, y_0, \zeta_0)$, $y_0 \neq 0$, on the "y-axis" has $A^2 = \gamma^2$. If we calculate the angle θ it forms with the "y-axis," we get $\cos \theta = A/\sqrt{A^2 + B^2 - \gamma^2} = A/B = \pm y_0/\zeta_0$ because $A^2 = \gamma^2$ and $By_0 = \gamma \zeta_0$. Since P_0 is not the "origin," $\pm y_0/\zeta_0 \neq 0$ and θ is not a right angle. Using $y_0^2 + \rho^2 = \zeta_0^2$ and $\cos^2 \theta + \sin^2 \theta = 1$, we get $\sin \theta = \pm \rho/\zeta_0$, so we also notice that θ varies for different points P_0 on the "y-axis." To see how θ depends on P_0, we can use the distance formula and find the distance δ from P_0 to $(0,0,\rho)$; $\cos (\delta/i\rho) = \zeta_0 \rho/\rho^2 = \zeta_0/\rho$. It follows that $\cos (\delta/i\rho) \sin \theta = \pm 1$. This means that, as P_0 approaches the "origin" (the distance δ goes to zero), $\cos (\delta/i\rho)$ approaches 1, $\sin \theta$ approaches ± 1, and θ approaches $\pi/2$ or $\frac{3}{2}\pi$. As we get closer to the "origin," as far as angles are concerned, we approach the Euclidean situation.

Exercises

1. Prove that there are infinitely many lines through $(0, y_0, \zeta_0)$ which do not intersect the "x-axis."

2. Find the angle between the "x-axis" and the "y-axis."

3. Find a line which is parallel to both the "x-axis" and the "y-axis." How many such lines are there? Find a line which is divergent with respect to both the "x-axis" and the "y-axis." How many of these lines exist?

4. Show that the two parallels to the "x-axis" through the point $(0, y_0, \zeta_0)$ from angles of equal magnitude with $x = 0$.

5. Prove that the length of the line segment joining the midpoints of two sides of a triangle is less than one half of the third side.

6.9 TRIANGLES

If we have developed our geometry correctly, the sum of the magnitude of the angles of any triangle should be less than π. Since we have a formula

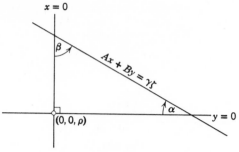

Fig. 6.9a

for angle, we can check. Here we are dealing with a triangle in the Euclidean sense: any two sides intersect. (We could talk about triangles where the sides are parallel, but that is not the case that we want to consider here.) Since any triangle can be split into two right triangles, it is sufficient to check the case of a right triangle. We can make use of our transformations to simplify the situation. We send the right angle to the "origin" so that $y = 0$ and $x = 0$ are two sides of the triangle (Figure 6.9a). Let the third side be $Ax + By = \gamma\zeta$. We must have $A^2 > \gamma^2$ and $B^2 > \gamma^2$ so that it intersects $y = 0$ and $x = 0$. Furthermore, $\gamma \neq 0$ because the line does not contain $(0,0,\rho)$ and we can transform the triangle in such a way that $A > 0$ and $B > 0$.

Let α and β be the angles between $Ax + By = \gamma\zeta$ and $y = 0$, and $Ax + By = \gamma\zeta$ and $x = 0$. We must show that $\alpha + \beta < \pi/2$, or that $\cos(\alpha + \beta) > 0$. Using the formulas, $\cos\alpha = B/\sqrt{A^2 + B^2 - \gamma^2}$ and $\cos\beta = A/\sqrt{A^2 + B^2 - \gamma^2}$. Using $\cos^2\theta + \sin^2\theta = 1$, we get $\sin\alpha = \sqrt{A^2 - \gamma^2}/\sqrt{A^2 + B^2 - \gamma^2}$ and $\sin\beta = \sqrt{B^2 - \gamma^2}/\sqrt{A^2 + B^2 - \gamma^2}$. Therefore,

$$\cos(\alpha + \beta) = \cos\alpha\cos\beta - \sin\alpha\sin\beta$$
$$= \frac{AB - \sqrt{A^2 - \gamma^2}\sqrt{B^2 - \gamma^2}}{A^2 + B^2 - \gamma^2}.$$

We must show that this is positive. The denominator is positive because $A^2 + B^2 > \gamma^2$. Since $\gamma \neq 0$, $A > \sqrt{A^2 - \gamma^2}$ and $B > \sqrt{B^2 - \gamma^2}$. Furthermore, we have $AB > 0$, so $AB - \sqrt{A^2 - \gamma^2}\sqrt{B^2 - \gamma^2} > 0$ and the whole fraction is positive, or $\alpha + \beta < \pi/2$.

Exercises

1. Prove that, in hyperbolic geometry, any triangle can be split into two right triangles.

2. Show that any right triangle can be transformed so that $y = 0$ and $x = 0$ are two of its sides and the third side $Ax + By = \gamma\zeta$ has $A > 0$ and $B > 0$.

3. Why is it impossible for $\cos(\alpha + \beta)$ above to be greater than or equal to 1?

6.10 THE DISTANCE FROM A POINT TO A LINE

With the formulas that we have developed, we have the tools necessary for solving any problem that involves points, lines, distance, or angle. We shall suggest some problems as exercises. In order to get ready for the next section, we shall solve one such problem here, the distance from a point to a line.

We already know how to find the distance from a point on the "y-axis" to the "x-axis," but now we want to consider any point $P' = (x',y',\zeta')$ and find the distance to any line $Ax + By = \gamma\zeta$. Let the perpendicular from P' to this line be $ax + by = \Gamma\zeta$ and the foot of the perpendicular be the point $P = (x,y,\zeta)$. Since P' and P are on the perpendicular,

$$ax' + by' - \Gamma\zeta' = 0$$

and

$$ax + by - \Gamma\zeta = 0.$$

Since the lines are perpendicular, we also have

$$aA + bB - \Gamma\gamma = 0.$$

The existence of the perpendicular means that there is a nontrivial solution to this system of homogeneous equations, so

$$\begin{vmatrix} x' & y' & \zeta' \\ x & y & \zeta \\ A & B & \gamma \end{vmatrix} = 0.$$

If we multiply the last column by i and square the determinant, we get

$$\begin{vmatrix} x'^2 + y'^2 - \zeta'^2 & x'x + y'y - \zeta'\zeta & Ax' + By' - \gamma\zeta' \\ x'x + y'y - \zeta'\zeta & x^2 + y^2 - \zeta^2 & Ax + By - \gamma\zeta \\ Ax' + By' - \gamma\zeta' & Ax + By - \gamma\zeta & A^2 + B^2 - \gamma^2 \end{vmatrix} = 0.$$

We know something about all of the elements of this determinant: $x'^2 + y'^2 - \zeta'^2$ and $x^2 + y^2 - \zeta^2$ each equal $-\rho^2$; $Ax + By - \gamma\zeta = 0$; $xx' + yy' - \zeta\zeta' = F$ is the negative of the numerator of the fraction which expresses the distance that we are interested in. The determinant now reduces to

$$\begin{vmatrix} -\rho^2 & F & Ax' + By' - \gamma\zeta' \\ F & -\rho^2 & 0 \\ Ax' + By' - \gamma\zeta' & 0 & A^2 + B^2 - \gamma^2 \end{vmatrix} = 0$$

or $\rho^4(A^2 + B^2 - \gamma^2) + \rho^2(Ax' + By' - \gamma\zeta')^2 - F^2(A^2 + B^2 - \gamma^2) = 0$. Since $\cos(\delta/i\rho) = -F/\rho^2$, we have

$$\sin^2(\delta/i\rho) = 1 - F^2/\rho^4 = (\rho^4 - F^2)/\rho^4$$
$$= -(Ax' + By' - \gamma\zeta')^2/[\rho^2(A^2 + B^2 - \gamma^2)].$$

Thus, the distance from (x',y',ζ') to $Ax + By = \gamma\zeta$ is given by

$$\sin(\delta/i\rho) = \pm i \frac{Ax' + By' - \gamma\zeta'}{\rho\sqrt{A^2 + B^2 - \gamma^2}}.$$

Exercises

1. Compare the formula for $\sin(\delta/i\rho)$ with the formula for the distance from a point to a line on a real sphere.
2. Given a point (x',y',ζ') and a line $Ax + By = \gamma\zeta$, find the equation of the perpendicular from the point to the line.
3. Find the conditions for the parallelism and divergence of any two lines $A_1x + B_1y = \gamma_1\zeta$ and $A_2x + B_2y = \gamma_2\zeta$.
4. Show that a pentagon with five right angles exists.
5. Prove that two divergent lines have a common perpendicular. Find an expression for the length of the common perpendicular and compare it with the "angle" between the two lines.
6. Prove that if a quadrilateral has three right angles then the fourth angle is acute. (This is known as the Lambert quadrilateral.)
7. Let $ABCD$ be a quadrilateral (vertices are listed consecutively) with $\angle B = \angle C = \pi/2$ and side AB equal to side CD. Prove that the line joining the midpoint of BC and AD is perpendicular to both BC and AD and that $\angle A = \angle D < \pi/2$. (This is known as the Saccheri quadrilateral.)
8. Prove that, in the quadrilateral described in Exercise 7, AD and BC are divergent.

6.11   ANALOGS OF CIRCLES

Thus far, we have been considering only straight lines. Now we shall try to discover what in hyperbolic geometry corresponds to circles. In

Euclidean geometry, we define a circle as the locus of points equidistant from a fixed point. Let us try to adjust this to our new geometry.

Let $P_0 = (x_0, y_0, \zeta_0)$ be a fixed hyperbolic point. If a variable point (x, y, ζ) is at a constant distance from P_0, then $(\zeta\zeta_0 - xx_0 - yy_0)/\rho^2$ is a constant or, equivalently, $\zeta\zeta_0 - xx_0 - yy_0 = D$ where D is a constant. To make this look more like the equations we have been dealing with we can rename P_0 and let $(x_0, y_0, \zeta_0) = (A, B, \gamma)$; then the equation becomes $Ax + By + D = \gamma\zeta$. Because P_0 is a point, we know that $x_0{}^2 + y_0{}^2 + \rho^2 = \zeta_0{}^2$, or $A^2 + B^2 + \rho^2 = \gamma^2$, so $A^2 + B^2 < \gamma^2$. We shall say that a circle (on a sphere of radius $i\rho$) with center at (A, B, γ) and having radius $i\rho$ arc cos (D/ρ^2) is given by the equation $Ax + By + D = \gamma\zeta$; we note that this means that A, B, γ, D are real, that $A^2 + B^2 < \gamma^2$, and $D \geq \rho^2$.

We should comment on two things about the equation of a circle. First, it may seem strange that a circle is represented by an equation of the *first* degree. This is due to the fact that we are using three coordinates for points and that the quadratic nature of the equation of a circle is taken care of by the quadratic condition on x, y, ζ. Second, the condition $A^2 + B^2 < \gamma^2$ is not necessary to guarantee the existence of some locus (as in the case of the inequality for the existence of a line) but, instead, arises from the way in which we define a circle. This raises a question. What does $Ax + By + D = \gamma\zeta$ represent if $A^2 + B^2 \geq \gamma^2$? Let us try to find out.

For a hint, we examine a real sphere. There we see that a circle, in addition to being the locus of points equidistant from a fixed *point*, is also a locus of points equidistant from a fixed *great circle*. These are usually called small circles of a sphere and are cut from the sphere by planes which do not contain the center of the sphere. Since the center of the sphere is at the origin, these planes have equations of the form $Ax + By + Cz + D = 0$. We could proceed as before and find the analog of this on a sphere of imaginary radius, but instead we shall look at the distance formula developed in the last section.

We have found that the distance δ from a point (x, y, ζ) to a line $Ax + By = \gamma\zeta$ is given by the formula

$$\sin(\delta/i\rho) = \pm \frac{i(Ax + By - \gamma\zeta)}{\rho\sqrt{A^2 + B^2 - \gamma^2}}.$$

We want to consider the locus of points equidistant from this line, so $Ax + By - \gamma\zeta$ must be a constant and we can use either the positive or negative value of the fraction. This may seem like a strange condition until we realize that we should expect the locus to consist of two parts or branches—one on each side of the line $Ax + By = \gamma\zeta$. We could write the locus of points equidistant from $Ax + By = \gamma\zeta$ as $Ax + By - \gamma\zeta = \pm D$ or $Ax + By \mp D = \gamma\zeta$. Since $Ax + By = \gamma\zeta$ is the equation of a line, we have the condition $A^2 + B^2 > \gamma^2$.

This gives a partial answer to the question that we asked (what does $Ax + By + D = \gamma\zeta$ represent if $A^2 + B^2 \geq \gamma^2$?) We shall still have to look at the case $A^2 + B^2 = \gamma^2$.

Before we take up this next case, however, we should emphasize that, unlike the situation in Euclidean geometry, the locus of points equidistant from a straight line is *not* a straight line but a curve. This curve is called an *equidistant* (here equidistant is a noun, not an adjective).

One approach to the problem of parallels before the introduction of non-Euclidean geometries was to define a parallel to a straight line as a locus of points equidistant from that line (and lying on one side of it). The uniqueness part of the parallel postulate then follows easily. The fallacy lies in the tacit assumption that this locus is a straight line—an assumption which is equivalent to the parallel postulate; we can see from the above that it is *not* a straight line in hyperbolic geometry.

Now we look at the locus satisfying $Ax + By + D = \gamma\zeta$ when $A^2 + B^2 = \gamma^2$. We could say that this locus occupies an intermediate position between a circle and an equidistant; it is the limiting case of either. This locus is called the *oricycle* (sometimes horocycle, or limiting curve). We use the definite article "the" because there is only one oricycle; in other words, any two oricycles are congruent—they differ in position only. To prove this, we could show that the equation of any oricycle can be transformed into $x + \rho = \zeta$. We shall leave this as an exercise.

To show that the oricycle occupies an intermediate position between a circle and an equidistant, we consider two curves

$$x_0 x + \zeta_0 \rho = \zeta_0 \zeta \quad \text{and} \quad \zeta_0 x + x_0 \rho = x_0 \zeta,$$

or

$$(x_0/\zeta_0)x + \rho = \zeta \quad \text{and} \quad (\zeta_0/x_0)x + \rho = \zeta$$

with $x_0 > 0$. They both contain the "origin." The first is a circle with center at $(x_0, 0, \zeta_0)$ on the "x-axis." The second is an equidistant to a line $\zeta_0 x + 0y = x_0 \zeta$ through $(x_0, 0, \zeta_0)$. As the point $(x_0, 0, \zeta_0)$ moves away from the "origin," x_0 and ζ_0 increase indefinitely. From $x_0^2 + \rho^2 = \zeta_0^2$, we have $(x_0/\zeta_0)^2 + (\rho/\zeta_0)^2 = 1$. As ζ_0 gets infinitely large $(x_0/\zeta_0)^2$ goes to 1. Since $x_0 > 0$, x_0/ζ_0 goes to 1 and both equations $(x_0/\zeta_0)x + \rho = \zeta$ and $(\zeta_0/x_0)x + \rho = \zeta$ go to $x + \rho = \zeta$. So the oricycle is the common limit of a circle and an equidistant.

Exercises

1. Find the equation of a circle with center at the "origin."
2. Find the equation of the locus of an equidistant to $y = 0$ Also find the equation of an equidistant to $x = 0$.
3. Using the first four axioms of Euclidean geometry, prove that the assumption that a parallel to a line is the locus of points at a fixed distance and to one side of the line implies the parallel postulate.
4. Prove that any oricycle can be transformed into $x + \rho = \zeta$.
5. What happens to the radii of a circle when the circle passes to an oricycle?
6. Show that a pencil of divergent lines plays the same role with respect to an equidistant as the radii do with respect to a circle.
7. Consider a three-dimensional space analogous to the hyperbolic plane. In this space, we could speak of a surface of revolution obtained from an oricycle; call it an orisphere. Prove that the geometry on the orisphere is the geometry of the Euclidean plane.

6.12 THE CAYLEY–KLEIN MODEL

The Lambert model of hyperbolic geometry which we have been using is not the only interpretation of that geometry. There are many models— each has its advantages and defects. One disadvantage of Lambert's sphere of imaginary radius is that a point in a two-dimensional geometry is given by three coordinates instead of two. This defect can be remedied (but of course, we expect that, in doing so, other undesirable features will appear).

We correct the three coordinate representation of points by a procedure similar to that which we used in projective geometry. In projective geometry, we were able to represent a point by three homogeneous coordinates (U,V,W). These were obtained from ordinary analytic coordinates (x,y) by setting $x = U/W$ and $y = V/W$. We shall reverse this procedure. In hyperbolic geometry, we have a point represented by three coordinates (x,y,ζ). Let $\lambda = x/\zeta$ and $\eta = y/\zeta$. This is possible because $\zeta \neq 0$. Because (x,y,ζ) satisfies the condition $x^2 + y^2 + \rho^2 = \zeta^2$, we notice that there is also a condition on λ and η. Since $x = \lambda\zeta$ and $y = \eta\zeta$, $(\lambda\zeta)^2 + (\eta\zeta)^2 + \rho^2 = \zeta^2$ or $\zeta = \rho/\sqrt{1 - \lambda^2 - \eta^2}$. Since ζ exists and is real, we must have $\lambda^2 + \eta^2 < 1$. This restriction on λ and η tells us that the coordinates (λ,η) can be thought of as the Cartesian coordinates of a point in the Euclidean plane, a point that is interior to a unit circle about the origin. We shall call this circle the CK circle (Cayley–Klein), because the English mathematician Arthur Cayley and the German mathematician Felix Klein were the first to use this representation.

What happens to the equation $Ax + By = \gamma\zeta$ when we change to two coordinates? We get $A\lambda\zeta + B\eta\zeta = \gamma\zeta$ or $A\lambda + B\eta = \gamma$. This looks like the equation of a straight line in ordinary analytic geometry, but there is a difference: the coefficients are restricted by the inequality $A^2 + B^2 < \gamma^2$. If we remember that, in analytic Euclidean geometry, the distance of a straight line $Ax + By = C$ from the origin is given by $|C|/\sqrt{A^2 + B^2}$, then we see that the inequality means that the line is at a distance of less than one from the origin. In other words, all the lines of this new form that we derive from the lines of hyperbolic geometry will intersect the CK circle.

We can now say that hyperbolic points are represented by the interior points of a unit circle about the origin and that hyperbolic lines are represented by the chords of the CK circle (chords without endpoints, because the endpoints do not satisfy $\lambda^2 + \eta^2 < 1$).

In this Cayley–Klein model, the intersection of lines is the intersection of chords in the CK circle. Three situations can occur: two chords may

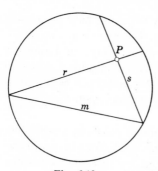

Fig. 6.12a

have (1) an interior point in common, (2) a point on the circumference in common, or (3) no point in common. This corresponds to two intersecting hyperbolic lines, two parallel lines, and two divergent lines. Through a point P not on a chord m (Figure 6.12a) there are two chords r and s that meet m on the circumference. These chords represent the two hyperbolic parallels to the line represented by m. Sometimes s is called a right parallel and r is called a left parallel. If two lines are right parallel to a third line, it is easy to see that they are right parallel to each other. Thus, right parallelism (and left) is an equivalence relation as parallelism is in Euclidean geometry.

The ease with which we can examine the theory of parallelism in the Cayley–Klein model is one of its advantages—but there are disadvantages. The angle between two chords has no simple relation with the hyperbolic angle between the lines represented by these chords. Distance is another problem; the distance between two points in the CK circle is not connected in a simple way with the distance between the two hyperbolic points represented by them. Although the relationship is not simple, it does exist. The distance between two points in hyperbolic geometry is equal (except for a numerical factor) to the logarithm of the cross ratio of four points, two of which are the Cayley–Klein representatives of the hyperbolic points and the other two are the intersections of the CK circle with the chord through these two points. There are several steps involved in proving this and we shall outline them for you in the exercises.

Exercises

1. Prove the following as a lemma. If arc cos $\beta = \alpha$, then

$$\alpha = \frac{i}{2} \log \frac{\beta - \sqrt{\beta^2 - 1}}{\beta + \sqrt{\beta^2 - 1}}.$$

   (*Hint.* Use Euler's formula which says that $\cos \alpha + i \sin \alpha = e^{i\alpha}$.)

2. Prove that the distance δ between $(x_1, 0, \zeta_1)$ and $(x_2, 0, \zeta_2)$ in hyperbolic geometry is given by

$$\delta = \left| \frac{-\rho}{2} \log \left(\frac{\lambda_1 + 1}{\lambda_1 - 1} \Big/ \frac{\lambda_2 + 1}{\lambda_2 - 1} \right) \right|$$

   where $\lambda_i = x_i / \zeta_i$ for $i = 1, 2$.

3. Exercise 2 says, in effect, that the distance between two hyperbolic points on the x-axis is equal (except for a numerical factor) to the logarithm of the cross ratio of four points, two of which are the Cayley-Klein representatives of the hyperbolic points and the other two are the intersections with the CK circle of the chord through these two points. Now show that this result is true, in general, and that we need not restrict ourselves to the points of the x-axis.

III

FOUNDATIONS OF GEOMETRY

In the first two parts of this book, we have discussed several geometries and have used a variety of approaches to build them. Now that you have seen these examples, you are in a position to do some thinking about the nature of geometry. What approaches can be used to develop geometries? How are the various geometries related to each other? Can we build geometries without using numbers that belong to some previous mathematical system? These are some of the questions that will be discussed in this last part of the book.

7 Axiom Systems

You may not have thought about it, but we have been using two different approaches as we talked about the various geometries. We could say that we have been emphasizing two different aspects of geometry. To understand what we mean by this, think of our first definition of geometry (we were speaking of Euclidean geometry then): geometry is the study of those properties of figures that are not affected by change of position. Later, we introduced other types of changes (for affine and projective geometry) and used the invariant properties under these changes as the characteristics of the geometries. Still later, we reversed this procedure (for inversive and hyperbolic geometries) and began by emphasizing the properties that we wanted to study (the propositions that we wanted to be true); transformations appeared only after the geometries were established. Thus, there are two views of geometry: the types of allowable changes and the content of the propositions. These aspects are interconnected, and every geometry may be studied from both viewpoints. We shall discuss content in this chapter and transformations in the next.

7.1 AXIOMATICS

When we talk about the content of the propositions (true statements) of a given geometry, we must consider the totality of all propositions about the geometry. In order to deal with all these propositions, we must organize them in some way. Such an organization can be based on the fact that some propositions can be derived from others. If we succeed in finding a few propositions from which the rest can be logically derived, we call such a set of propositions *axioms.*

However, it is not this simple. We cannot begin with the propositions of a geometry; we first need some vocabulary in order to state the propositions. This means that we need some undefined terms and possibly some definitions. The definitions and undefined terms will have to be about elements (objects) and relationships between these elements if we are

165

going to be able to formulate meaningful propositions. An axiom system consists of undefined notions, axioms, and usually some definitions.

(It would be possible to build a system without definitions. If definitions are in an axiom system, they may add nothing to the system but only name something that is already there. On the other hand, a definition may play a creative role in the axiom system; that is, it may act like an axiom and make it possible to prove propositions that cannot be proved in its absence. The task of distinguishing a creative from a noncreative definition is sometimes very difficult.)

An axiom system (with its undefined terms, definitions, and axioms) determines the content of a geometry; if we know the axiom *simplicity*, we can almost dispense with the consideration of the rest of the propositions. This is especially true when we are looking for the relationship between different geometries and when we are trying to determine the transformations of a certain geometry.

Let us talk now about some of the qualities of a good axiom system for a geometry.

There are two absolute requirements that a system of axioms must meet, *consistency* and *adequacy*. It must be free from contradictions, be consistent; for example, a system in which it is possible to prove both Playfair's axiom (Section 6.1) and its negative would not be consistent. A system is adequate if it is possible to derive all the propositions of the geometry from it.

In addition, there are some desirable features which are not absolutely necessary and are often difficult to achieve. One feature is *simplicity*—we want the individual axioms to be simple. Another feature is a *small number of axioms*. Notice that these two characteristics could contradict each other if we had a complicated axiom that we could break up into several simple axioms; on one hand the axiom is complicated, on the other, we have too many axioms. It would be nice if the axioms of a system were *independent*—if no axiom could be proved on the basis of the other axioms. There is difficulty with this characteristic also. Sometimes an axiom can be split into two parts, one of which can be proved (and so can be eliminated) while the other part cannot. The problem is that it is very difficult to prove that, for some given axiom, this cannot happen. Another characteristic that we shall mention is *completeness*. Completeness means that every question that can be formulated in terms of the concepts involved in the axioms can be answered on the basis of the axioms. In Section 7.5 we shall discuss completeness along with *categoricity*, a closely related characteristic.

In Euclid's time, and for almost two thousand years after, besides the absolute and desirable features that we have mentioned, mathematicians wanted the axioms, to be *self-evident*; later, some mathematicians wanted them to be *true*, that is, in some way verifiable. We do not want to discuss this question, except to remark that the correspondence of a set of axioms to reality does not necessarily mean that all the propositions will correspond to reality. Verifiability means testing by experiment and this involves observational errors. If one proposition is a logical consequence of another, it does not mean that both are equally sensitive to error. In order to discuss the question of the correspondence of a theory to reality (the applicability of a theory), we must confront the whole body of propositions with experience of the outside world, not just a part of it.

In the remainder of the chapter, we shall look at the geometries that we have already studied and discuss some of the questions that arise when we want to find axiom systems for them. We shall not try to give finished axiom systems for these geometries; instead, we shall indicate some of the possibilities and emphasize the interconnections between the geometries. In keeping with the remarks above about the nature of an axiom system, we shall consider a system of axioms as a basis of study for a geometry—an organizing principle for a body of propositions already existing (that is why this section on axioms has been placed near the end of this book). Besides discussing axiom systems for geometries that we have already studied, we shall briefly introduce two new geometries (equiform and equiaffine) and discuss categoricity and completeness.

Exercises

1. How could you prove that an axiom system is inconsistent? What difficulties arise if you attempt to prove that an axiom system is consistent?
2. What method could be used to prove that one axiom in a system is independent of all the other axioms?
3. What is the difference between adequacy and completeness?

7.2 AXIOMS FOR EUCLIDEAN GEOMETRY

One system of axioms for Euclidean geometry was discussed in Chapter 2. Another system is that found in Euclid's *Elements*; we discussed one of these axioms, the parallel postulate, in Section 6.1. In this section, we shall discuss a third set of axioms for Euclidean geometry: Hilbert's.

Historically, the first geometry to be axiomatized was Euclidean. For two thousand years, Euclid's axioms were discussed while the existence of other geometries was not even suspected. When non-Euclidean geometries appeared, investigations of Euclid's system were intensified; they culminated in Hilbert's work—a system of axioms for Euclidean geometry published in his *Foundations of Geometry* (1897).

Euclid's axioms had several defects, the most serious being that several of his assumptions were not explicitly stated (for instance, the axiom of Pasch discussed in Section 2.6). Hilbert's was the first system from which all of the propositions of Euclid could actually be derived. Aside from this, Hilbert's book reflects a change of view which took place in the last century. Hilbert speaks of points, lines, and planes as things that are in certain relationships to each other; he says that the axioms give a complete description of these relations which is sufficient for mathematical purposes. This is a good example of the *formal* viewpoint which had entered mathematics (see the introduction to Chapter 2).

Hilbert considers points, lines, and planes as undefined (primitive) objects, and incidence, betweenness, and congruence for segments and angles as undefined (primitive) relations. Segment, ray, angle, triangle, and collinear are some of his defined terms. He divides his axioms into five groups: (1) postulates of connection (incidence), (2) postulates of order (betweenness), (3) postulates of congruence, (4) the postulate of parallels, and (5) postulates of completeness. We shall list his axioms for *plane* Euclidean geometry.

The first group, the postulates of connection, deals with the properties of incidence. The axioms of this group include the following: *Two distinct points determine one and only one straight line; there are at least two distinct points on every line; and there exist three noncollinear points.*

The postulates of order are about betweenness. Pasch's axiom is found in this group (Section 2.6) and the properties of betweenness listed in Exercise 5 of Section 2.5.

The third group deals with congruence of segments, angles, and triangles. The axioms on congruence for segments are the following.

1. *If A,B are two points on a line a and A' is a point on the same line or another line a', then there exists on a given side of A' on a' a point B' such that segments AB and $A'B'$ are congruent.*

2. *If two segments are congruent to a third, they are congruent to each other.*

3. *If AB and BC are two segments on a line a having only point B in common, $A'B'$ and $B'C'$ are two segments on the same or another line a' having only B' in common, and if $A'B'$ and $B'C'$ are congruent to AB and BC respectively, it follows that $A'C'$ is congruent to AC.*

The axioms of congruence for angles are analogous to the first two axioms for segments just given, and the axiom of congruence for triangles is the familiar SAS of high-school geometry.

The postulate of parallels is Playfair's (Section 2.4 and 6.1). The last group of axioms (which appears in different forms in various editions of Hilbert's work) contains the postulate of Archimedes and a postulate of linear completeness. The postulate of Archimedes states that *if AB and CD are any two segments, then there is an integer n such that, if the segment CD is layed off consecutively n times from A on the ray containing B, then it will extend beyond B.* Hilbert's postulate of linear completeness says that *all the points of a line are such that no new points can be added and still satisfy all the postulates about points and lines.*

Exercises

1. Which of Hilbert's axioms given above belong to affine geometry (Section 3.1)?
2. A system of axioms for hyperbolic geometry can be obtained easily from the Hilbert axioms given in this section; the postulate of parallelism is replaced by: *Through a point on a line there is more than one line which does not intersect the given line.* See if you change the axiom system for Euclidean geometry given in Chapter 2 into a system of axioms for hyperbolic geometry.
3. Let $r(ABC)$ mean that the points A,B,C are the vertices of a right triangle. Try to formulate some axioms for Euclidean geometry using only this relation.
4. Let $t(ABCD)$ mean that A,B,C,D are the vertices of a trapezoid. Using only this relation, try to set up a system of axioms for affine geometry. Can the relation $t(ABCD)$ alone be used as a basis for Euclidean geometry? Why, or why not?

7.3   AXIOMS FOR PROJECTIVE GEOMETRY

Projective geometry was discussed before—in Chapter 3, where we used Euclidean geometry and intuition, and in Chapter 4, where we used vectors. The approach of Chapter 4 could lead to an axiom system for plane projective geometry. Some of the vector properties that we would need are given by part of the axiom system in Chapter 2; these together with the necessary properties of cross product and the representation of points (rays) and lines (flats) by vectors (Section 4.1) would form an axiom system for projective geometry. This approach has an undesirable feature, that is, the use of real numbers. It would be better if we could talk about projective geometry without using concepts borrowed from other mathematical systems. In this section, we shall indicate how this can be done without numbers (in the last chapter, we shall show how numbers, or something like numbers, can be introduced into such a system after it is established).

Our job now is to organize the body of propositions of projective geometry without using numbers. We must first decide what we are going to use as primitive notions—the undefined elements and relations.

If we were interested in projective geometry for its own sake, we would keep the notion of duality closely in mind. This would lead us to use points and lines as the undefined elements and incidence as the undefined relation. With these terms, two of our early axioms could be that *two points determine one and only one line*, and the dual of this proposition.

If we wanted to compare projective geometry with Euclidean geometry, and if we were using Hilbert's axioms for Euclidean geometry, we would probably make the same decision about the primitive notions for projective geometry.

In spite of these two strong reasons for using points, lines, and incidence as undefined terms, we shall *not* do this. We choose instead to use points as the only primitive elements and collinearity as the only primitive relation. One reason for this decision is that we already know many of the properties of collinearity from our vector development of projective geometry. Another reason is that, in the next section, we shall discuss an axiom system for inversive geometry which has similar primitive notions.

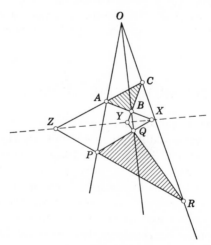

Fig. 7.3a

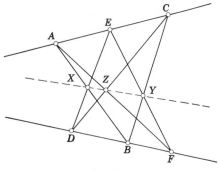

Fig. 7.3*b*

Still another reason is that in spaces of higher dimensions the point–line duality does not apply.

In what follows, upper case *italic* letters, $A,B,C, \ldots$, indicate points. If we want to say that the points A,B,C are collinear, we shall write ABC. [Notice that this is a shortened form of $(ABC) = 0$ which stood for the collinearity of A,B,C in Chapter 4.] This brief notation should not cause confusion because collinearity will be the only ternary relation used in this section.

Let us list some of the properties of collinearity that we want to be true.

1. *Collinearity is independent of the order of the points.* (This means that, if ABC, then we can also write ACB, BAC, BCA, CAB, and CBA.)

2. *Given three points, if two of them are identical, then the points are collinear.* (This means that we can always write BBA, and other similar expressions.)

3. *If $P \neq Q$, PQR and PQS, then QRS.*

4. (The Desargues proposition) *If OAP, OBQ, OCR, ABX, PQX, BCY, QRY, CAZ, and RPZ, then XYZ* (Figure 7.3*a*).

5. (The Pappus proposition) *If A,B,C,D,E,F are six distinct points, ACE, BDF, ABX, BCY, CDZ, DEX, EFY, and FAZ, then XYZ* (Figure 7.3*b*).

These five properties of collinearity probably do not constitute a set of axioms for projective geometry. We have probably forgotten some essential properties; also, some of these properties may be redundant and could be removed from the list (if the list were adequate, we would be able to prove Axiom 4 from Axiom 5 and the others.)

In order to test this tentative list of axioms for projective geometry, let us see if it is possible to prove that a Pascalian hexagon (we shall define this the same way as we did in Chapter 3) remains Pascalian if two adjacent vertices are interchanged.

Theorem. *If ABCDEF is a Pascalian hexagon with distinct vertices, its opposite sides, AB and DE, BC and EF, and CD and FA, intersect respectively in three distinct collinear points X,Y,Z none of which are vertices of the hexagon, and the hexagon ACBDEF has its opposite sides AC and DE, and BD and FA intersecting in the points X' and Z' respectively, then ACBDEF is Pascalian* (Figure 7.3c).

Proof. We must show that, if A,B,C,D,E,F,X,Y,Z are distinct, ABX, BCY, CDZ, DEX, EFY, FAZ, XYZ, ACX', BCY, BDZ', DEX', EFY, and FAZ', then $X'YZ'$ follows. This means that eleven collinearities (BCY and EFY appear twice) must be used to prove $X'YZ'$. We shall prove this by considering hexagon $DXZACB$. This is a hexagon with distinct vertices and it satisfies the hypothesis of the Pappus proposition: DZC, XAB, DXX', XZY, ZAZ', ACX', CBY, BDZ' (DXX' follows from $D \neq E$, DEX, DEX' and Axiom 3; ZAZ' can be proved similarly if we also use Axiom 1; and all the other collinearities are given or follow from a given collinearity and Axiom 1). Using Axiom 5, we can conclude that $X'YZ'$ and $ACBDEF$ is Pascalian. |

In this last theorem, we have interchanged the second and third symbols. It would be nice if we could conclude that any two adjacent symbols can be interchanged. Then, by using Exercise 3 of Section 4.2 (which says

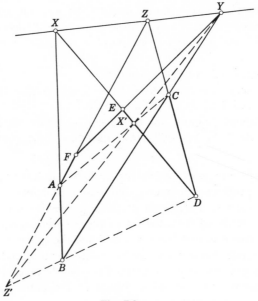

Fig. 7.3c

that any permutation of six symbols can be achieved by a finite number of changes of two neighboring symbols), we would know that, if six points form a Pascalian hexagon in some given order, then they form a Pascalian hexagon considered in any order. From Chapter 4 we know that we want this proposition to be true. However, a difficulty arises if we try to rewrite the last theorem for some other pair of adjacent vertices— a similar proof is valid only if the intersections of certains pairs of opposite sides exist and are distinct from each other and the vertices. The existence of these intersections can be taken care of if we add another axiom to our tentative list:

·6. *If $A \neq B, C \neq D$, then there exists a point X such that ABX and CDX.*

This type of axiom is called an existence axiom. If we were going to completely develop this axiom system for projective geometry, we would have to add more axioms of this type.

The requirement of distinctness in the last theorem seems to be a greater difficulty than the problem of the existence of certain points. Are there Pascalian hexagons with meets of opposite sides which coincide with each other or with the vertices? Could we have a Pascalian hexagon with vertices which are not all distinct? We needed to know about the distinctness of certain points at two places in the proof: when we apply Axiom 3 and again when we apply Axiom 5. It is not possible to remove the condition of distinctness in Axiom 3, but perhaps the condition in Axiom 5 is not necessary. If we were going to complete this axiom system, we would have to settle these questions first.

The theorem that we have just been discussing illustrates several things. It indicates how geometry can be treated in a formal way; it shows how the attempt to prove a known proposition of a geometry can lead us to change our tentative list of axioms; it also points out how an apparently small requirement in an axiom (distinctness) can lead to some rather big questions.

There is another important proposition that we want to be true; it arises from our desire to define harmonic points. We would like to define two pairs of points on a line to be harmonic if one pair is a pair of diagonal points of a quadrifigure and the other pair is formed by the meets of the line with the two diagonals of the quadrifigure. This definition is meaningful only if the diagonal lines of a quadrifigure do not meet on the join of the diagonal points (otherwise we are speaking of only *three* points). This proposition about the diagonal lines of a quadrifigure cannot be proved on the basis of our axioms. We could add it to our list in a negative way by saying that a certain collinearity does *not* hold. It is interesting that the same proposition can be formulated in an affirmative manner by saying that, if the meet of the diagonals is collinear with the diagonal points, the whole figure collapses; that is, all the points are collinear. In our symbolism, this becomes the following axiom:

7. (Axiom of Fano) If *ACD*, *BEC*, *AEF*, *BFD*, *FGC*, *DGE*, and *AGB*, then *ABC*.

Exercises

1. Try to set up an axiom system for projective geometry following the vector approach of Chapters 2 and 4.
2. Why is the condition $P \neq G$ necessary in Axiom 3?
3. Try to draw a Pascalian hexagon with six distinct vertices and in which two meets of the opposite sides are not distinct. Try to draw a Pascalian hexagon with six distinct vertices and in which a meet of opposite sides coincides with a vertex. Remove the restriction of six distinct vertices and repeat both of these experiments.

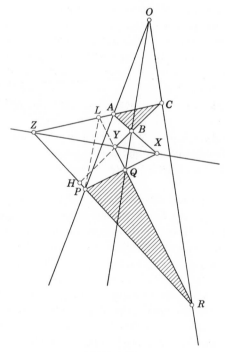

Fig. 7.3*d*

4. If some of the vertices in the Pappus proposition coincide, this is known as a degenerate case of the Pappus proposition. Experiment with drawings to determine if there are some valid degenerate cases. Prove them, using any approach to projective geometry developed in this book.

5. In stating Axiom 4, we did not include any requirement of distinctness of points. Perhaps we should have. Experiment to see whether some of the degenerate cases of Desargues are false.

6. Show that Axiom 4 (without Axiom 5) can be used to prove that if six distinct vertices form a Pascalian hexagon in some order, then the hexagon formed by interchanging two vertices separated by a third is still Pascalian.

7. Assume that, whenever needed, any requirement of distinctness is satisfied and use the theorem proved in this section to show that, in the presence of the other axioms, Desargues follows from Pappus (Figure 7.3d).

8. Show that Axioms 1 to 7 given in this section do not guarantee that there are any points at all in our geometry. Formulate some existence axioms which eliminate this difficulty and give us a sufficient number of points to make the geometry interesting.

9. Prove that Axiom 7 is independent of Axioms 1 to 6.

7.4 AXIOMS FOR INVERSIVE GEOMETRY

There is a surprising analogy between inversive geometry and projective geometry. In projective geometry, the simplest locus is a straight line and, in inversive geometry, the simplest locus is a circle. This leads us to feel that collinearity of three points in projective geometry should correspond to cocircularity of four points in inversive geometry. This correspondence, and the work of the last section on projective axioms, gives us an idea of how to start setting up an axiom system for inversive geometry.

Once again, we choose points as the only primitive elements, and this time cocircularity is the only undefined relation. We shall write $PQRS$ if we want to say that the points $P, Q, R,$ and S are cocircular. Following the axioms of the last section, we can start listing some propositions that we want in our axiom system for inversive geometry.

I. *Cocircularity is independent of the order of points.*

II. *Given four points, if two of them are identical, then the points are cocircular.*

III. *If P, Q, R are three distinct points, $PQRS$ and $PQRT$, then $QRST$.*

This last proposition permits us to define a circle as a set of points such that any four points of the set are cocircular, and guarantees that if two circles have three points in common, then they coincide. Since Axiom II tells us that any three points are cocircular, we can conclude that there always exists a circle through three given points.

Before we look for an analog of Pappus (since Desargues can be proved from Pappus, we shall not bother with the analog of Desargues), let us state the analog of Axiom 6 in the last section.

IV. *If two distinct circles have a point in common then they have at most, two points in common.*

We are now ready to look for an analog of the Pappus proposition. The theorem of Pappus says that a certain set of collinearities implies still another collinearity. We would expect our analog to say that a certain set of cocircularities implies still another cocircularity. Since the transformation of inversion is so important in inversive geometry, perhaps we should try to define inversion in terms of our present list of axioms; this attempt may uncover the analog of Pappus.

In Section 5.7 we found an inversive definition of inversion; this is the definition that we want to formulate now in terms of our axioms. Given four cocircular points A,A',B,B' and a fifth point P, we consider the circles through A,A',P and B,B',P; if P is not on the circle through A,A',B,B', then these two new circles are distinct and may have another point in common by Axiom IV. If this second point P' is distinct from P, we assign P to P'. If P is the only common point, it is assigned to itself. (If P is on the circle through A,A',B,B', we use the procedure described in Section 5.7.)

Assume now that we have assigned P to its inverse P' as above and that P and P' are not identical. We should be able now to use P and P' instead of B and B' in our construction and still get the same result. That is, if R and R' are cocircular with A and A' and also with B and B', they must also be cocircular with P and P'. To guarantee this, we add another axiom.

V. *If $AA'BB'$, $AA'PP'$, $BB'PP'$, $AA'RR'$, $BB'RR'$, then $PP'RR'$.*

This proposition seems to have first been stated by Miquel in 1844. It plays a role in inversive geometry similar to the role played by the Pappus proposition in projective geometry.

The five axioms that we have just listed are a beginning for an axiom system for inversive geometry. Other axioms are probably necessary; for example, we want every circle to contain an infinite number of points and we must be sure that circles exist. The five axioms that we have mentioned will be sufficient, however, to show how we could begin.

Exercises

1. Use any technique developed in Chapter 5 and prove the Miquel proposition.
2. Why does the Miquel proposition in inversive geometry resemble the Pappus proposition in projective geometry?
3. Another analog between inversive geometry and projective geometry is found in the formula for finding the inverse of any point z with respect to a circle of radius R about a point a.

$$z' = a + \frac{R^2}{\bar{z} - \bar{a}} \cdot$$

In projective geometry, the harmonic conjugate x' of a point x with respect to two fixed points c and d (assume that we are dealing with one line transformed to the x-axis and that these are the abscissas of the points) can be found by the formula

$$x' = s + \frac{\rho^2}{x - s}$$

where $s = (c + d)/2$ and $\rho = (c - d)/2$. For real values of z, these two formulas coincide (however, the inversive transformation applies to the whole plane, while the projective transformation is limited to a single line.) Prove that the projective formula given here is correct.

7.5 REALIZATIONS OF GEOMETRIES

In the last three sections, we have been talking about various axiom systems. As we listed the axioms, we used words like "given," "there exists," and "two"; these words have a definite meaning for us, and they had this meaning before we stated the axioms. We also used another type of word: "point," "incident," "vector," and "congruent"; these words are regarded as having no properties other than those specified in the axioms. This second class of words stands for something, but it is possible to interpret them in different ways. We want to talk now about this question of interpretation.

Among the words that have no definite meaning are two types, *objects* (points, vectors, lines) and *relations* between objects (collinear points, one vector being the sum of two other vectors, parallel lines). We have already talked about these words as being defined or undefined; now we are interested in the *possible meanings* of these words, their interpretations.

Let us assume that we have an actual set of objects and that, between these objects, actual relations are established in such a way that we are able to tell whether a certain relation holds or fails to hold for some given set of objects (for example, the objects could be the set of all ordered pairs of real numbers, one of the actual relations between three of these ordered pairs could be betweenness, and we could check to determine if one of the three given ordered pairs is between the other two by showing that the three ordered pairs satisfy certain distance formulas). If we have this type of actual situation and find that the properties of the relations, when expressed in words, are identical with some system of axioms, we say that we have a *realization*, or interpretation, of the system of axioms (the example that we just gave would be an interpretation of Hilbert's axioms for plane geometry).

An axiom system may have several different realizations; they may differ from each other in the nature of their objects and in the methods of establishing the relations. To understand this better, let us consider two different realizations of the axiom system described in Section 2.1.

One realization of these vector axioms for Euclidean geometry would consist of the set of all vectors (classes of ordered pairs of points) in a plane. We can add these vectors, find their dot products, and so on, as described in Chapter 1. Another realization would be the set of all ordered pairs of real numbers. The sum of two pairs $\{x_1, y_1\}$ and $\{x_2, y_2\}$ is defined to be the pair $\{x_1 + x_2, y_1 + y_2\}$, the dot product of these two pairs is $x_1 x_2 + y_1 y_2$, and other relations could be expressed in similar ways.

If we have two realizations of a system of axioms, we can compare them. Of course, they have in common the fact that they are both realizations of the same system of axioms. But there may be more; in some cases, it is possible to establish a correspondence between the objects of one realization and the objects of the other so that every object of the first corresponds to one and only one object of the second and vice versa (a one-to-one correspondence). For example, if we represent the vectors in a plane by ordered pairs of points having a fixed first point O (a common tail), and consider two perpendicular lines through O (coordinate axes), we can associate an ordered pair of real numbers with each vector by considering the length of the projection of the vector on each of the axes. Conversely, given an ordered pair of real numbers, we can consider segments of these lengths on the axes and find the vector that corresponds to the pair of real numbers. In this example, it is true that the same relations hold for vectors and for ordered pairs of real numbers; we say that the correspondence or mapping between the vectors and the numbers preserves relations. If two realizations of a system of axioms are mapped in a one-to-one manner on each other with preservation of relations, we say that the realizations are *isomorphic*, and the relation preserving mapping is called an isomorphism.

We should notice that, in the above discussion, we were interested in preserving only the relations that appear in the axiom system; in our case, the relations which are a combination of vector addition, multiplication by scalars, and dot multiplication. Some vectors could have been parallel to an axis, of unit length, and some numbers prime, composite, rational or irrational—none of these things concerns us when we discuss realizations of this axiom system.

Now we are in a position to continue our discussion of categoricity and completeness begun in Section 7.1. If a system of axioms is such that given any two of its realizations, they are isomorphic, then the axiom system is *categorical*.

An example of a categorical axiom system is given by the axioms in Group 1, 2, and 3 of Section 2.1. For example, assuming that n is 3 in Group 3, we shall prove that this axiom system is categorical. Assume that we have two realizations. In one realization, objects $\mathbf{a},\mathbf{b},\mathbf{c},\ldots$ correspond to the vectors in the axiom system. In the other realization, $\mathbf{A},\mathbf{B},\mathbf{C},\ldots$ correspond to the vectors. In each realization according to Axiom 3b, there exist three linearly independent vectors. Let $\mathbf{a},\mathbf{b},\mathbf{c}$ be linearly independent in the first system, and $\mathbf{A},\mathbf{B},\mathbf{C}$ in the second. Using axioms from Groups 1, 2, and 3 it can be shown that any vector $\mathbf{x}$ of the first system can be writen as $\mathbf{x} = \alpha\mathbf{a} + \beta\mathbf{b} + \gamma\mathbf{c}$ where α,β,γ are some unique real numbers. Similarly, any vector $\mathbf{Y}$ in the second realization can be expressed as $\mathbf{Y} = \delta\mathbf{A} + \varepsilon\mathbf{B} + \varphi\mathbf{C}$ where $\delta,\varepsilon,\varphi$ are some unique real numbers. In order to establish an isomorphism between the two systems, we simply assign vector $\mathbf{x}$ to vector $\mathbf{X}$ if the coefficients of their expressions in terms of $\mathbf{a},\mathbf{b},\mathbf{c}$ and $\mathbf{A},\mathbf{B},\mathbf{C}$ are identical; that is if $\mathbf{x} = \alpha\mathbf{a} + \beta\mathbf{b} + \gamma\mathbf{c}$ and $\mathbf{X} = \alpha\mathbf{A} + \beta\mathbf{B} + \gamma\mathbf{C}$. It is easy to prove that this mapping preserves relations. Thus, any two realizations are isomorphic and the axiom system is categorical.

We can also give an example of a system that is not categorical; such a system would be the axioms of Groups 1 and 2. No statement is made in these axioms about the number of dimensions; consequently, the set of vectors in a plane and the set of vectors in three-space are both realizations of this system. We can prove that these realizations are *not* isomorphic. In the three-dimensional realization, let $\mathbf{a},\mathbf{b},\mathbf{c}$ be three linearly independent vectors; assume that there is a relation preserving mapping between the objects of the two realizations and that $\mathbf{A},\mathbf{B},\mathbf{C}$ in the plane realization correspond to $\mathbf{a},\mathbf{b},\mathbf{c}$. Since $\mathbf{A},\mathbf{B},\mathbf{C}$ are in a plane, there exists real numbers

α,β,γ not all zero such that $\alpha A + \beta B + \gamma C = 0$. Since the mapping preserves relations $\alpha a + \beta b + \gamma c = 0$ must also hold. However, since **a,b,c** are linearly independent, this cannot happen. It follows that there is no relation preserving mapping, no isomorphism, and thus the axiom system is not categorical.

Categoricity is a desirable property of a system of axioms, but it is not necessary, and in many cases we have useful noncategorical systems.

Another desirable property that we mentioned is *completeness*. If an axiom system has this property, it must be possible to derive from the axioms an answer to every question formulated in terms of the axioms. This property is connected with categoricity; in fact, if a system is categorical, it is also complete or, equivalently, if a system is not complete, it is not categorical. For example, the axioms of Groups 1 and 2 are not complete because the question of the number of dimensions can be formulated in terms of the axioms but cannot be answered; we have also just shown that this system is not categorical.

Exercises

1. Verify that, on the basis of the Axioms of Groups 1, 2, and 3 in Chapter 2, if n is 3 and **a,b,c** are linearly independent vectors, then any vector **x** can be written as $x = \alpha a + \beta b + \gamma c$ for some unique real numbers α,β,γ.
2. Prove that the mapping described in this section between the two realizations of the axiom system of Groups 1, 2, and 3 of Chapter 2 does preserve relations.
3. Prove that the axiom system of Groups 1 to 4, excluding 4*e*, is not categorical.
4. Prove that every axiom system that is categorical is complete.

7.6   EQUIFORM AND EQUIAFFINE GEOMETRIES

In this chapter, we have been talking about the content of different geometries. We have considered most of the important two-dimensional geometries: Euclidean, affine, hyperbolic, projective, and inversive. There are two more geometries that we shall mention here in order to make the list more comprehensive.

One of these geometries is *equiform geometry* (we mentioned it in Section 3.1). Equiform geometry studies properties of figures which are not affected by change of size. In this geometry, angle is a significant concept, but length of segment has no meaning. There is no difference between similar figures, no difference between circles, no difference between squares, and there is no such thing as a unit vector. More precisely, two circles that are different in Euclidean geometry because they are different sizes would not be considered different here. Similarity plays the same role in this geometry as congruence plays in Euclidean geometry.

The other geometry is closely related to affine geometry. It is *equiaffine* geometry. In fact, equiaffine geometry is related to affine geometry as Euclidean geometry is related to equiform geometry. The important concept in equiaffine geometry is *area*; two rectangles with the same area are equivalent, so that there is no difference between a rectangle and a square (if they have the same area). Area has no meaning in affine geometry. In a sense, equiform and equiaffine geometries contrast with each other. The important thing in equiform geometry is shape (size is immaterial), and in equiaffine geometry, the important thing is size as measured by area (shape is immaterial). The question of the allowable changes in these two geometries will be discussed in the next chapter.

Exercise

Try to formulate some of the axioms of equiform geometry. Do the same thing for equiaffine geometry. (The task of setting up actual axiom systems for these geometries is not a trivial question.)

8 Groups

8.1 CONGRUENCE AND MOTION

We have just finished a discussion of one aspect of geometry: content. We are now ready to talk about the second aspect: transformations, or allowable motions. Since Euclidean geometry is the one that is most familiar to us, let us consider the role of motion in Euclidean geometry before we get into a general discussion of transformations.

Independence of position is one of the major ideas in Euclidean geometry. We say that two figures (or bodies, if we are considering three-space) are congruent if they differ only in position. Another way to say this is that two figures are congruent if one can be superimposed on the other, or if there exists a displacement that makes them coincide. The properties of congruence depend on the properties of displacement (motion). It appears that the ancient Greeks were reluctant to bring this idea of motion explicitly into geometry; it seemed to belong to mechanics and not to geometry. Whatever the opinion of the ancients, we shall take a more courageous and, in a way, a more honest attitude. Since displacement, or motion, is at the very basis of the notion of Euclidean geometry, we want to analyze it and make it a part of the study of geometry. Of course, we shall free it from any nongeometrical aspects, for instance, the role of time. We shall use only the geometrical content of the idea.

If we analyze the idea of superposition, we see that, to begin with, we must consider two figures, for example, two triangles. Geometrically, the only part of the process that interests us is the result; we are not interested in what happens to one figure "while it is being transported" onto the other. In fact, we do not actually move one figure onto the other, we just think about the correspondence. Mentally, we associate every point of one figure with a corresponding point of the other figure. The process has something in common with the process of counting. When we count, we associate with each object a word and a number. Superposition is a mental operation, rather than a mechanical operation. It is also an operation that is not strictly geometrical, but a fundamental logical operation—the operation of establishing a one-to-one correspondence between two sets. Superposition of course is not exactly like counting—it requires rigidity.

Let us look at another aspect of motion that needs some refinement, or reformulation, before we can incorporate it into our theory. We have been talking, thus far, about two individual figures. Any figure may be considered as a part of a more comprehensive figure and any motion that affects a part, of course, will determine a motion on the whole figure. The most comprehensive figure is the whole plane, this suggests that we consider displacements of the whole plane. Displacement is a correspondence, or mapping, so a displacement assigns to every point of the plane another point of the plane (it may happen to be the same point, of course). As a result of this, every figure is assigned to another figure. This is the general idea. When we are talking about Euclidean geometry and congruence, the correspondence will be such that the distance between any two points will be unchanged by the transformation; that is, the corresponding pair of points will have the same distance as the original pair.

To understand displacements or rigid motions of the entire plane, we can think of two sheets of paper, one opaque and, the other tracing paper. By drawing identical triangles on both pieces of paper and placing the tracing paper on the top, some of the rigid motions can be easily illustrated. Sliding the upper sheet along a straight line illustrates a translation; rotations can be illustrated by using a pin to fix the center of the rotation. (Reflections in lines cannot be illustrated as easily. The tracing paper would have to be lifted from the other sheet and turned over. It is because of this that some authors do not consider reflections to be rigid motions. However, we *are* calling reflections rigid motions.) This method of illustrating motions should make clear the connection between superposition of figures and motions of the plane as a whole.

We can say now that two figures A and B are congruent to each other if there exists a rigid motion (a distance-preserving transformation of the plane) that brings A into B.

We have already mentioned that the properties of congruence and the properties of motions are closely related. Let us see if we can discover which properties of motion determine the properties of congruence. Since ancient times, the following properties of congruence were considered.

1. *A figure is congruent to itself.*
2. *If A is congruent to B, then B is congruent to A.*
3. *If two figures are congruent to a third, they are congruent to each other.*

Notice that congruence is a special case of equivalence discussed in Section 1.7. Let us look now for the properties of motion which will give the three properties of congruence just listed.

From our point of view, rest must be considered as a special case of motion. This means that we may assign every point of the plane to itself; distances are obviously preserved by this mapping, so we have a rigid motion. Every figure is assigned to itself by this mapping. We call this mapping the *identity* transformation and it is the property of motion which makes property 1 possible.

Since we have been assigning points to points in a one-to-one manner, together with any distance-preserving mapping, we may consider the *inverse* mapping; that is, if *P* is assigned to *P'* by a mapping, *P'* is assigned to *P* by the inverse of the mapping, and of course distances are preserved. If figure *A* is assigned to figure *B* by a mapping, the inverse assigns *B* to *A*. Property 2 above is the consequence of the fact that, for every rigid motion, there is an inverse mapping which is also a rigid motion.

Finally, if *A* is congruent to *C*, this means that there is a distance preserving mapping that takes *A* into *C*. If *B* is congruent to *C*, there is a mapping that takes *B* into *C*; the inverse of this mapping takes *C* into *B*. Combining the first mapping with the inverse of the second, we get a distance preserving mapping that takes *A* into *B*. From this we see that property 3 depends on the possibility of combining two distance-preserving mappings into a single mapping by performing one and then applying the other to the result. This single mapping is usually called the *product* of the two mappings.

Summarizing, we see that the properties of congruence depend on the following properties of the rigid motions.

1. *The existence of the identity mapping.*
2. *The existence of the inverse of every mapping.*
3. *The existence of the product of any two mappings.*

Exercises

Show that the stretchings in lines (or affinities, described in Section 3.1) have the three properties listed above for the rigid motions. Do the same thing for inversions (Section 5.1).

8.2 GROUPS

Now we want to generalize the discussion that we just had on congruence and motion. We shall find that an analogous situation exists in many other cases. The generalization will affect both terms of the relationship; we shall generalize the idea of congruence and the idea of motion.

Let us begin with the idea of motion. Instead of restricting ourselves to the rigid motions, we can consider any transformations of the plane that have the three properties that we listed for the rigid motions. We shall say that a set of transformations is a *group* if it has the following properties.

1. *The set contains the identity transformation.*
2. *If a transformation belongs to the set, its inverse belongs to the set also.*
3. *If two transformations belong to the set, their product belongs to the set also.*

You have probably met the concept of a group before. In this book, it was used in some of the exercises of Section 5.4. What we are concerned about now is not a study of groups themselves, but an understanding of the relationship between groups and geometry.

The rigid motions considered in the last section form a group. We can also think of several other groups that we have encountered in discussing the various geometries. Translations constitute a group, rotations about a point are another example, and the fractional linear transformations (Section 5.4) are still another. Groups play an important role not only in geometry but also in other branches of mathematics.

You might be wondering why groups have appeared so frequently in the gometries that we have studied. Speaking loosely, we could give the following explanation. The reason is that groups are very closely connected with the notion of invariance. If a transformation T does not affect something, and another transformation S does not affect it either, then the product of S and T will not affect it. In fact, the totality of all transformations that do not affect something will have all the properties of a group. Since invariance is so basic and transformations are so closely related to invariance, we should not be surprised that groups appear so often.

Let us make some of the notions in this last discussion a little more precise and this will bring us to the generalization of congruence which we mentioned at the beginning. We were vague when we just talked about "something" that was left invariant under transformations because it could be a point, a line, a figure, a property, a relation, an equation, and so on. In order to be able to discuss all geometries at the same time, we shall have to restrict our invariants to something that is common to all geometries. Since all the geometries that we have discussed can be axiomatized and the axioms can be stated in terms of relations, *relations* will be something which can be left invariant by the transformations of every geometry. In Euclidean geometry, congruence is not affected by the rigid motions; this is a relation between two figures. In projective geometry, incidence is not affected by projective transformations; it is a relation between a line and a point. Cross ratio is also not affected by projective transformations; it is a relation between four collinear points. In inversive geometry, cocircularity is the relation which is not affected by inversions.

We have many relations and often, if we know that one relation is invariant under certain transformations, we can prove that other relations are invariant also. In inversive geometry, for example, we proved the invariance of angles under inversions from the invariance of cocircularity. Thus in determining the transformations under which different relations of a geometry are invariant, it is not necessary to consider all relations. If a geometry is given by a system of axioms, it is natural only to consider the relations that occur explicitly in the axioms.

Now that we know which transformations we shall consider (those that preserve the relations in the axioms), we must determine to what the transformations will be applied. We cannot apply transformations directly to the axioms. Transformations have to be applied to the *objects of a realization*. Thus, given a geometry specified by a set of axioms and a realization of that system, we can consider the transformations on the objects of that realization—all the transformations that preserve the relations which occur in the axioms.

Now that our ideas are more precise, let us check that these transformations do form a group. The identity transformation does not affect any relations (it does not affect anything); transformations are one-to-one reversible mappings, and if any mapping does not affect a relation, its inverse will not affect it either. Since we are considering all the transformations that preserve the relations, the product of two such transformations will also belong to the set and the last property of a group is also satisfied. The set of all the transformations of a geometry does form a group.

In Section 7.5 we talked about an isomorphic mapping of one realization onto another. We could just as well map a realization onto itself; in fact, this is what we do when we apply the transformations of a geometry. Such a mapping (a mapping of a realization onto itself preserving relations) is called an *automorphism*. From the discussion above, we see that the automorphisms of a realization form a group.

An axiom system usually has several different realizations. The automorphisms of each realization form a group. Thus we have many groups of transformations connected with the axiom system of a given geometry. Is there any relation between these different groups? In order to answer this question, we have to examine the relationship between the different realizations of the same axiom system. We shall do this in Section 8.4.

Before we consider this relationship, we shall look at a particular example in the next section which will illustrate how we shall approach the problem.

Exercises

1. Prove that the product of a mapping and its inverse mapping is the identity mapping.
2. An associative law for products is usually included in the definition of a group. Why could we leave it out of our definition of a group of transformations?
3. Prove that, in a plane, the rotations about a point constitute a group.
4. Prove that the set of all translations of a plane is a group.
5. Prove that the set of all rotations in a plane is *not* a group.
6. Prove that the set of all cross ratio-preserving transformations is a group.

8.3   AN EXAMPLE OF AN AUTOMORPHISM

We have spoken about automorphisms and isomorphisms. In both cases, we were considering mappings that preserve relations. In the first case, we mapped a realization onto itself, in the second, we mapped a realization to some other realization. Let us now consider an example in which both of these concepts will appear.

Consider a set of vectors in a plane having a common tail at a point O. We can set up a coordinate system in the usual way and map a vector $\mathbf{V}$ to an ordered pair of real numbers $\{x,y\}$; this is a one-to-one mapping preserving relations. On the ordered pairs, we can define a second mapping by

$$x' = x \cos \theta - y \sin \theta, \qquad y' = x \sin \theta + y \cos \theta.$$

This second mapping is an isomorphism—actually, an automorphism on the set of ordered pairs of real numbers. This automorphism preserves the relations described in the vector axioms. For example, we could verify that dot product is preserved; if $\{x_1,y_1\}$ and $\{x_2,y_2\}$ are mapped to $\{x_1',y_1'\}$ and $\{x_2',y_2'\}$, it is easy to show that $x_1 x_2 + y_1 y_2 = x_1' x_2' + y_1' y_2'$.

Combining these mappings, we can first map a vector $\mathbf{V}$ to an ordered pair $\{x,y\}$, then map $\{x,y\}$ to $\{x',y'\}$, and, finally, by the inverse of the first map, we can take $\{x',y'\}$ to a vector $\mathbf{V}'$ in the original realization. The total effect is a mapping of the set of vectors onto itself, and $\mathbf{V}$ goes to $\mathbf{V}'$. Each step preserves the fundamental relations; thus, in sending $\mathbf{V}$ to $\mathbf{V}'$, relations are preserved.

We can speak a little easier about the above situation if we use symbols to represent the mappings. Let the formulas that take $\{x,y\}$ to $\{x',y'\}$ be represented by T, that is, $\{x',y'\} = T(\{x,y\})$. Let the mapping φ assign the number pairs to the vectors, $\varphi(\{x',y'\}) = \mathbf{V}'$. There is no formula for φ, but there is a definite method for finding the vector, given its coordinates. The mapping that takes the vectors to the ordered pairs must then be φ^{-1}, since $(\varphi^{-1})^{-1} = \varphi$. The transition from $\mathbf{V}$ to $\mathbf{V}'$ is achieved by first applying φ^{-1}, then T, and finally φ,

$$\mathbf{V}' = \varphi T \varphi^{-1}(\mathbf{V}).$$

This is the product of three mappings. We could let $t = \varphi T \varphi^{-1}$ and write

$$\mathbf{V}' = t(\mathbf{V}).$$

Here, t is an automorphism on the set of vectors; it is a rotation. An automorphism on the set of ordered pairs of numbers has led to an automorphism on the set of vectors.

Exercises

1. Show that $(\varphi^{-1})^{-1} = \varphi$.

2. In the product $\varphi T \varphi^{-1}$, we have omitted parentheses. Why are we justified in doing this?

3. Is the product of two mappings commutative? Why, or why not?

8.4   THE GROUP OF A GEOMETRY

We mentioned, in Section 8.2, that a geometry may have several realizations and that each of these realizations will be associated with a group of transformations. In order to speak about *the* group of a geometry, it will be necessary to show that all the groups of the various representations are essentially the same.

Let us consider two isomorphic realizations of a geometry as we did in a particular case in the last section. Let the objects in one realization be represented by capital letters $A,B,C,\ldots$, and the objects in the other realization by lower case letters $a,b,c,\ldots$. If φ is the isomorphic mapping that takes the objects of the first realization to those of the second, we write $a = \varphi(A)$ and also $\varphi^{-1}(a) = A$.

If T is an automorphism of the first realization, we can construct an automorphism of the second, that is, $t = \varphi T \varphi^{-1}$. Let us check this. If x is any object of the second realization, $\varphi^{-1}(x) = X$ is an object in the first.

$T(X) = T\varphi^{-1}(x)$ is another object in the first realization, and $\varphi T(X) = \varphi T\varphi^{-1}(x)$ is an object in the second assigned to x. Since relations are preserved in each of the transformations φ^{-1}, T, and φ, they are preserved in $t = \varphi T\varphi^{-1}$ and t is an automorphism on the second realization.

The formula $t = \varphi T\varphi^{-1}$ assigns to each automorphism of a realization an automorphism of another realization (*if the realizations are isomorphic to each other* and of course any two realizations are if the system is categorical; if not, the situation is more complicated). From Section 8.2 we know that the automorphisms of each realization form a group; we can say, then, that this formula shows the connection between the groups of the various isomorphic realizations.

In order to understand the relationship between the groups of different realizations, we must extend the idea of isomorphism. Section 7.5 we talked about isomorphic realizations of an axiom system. The term isomorphic has a more general meaning; it can be used any time we have two sets of objects and one relation (or more) defined on each of these sets (as two groups). If a one-to-one correspondence is established in such a way that the relations are preserved, then we say that the two systems are isomorphic *with respect to these relations.* Whenever we speak of an isomorphism, it is either explicitly stated or clearly implied what relations are preserved. For example, when we speak of an isomorphism between two realizations of an axiom system, it is understood that the isomorphism is with respect to the relations used in the axioms; two isomorphic realizations may not be isomorphic with respect to some other relations. (The objects of one system may be ordered pairs of real numbers so some of them may satisfy the relation of both being integers, while the objects in another realization may be pairs of points with some satisfying the relation of lying on a certain line. The isomorphism between these two realizations probably will not preserve these relations.) When we speak of isomorphic groups, we mean (without explicitly saying so) that the relations with respect to which the groups are isomorphic are the relations expressed in terms of products of the elements (for example, three transformations considered in a certain order are related if the third is the product of the first and second). If $ST = U$ is a product in one group and this group is isomorphic to a second group where s,t,u correspond to S,T,U, then we must have $st = u$.

Using our new terminology, we can now formulate an answer to our question about the relationship between the groups of automorphisms of different realizations of the same axiom system.

Theorem. *If two realizations of an axiom system are isomorphic, then their groups of automorphisms are isomorphic.*

(We should notice that the word isomorphic is used here in two different senses; the isomorphism of the realizations is with respect to the relations occurring in the axioms, and the isomorphism of the groups is with respect to the group multiplication.)

Proof. We have already shown that an automorphism T of the first realization is related to an automorphism $\varphi T \varphi^{-1}$ of the second. We must show that this correspondence is an isomorphism in the sense that the relation expressed in terms of multiplication of mappings is preserved. To do this, we must consider three automorphisms of the first realization S, T, and U such that $ST = U$. We want to show that the corresponding automorphisms of the second realization, that is, $s = \varphi S \varphi^{-1}$, $t = \varphi T \varphi^{-1}$, and $u = \varphi U \varphi^{-1}$ are similarly related, $st = u$. We can write

$$st = \varphi S \varphi^{-1} \varphi T \varphi^{-1},$$

and since $\varphi^{-1}\varphi$ is the identity mapping, $st = \varphi ST \varphi^{-1} = \varphi U \varphi^{-1} = u$. |

Because of this theorem, it follows that, if an axiom system is categorical (remember, this means that any two realizations are isomorphic), then the groups of automorphisms are isomorphic to each other. There is an abstract group to which all of these groups are isomorphic (of which, in a sense they are realizations) and this abstract group is *the* group of a geometry that has a categorical axiom system.

The rigid motions form the group of Euclidean geometry (Section 5.3). The rest of this chapter will be concerned with the groups of the other geometries. We have been dealing with these groups all along, although we have not used this terminology—we have called them allowable changes. We already know that these groups, or allowable changes, tell us much about a geometry. In many cases, it seems that if we know the group of a geometry, we know all about the geometry; sometimes we say that the group of a geometry characterizes that geometry. This is not completely true, as the following illustrates.

Let us examine a number of geometries. Each geometry will be on a different surface (a plane, sphere, ellipsoid, etc.) but all of the geometries will have congruence as one of their relations. The transformations in the groups of these geometries are manifestations of free mobility because congruence is one of the relations. For example, in a plane, congruence arises because we can move the plane in itself without distorting figures. If we consider a geometry on the surface of a sphere, we can rotate the spherical surface and a similar thing occurs. However, if we look at geometries on other surfaces, this does not always hold. A figure on the surface of an ellipsoid cannot be freely moved on that surface without distortion. In general, there is only one figure on the surface of an ellipsoid that is congruent to a given figure. (An ellipsoid of revolution would be the intermediate case; there is some mobility, but less than on a sphere.) If we consider a surface even less "regular" than an ellipsoid, there is, in general, no mobility; for a given figure, there is no distinct congruent figure. In all of these cases, the question of free mobility is connected with the group of the geometry. There is, of course, always a group for a given geometry, but it may consist of only the identity transformation. There are a great many surfaces such that the geometry on those surfaces has the group consisting of only the identity transformation. These geometries all have the same group, but they can be very different from each other. Therefore, the group of a geometry does *not* completely characterize a geometry.

Exercises

1. Prove (by any method) that the set of all rigid motions of the Euclidean plane forms a group under composition.
2. Prove that the set of all rotations and translations of the Euclidean plane form a subgroup of the group of rigid motions.
3. Prove that, on an ellipsoid, there is only one figure congruent to a given figure.

8.5   THE AFFINE GROUP AND ITS SUBGROUPS

Now we want to look at the groups of the various geometries we have studied. We do not want, however, to consider these geometries in isolation from each other; we want to consider how they are related. Their relationships can be conveniently studied from the viewpoint of their groups. To make comparisons of the groups easier, we shall treat the geometries analytically.

We mentioned, in Section 5.3, that the rigid motions can all be expressed as a composition of a finite number of rotations, reflections, and translations. If we treat Euclidean geometry analytically, the rigid motions that carry a point (x,y) to a point (x',y') are given by the formulas

$$x' = ax + by + h$$
$$y' = cx + dy + k$$

where $a^2 + c^2 = b^2 + d^2$ and $ab + cd = 0$ (a,b,c,d,h,k all real numbers). We shall suggest a way to prove this in the exercises.

In Section 3.1 we described affine geometry as the study of those properties of figures which are left unchanged by stretchings in lines. If we set $\alpha = -1$ in that description, the stretching is actually a reflection in a line. Since reflections are among the affine transformations, it follows that rotations and translations are also affinities since they can be expressed as a composition of reflections (Section 5.3).

In order to find an analytic formula for the stretchings in lines, we can simplify the problem by considering only stretchings in the y-axis. These are given by $x' = \alpha x$ and $y' = y$. Any stretching in a line can be accomplished by first translating the plane so that the intersection of the line of the stretching with either the x-axis or the y-axis is moved to the origin, and then, if necessary, rotating the plane until the line coincides with the y-axis. After the stretching in the y-axis is performed, the plane can be returned to its original position by the inverses of the rotation and the translation.

Since translations have the form $x' = x + h$, $y' = y + k$ and rotations about the origin are given by $x' = x \cos \theta - y \sin \theta$, $y' = x \sin + y \cos \theta$, the composition of all of these transformations will have the form

$$x' = ax + by + h$$

$$y' = cx + dy + k,$$

the same as the Euclidean group, except that we can no longer expect such a strong condition on the coefficients. It is easy to find particular transformations which illustrate that $a^2 + c^2 = b^2 + d^2 = 1$ and $ab + cd = 0$ are no longer satisfied. We would expect, however, that there is some condition necessary on the coefficients a,b,c,d; it does not seem likely that any arbitrary choice of coefficients will always turn out to be an affinity. One condition that is certainly necessary is that every affinity have an inverse; analytically, this means that $ad - bc \neq 0$. The proof of this, as well as the sufficiency of this condition, will be left as an exercise. This means that all affine transformations can be represented by the formulas

$$x' = ax + by + h$$

$$y' = cx + dy + k$$

where $ad - bc \neq 0$ (a,b,c,d,h,k all real numbers).

Next, we consider equiaffine geometry, the geometry in which the area of a figure is the basic invariant. The rigid motions certainly preserve the area of figures, but we would expect that there are many more transformations which preserve area. For example, if we consider the double stretching

$$x' = \alpha x$$

$$y' = \beta y$$

in the axes, a unit square with a vertex at the origin and sides along the axes will become a rectangle. In general, area is not preserved by this transformation, but if $\alpha\beta = 1$, then the sides have length α and $1/\alpha$; thus, the area of the rectangle is 1. From this discussion, it seems that the transformations of equiaffine geometry are a subset of the affine transformations and that they contain all the Euclidean transformations. This leads us to suspect that they have the same form as the affine and Euclidean groups

$$x' = ax + by + h$$

$$y' = cx + dy + k$$

with some intermediate condition on the coefficients.

To find this condition, we shall consider what these transformations do to a triangle with vertices (x_1, y_1), (x_2, y_2), and (x_3, y_3). The area of this triangle is

$$\frac{1}{2}\begin{vmatrix} x_1 & y_1 & 1 \\ x_2 & y_2 & 1 \\ x_3 & y_3 & 1 \end{vmatrix}.$$

After applying the transformation, the area is

$$\frac{1}{2}\begin{vmatrix} ax_1 + by_1 + h & cx_1 + dy_1 + k & 1 \\ ax_2 + by_2 + h & cx_2 + dy_2 + k & 1 \\ ax_3 + by_3 + h & cx_3 + dy_3 + k & 1 \end{vmatrix}.$$

Using the properties of determinants, we can show that this is equal to

$$\tfrac{1}{2}(ad - bc)\begin{vmatrix} x_1 & y_1 & 1 \\ x_2 & y_2 & 1 \\ x_3 & y_3 & 1 \end{vmatrix}.$$

It follows that a necessary and sufficient condition for the transformation to preserve area is that $ad - bc = 1$.

Although we have only considered the area of a triangle, all other areas can be derived from triangular regions, and therefore we can accept this as the general condition. Thus, the transformations of equiaffine geometry are

$$x' = ax + by + h$$
$$y' = cx + dy + k$$

where $ad - bc = 1$ $(a,b,c,d,h,k$ all real numbers).

There is one more geometry that we would expect to be closely related to affine geometry: equiform geometry. Equiform geometry is concerned with figures that have the same shape, figures that are homothetic (Section 3.9) or similar to each other. Again, we see that the rigid motions belong to the transformations of this geometry because they do not alter shape) Besides the rigid motions, any transformation that stretches (or shrinks. the distance between any two points by a constant factor α will also preserve shape. Thus, if the distance between any two points (x,y) and (u,v) is d, and the distance between their images (x',y') and (u',v') or $(ax + by + h, cx + dy + k)$ and $(au + bv + h, cu + dv + k)$ is αd, then this is a similarity transformation. Using the distance formula, we must have

$$\alpha\sqrt{(x - u)^2 + (y - v)^2}$$

$$= [(a^2 + c^2)(x - u)^2 + (b^2 + d^2)(y - v)^2 + 2(ab + cd)(x - u)(y - v)]^{1/2}$$

so the condition on the equations is that $a^2 + c^2 = b^2 + d^2 = \alpha^2$ and $ab + cd = 0$. The Euclidean transformations are a subset of these transformations, as we expected, and these equiform transformations are a subset of the affine transformations.

Exercises

1. Use the fact that a rotation in a plane about the origin is given by the formulas $x' = x \cos \theta - y \sin \theta$ and $y' = x \sin \theta + y \cos \theta$, a reflection in the y-axis by $x' = -x$ and $y' = y$, and a translation by $x' = x + h$, $y' = y + k$ to show that every rigid motion can be expressed by $x' = ax + by + h$, $y' = cx + dy + k$ where $a^2 + c^2 = b^2 + d^2 = 1$ and $ab + cd = 0$.

2. Show that the formulas $x' = ax + by + h$ and $y' = cx + dy + k$ where $a^2 + c^2 = b^2 + d^2 = 1$ and $ab + cd = 0$ always represent a rigid motion; that is, the distance between two points is preserved.

3. Using the formulas of Exercise 2, prove that the rigid motions form a group.

4. Show that, in the group of Euclidean transformations, the only possible values for the coefficients are $a = \cos \theta$, $b = -\varepsilon \sin \theta$, $c = \sin \theta$, and $d = \varepsilon \cos \theta$ where $\varepsilon = \pm 1$.

5. If a transformation preserves distance, show that it also preserves the measure of an angle, perpendicularity, and dot product.

6. Show that $ad - bc \neq 0$ is a necessary and sufficient condition for the formulas $x' = ax + by + h$, $y' = cx + dy + k$ to represent an affine transformation.

7. Verify the equality of the two determinants used in this section to compute the area of a triangle.

8. Prove that the set of all transformations $x' = ax + by + h$, $y' = cx + dy + k$ with $ad - bc = 1$ form a group (the equiaffine group).

9. Prove that the set of all transformations $x' = ax + by + h$, $y' = cx + dy + k$ with $a^2 + c^2 = b^2 + d^2$ and $ab + cd = 0$ form a group (the equiform group).

10. Given the equiaffine group in Exercise 8, show that the only possible values for the coefficients are $a = r \cos \theta$, $b = -\varepsilon r \sin \theta$, $c = r \sin \theta$, and $d = \varepsilon r \cos \theta$, where $r \neq 0$ and $\varepsilon = \pm 1$.

11. Combine the rotations $x' = x \cos \theta - y \sin \theta$, $y' = x \sin \theta + y \cos \theta$ with the double stretching $x'' = \alpha x'$, $y'' = \beta y'$ and show that the resulting formulas do *not* represent a group.

12. Show that the symmetric transformations $x' = ax + by$, $y' = bx + cy$ do *not* form a group. Why are these called symmetric transformations?

13. Let the points of the plane be represented by complex numbers as in Chapter 5. Express equiform transformations in complex numbers.

8.6 THE PROJECTIVE GROUP

In this section, we shall determine the formulas for the projective transformations and show that the affine group is a subgroup of this projective group.

In Section 4.3 we learned how to establish the projective coordinates of a point X with respect to a fundamental triangle with vertices A,B,C and a fourth point E. This was done by means of cross ratios. Now we want to find an analytic representation of the cross ratio preserving transformations of the projective plane into itself in terms of these projective coordinates.

If A',B',C',E', and X' are the images of A,B,C,E, and X respectively under a cross ratio preserving transformation, then X' will have coordinates Y_1,Y_2,Y_3 with respect to A',B',C',E' where Y_1,Y_2,Y_3 have the same ratios as the coordinates X_1,X_2,X_3 of X with respect to A,B,C,E (because cross ratios are preserved and the cross ratios are ratios of the coordinates). Another way to say this is that the coordinates are the same except for a common numerical factor (when we use the first reference system for the coordinates of X and the second for X'). The problem now is to find coordinates X_1',X_2',X_3' of X' with respect to the first reference system A,B,C,E.

From Section 4.3, we know that we can write

$$X = X_1 A + X_2 B + X_3 C$$

(because in Section 4.3 we chose $a \cdot E = b \cdot E = c \cdot E = 1$ and only the ratios of the coordinates are significant). Since our two sets of coordinates have the same ratio, we can write

$$Y_1 = \lambda X_1, \qquad Y_2 = \lambda X_2, \qquad \text{and} \qquad Y_3 = \lambda X_3.$$

Furthermore A', B', C' can be written as linear combinations of A, B, C:

$$A' = \alpha_{11} A + \alpha_{21} B + \alpha_{31} C$$

$$B' = \alpha_{12} A + \alpha_{22} B + \alpha_{32} C$$

$$C' = \alpha_{13} A + \alpha_{23} B + \alpha_{33} C.$$

Substituting these last two facts into our formula for X' above and rearranging terms, we get

$$X' = \lambda [(\alpha_{11} X_1 + \alpha_{12} X_2 + \alpha_{13} X_3) A + (\alpha_{21} X_1 + \alpha_{22} X_2 + \alpha_{23} X_3) B$$
$$+ (\alpha_{31} X_1 + \alpha_{32} X_2 + \alpha_{33} X_3) C].$$

Thus, we can write the coordinates of X' with respect to A, B, C as

$$\rho X_1' = \alpha_{11} X_1 + \alpha_{12} X_2 + \alpha_{13} X_3$$

$$\rho X_2' = \alpha_{21} X_1 + \alpha_{22} X_2 + \alpha_{23} X_3$$

$$\rho X_3' = \alpha_{31} X_1 + \alpha_{32} X_2 + \alpha_{33} X_3.$$

This is the general analytic representation of a cross ratio preserving transformation taking points to points, if we add one restriction. The determinants of the coefficients cannot be zero; this will guarantee that the points are mapped in a one-to-one manner (and that inverses exist).

You may have noticed that the formulas for a cross ratio preserving transformation look exactly like the formulas for the transformation of coordinates derived in Section 4.3. This is because our coordinates specify the position of a point with respect to a projectively meaningful configuration. This happens in any geometry where the coordinates are developed in a similar way and has led to confusion between the two concepts—transformations of coordinates and the group of a geometry. In the general case, where the position of a point is specified in a way other than by giving its relation to a fixed configuration of invariants, there is no such relationship between the two concepts. For example, the group of a geometry could consist of only the identity transformation while there could be many coordinate transformations.

The cross ratio preserving transformations which we have just developed are called *collineations*—they take collinear points into collinear points. Actually, they are only a part of the projective group. If we take the notion of duality seriously, we would have to make no distinction between points and lines. Besides considering collineations, we would have to look for transformations that take points to lines (preserving projective properties) and lines to points—*correlations*. We have mentioned these transformations in Section 3.11 where we used a conic to assign every point (considered as a pole) to a line (its polar) and vice versa. The group of projective geometry consists of all correlations and collineations. We are not going to develop its analytic representation; however, we should notice that the situation here is similar to inversive geometry—the product of two correlations is a collineation, while there the product of two odd inversions was an even number of inversions.

In order to see the relationship between affine and projective geometry, we designate one of the lines of the projective plane as the line at infinity and exclude the points on this line from our consideration. If we choose the line c of the fundamental triangle, the points on this line have their third coordinate X_3 equal to zero because $X_3 = c \cdot X$ (Section 4.3). We shall want the projective transformations to take all the points on c into points on c; thus, the third equation must have $\alpha_{31} = \alpha_{32} = 0$. This reduces the formulas to

$$\rho X_1' = \alpha_{11}X_1 + \alpha_{12}X_2 + \alpha_{13}X_3$$

$$\rho X_2' = \alpha_{21}X_1 + \alpha_{22}X_2 + \alpha_{33}X_3$$

$$\rho X_3' = \qquad\qquad\qquad \alpha_{33}X_3$$

with

$$\alpha_{33} \begin{vmatrix} \alpha_{11} & \alpha_{12} \\ \alpha_{21} & \alpha_{22} \end{vmatrix} \neq 0.$$

Since the points with third coordinate zero are excluded, we can deal with coordinate ratios rather than with coordinates and, thus, write the formulas as

$$\frac{X_1'}{X_3'} = \frac{\alpha_{11}(X_1/X_3) + \alpha_{12}(X_2/X_3) + \alpha_{13}}{\alpha_{33}}$$

$$\frac{X_2'}{X_3'} = \frac{\alpha_{21}(X_1/X_3) + \alpha_{22}(X_2/X_3) + \alpha_{23}}{\alpha_{33}}$$

If we introduce the notation $X_1/X_3 = x$, $X_2/X_3 = y$, $X_1'/X_3' = x'$, $X_2'/X_3' = y'$, $\alpha_{11}/\alpha_{33} = a$, $\alpha_{12}/\alpha_{33} = b$, $\alpha_{13}/\alpha_{33} = h$, $\alpha_{21}/\alpha_{33} = c$, $\alpha_{22}/\alpha_{33} = d$, $\alpha_{23}/\alpha_{33} = k$, the formulas become

$$x' = ax + by + h$$
$$y' = cx + dy + k$$

with $ad - bc \neq 0$.

This shows that the formulas for the affine group are a special case of the projective group. Actually, if we disregard the change of notation, they are a subgroup of the projective group. It follows that Euclidean, equiform, and equiaffine transformations are also subgroups of the projective group.

Exercises

1. Prove that the set of all transformations of the form

$$\rho X_1' = \alpha_{11}X_1 + \alpha_{12}X_2 + \alpha_{13}X_3$$
$$\rho X_2' = \alpha_{21}X_1 + \alpha_{22}X_2 + \alpha_{23}X_3$$
$$\rho X_3' = \alpha_{21}X_1 + \alpha_{32}X_2 + \alpha_{33}X_3$$

with the determinant of the coefficients not equal to zero form a group.
2. Explain why designating one line of the projective plane as the line at infinity gives affine geometry.

8.7   THE SPHERICAL AND HYPERBOLIC GROUPS

We saw, in Section 6.2, that it was easy to develop many of the formulas of spherical geometry if we made use of vectors to represent the points on the sphere. We did a similar thing in projective geometry except that the vectors representing projective points could be multiplied by arbitrary nonzero numbers (Section 4.1). In spherical geometry, the coordinates of the vectors were subject to the restriction $x^2 + y^2 + z^2 = R^2$ where R is the radius of the sphere.

Since the points of spherical geometry and projective geometry can both be represented by vectors, it seems that there would be little difference between the groups of these geometries. This is not true, because the restriction $x^2 + y^2 + z^2 = R^2$ has far-reaching consequences when we consider the transformations of spherical geometry. First, this restriction means that we must deal with vectors rather than with arbitrary multiples of vectors; thus, the transformation formulas will not contain the factor ρ; instead, they will be

$$x' = \alpha_{11}x + \alpha_{12}y + \alpha_{13}z$$

$$y' = \alpha_{21}x + \alpha_{22}y + \alpha_{23}z$$

$$z' = \alpha_{31}x + \alpha_{32}y + \alpha_{33}z.$$

Besides this, they must express the fact that x',y',z' are the coordinates of a vector whose tip is on the sphere; that is, $x'^2 + y'^2 + z'^2 = R^2$. This means that

$$(\alpha_{11}x + \alpha_{12}y + \alpha_{13}z)^2 + (\alpha_{21}x + \alpha_{22}y + \alpha_{23}z)^2 + (\alpha_{31}x + \alpha_{32}y + \alpha_{33}z)^2$$
$$= x^2 + y^2 + z^2.$$

Performing the operations indicated and equating the coefficients gives us the following necessary (and sufficient) conditions on the above formulas to specify them as the transformations of spherical geometry:

$$\alpha_{11}^2 + \alpha_{21}^2 + \alpha_{31}^2 = 1 \qquad \alpha_{11}\alpha_{12} + \alpha_{21}\alpha_{22} + \alpha_{31}\alpha_{32} = 0$$

$$\alpha_{12}^2 + \alpha_{22}^2 + \alpha_{32}^2 = 1 \qquad \alpha_{11}\alpha_{13} + \alpha_{21}\alpha_{23} + \alpha_{31}\alpha_{33} = 0$$

$$\alpha_{13}^2 + \alpha_{23}^2 + \alpha_{33}^2 = 1 \qquad \alpha_{12}\alpha_{13} + \alpha_{22}\alpha_{23} + \alpha_{32}\alpha_{33} = 0.$$

In Section 6.3 we developed hyperbolic geometry from spherical geometry by letting $z = i\zeta$ and $R = i\rho$. If we use these values in the formulas above, we get

$$x' = \alpha_{11}x + \alpha_{12}y + i\alpha_{13}\zeta$$

$$y' = \alpha_{21}x + \alpha_{22}y + i\alpha_{23}\zeta$$

$$i\zeta' = \alpha_{31}x + \alpha_{32}y + i\alpha_{33}\zeta.$$

Or, we could write the last line as

$$\zeta' = -i\alpha_{31}x - i\alpha_{32}y + \alpha_{33}\zeta.$$

The conditions on the coefficients then become

$$\alpha_{11}^2 + \alpha_{21}^2 - \alpha_{31}^2 = 1 \qquad \alpha_{11}\alpha_{12} + \alpha_{21}\alpha_{22} - \alpha_{31}\alpha_{32} = 0$$

$$\alpha_{12}^2 + \alpha_{22}^2 - \alpha_{32}^2 = 1 \qquad \alpha_{11}\alpha_{13} + \alpha_{21}\alpha_{23} - \alpha_{31}\alpha_{33} = 0$$

$$\alpha_{13}^2 + \alpha_{23}^2 - \alpha_{33}^2 = 1 \qquad \alpha_{12}\alpha_{13} + \alpha_{22}\alpha_{23} - \alpha_{32}\alpha_{33} = 0.$$

These are the formulas for the group of hyperbolic geometry.

It is clear, from this development, that the spherical group is a subgroup of the projective group. The hyperbolic transformations also have the same form as a special case of the projective group except that some of the coefficients are pure imaginaries instead of real numbers; because of this, we could say that hyperbolic geometry is a type of subgeometry of projective geometry, although, strictly speaking, in this development its group is not a subgroup of the projective group.

Exercises

1. Verify that the formulas for a spherical transformation leave the distance between any two points on the sphere invariant.
2. Show that the conditions on the coefficients of the spherical transformations guarantee that the determinant of the coefficients is not zero and, thus, the inverse of every spherical transformation exists.
3. Show that the formulas developed in Section 6.5 for hyperbolic geometry are a special case of the hyperbolic transformations given in this section.
4. Verify that the transformations of hyperbolic geometry form a group.

8.8   THE INVERSIVE GROUP

The group of inversive geometry has already been dealt with in Chapter 5. It is represented by the formulas

$$z' = \frac{az + b}{cz + d} \quad \text{and} \quad z' = \frac{a\bar{z} + b}{c\bar{z} + d}$$

where a,b,c,d,z are complex numbers and $bc - ad \neq 0$ (or, equivalently, $ad - bc \neq 0$).

In order to compare these formulas with the formulas representing the groups of the other geometries, we must replace z by $x + iy$, z' by $x' + iy'$, and do a similar thing for the coefficients a,b,c,d. Generally, we get somewhat complicated expressions involving x^2 and y^2; however, if we look at the special case where $c = 0$ and we set $d = 1$, we have the formula

$$z' = az + b$$

from the even inversive transformations. Now, if we write the complex number a as $a = \rho(\cos \theta + i \sin \theta)$ and b as $h + ik$, we get

$$x' + iy' = \rho(\cos \theta + i \sin \theta)(x + iy) + (h + ik)$$

or

$$x' = \rho x \cos \theta - \rho y \sin \theta + h$$
$$y' = \rho x \sin \theta + \rho y \cos \theta + k.$$

In this case, the coefficients satisfy the requirements for the equiform group, and if $\rho = 1$, then it would, of course, also mean that the transformations belong to the Euclidean group. This is sufficient to show that equiform and Euclidean geometry are subgeometries of inversive geometry. This is not surprising since we already saw, in Section 5.3, that all the Euclidean transformations were inversive transformations.

Exercise

Set $z = x + iy$, $z' = x' + iy'$ and derive the general formulas in terms of real numbers for the inverse transformations.

8.9 CLASSIFICATION OF GEOMETRIES

The best way to study the interconnections between the various geometries is by the theory of continuous transformation devised by Sophus Lie: Lie theory. Even without this theory, we can form a pretty good idea of the interconnections.

In this chapter we have seen that, in some cases, we have a chain of groups, each being a subgroup of the preceding, as

Projective—Affine—Equiform—Euclidean

and

Inversive—Equiform—Euclidean.

From Section 5.6, we could extend this second chain to

Conformal—Inversive—Equiform—Euclidean.

Not all of the connections can be written as chains; for example, the four geometries: affine equiaffine, equiform, and Euclidean. Both the equiaffine and equiform groups are subgroups of the affine group, but neither is a subgroup of the other. The Euclidean group is a subgroup of both the equiaffine and equiform groups. This relationship may be represented by the following diagram.

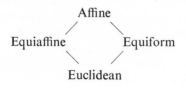

Similarly, the projective and the inversive groups both contain the equiform group as a subgroup, but neither is a subgroup of the other. This gives the following diagram.

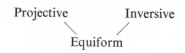

A more complete picture is given by the following.

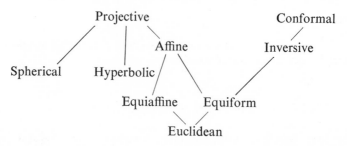

There are other groups that we could consider. Below the Euclidean group, we could consider the group of translations, or a group of rotations about a fixed point (the totality of all rotations do not constitute a group as was mentioned in Exercise 5 of 8.2). We could also obtain a geometry by selecting a point in projective geometry and proceeding in the same way that we did to get affine geometry in Section 8.6. However, due to the principle of duality, we would get a geometry that is formally indistinguishable from affine geometry.

The diagram above was developed on the basis of the groups of the various geometries. The geometries themselves are a body of propositions. If we have two geometries G_1 and G_2 and the group of G_1 is a subgroup of G_2, we ought to wonder about the relationship between the propositions of the geometries. If we take affine and Euclidean geometries as an example, we know that every affine proposition is also a Euclidean proposition. The converse is not true; there are concepts in Euclidean geometry (for instance, perpendicularity and circle) that have no meaning in affine geometry because they are not preserved by the affine transformations. Propositions containing words like perpendicularity have no meaning in affine geometry—they are not propositions of affine geometry. The effect of having more transformations in the affine group is that there are fewer propositions in affine geometry; the body of affine propositions is a part of the body of Euclidean propositions.

This is also true in general; as transformations are added to a group, there are fewer relations that are invariant under the group and the content of the geometry is decreased. Thus, if the group of transformations of a geometry G_1 is a subgroup of the transformations of another geometry G_2, then the propositions of G_2 are a subset of the propositions of G_1.

This relationship between the content of geometries and their groups of transformations was first clarified by Felix Klein when he classified geometries in his famous Erlangen Program of 1872.

Exercise

Develop the group of affine geometry from the projective group by specializing a point (instead of a line) as suggested in this section.

9 Numbers in Geometries

When we introduced our first axiom system in Chapter 2, we remarked that the use of numbers in the axioms of a geometry did not seem geometrical. Using numbers in the axioms is somewhat inconsistent with the idea that a geometry should be developed from undefined terms and unproved propositions. This last chapter will be devoted to some ways in which numbers, or some concepts analogous to numbers, may be developed within a geometry from its axioms instead of attaching the numbers to geometry ready-made from the extraneous subject of algebra or analysis.

9.1 SCALARS IN EUCLIDEAN, AFFINE, AND PROJECTIVE GEOMETRIES

In order to find a way to develop numbers from within a geometry, let us consider how we used numbers (the real numbers) in the vector axioms for Euclidean geometry in Chapter 2.

Real numbers appeared for the first time in the axioms of Group 2. Axiom 2 says: To every real number α and every vector $\mathbf{a}$, there corresponds a unique product which is a vector $\mathbf{x}$ and we write $\mathbf{x} = \alpha\mathbf{a}$.

If we consider how this product acts in vector geometry, we see that the relationship between $\mathbf{x}$ and $\mathbf{a}$ consists of two things.

1. $\mathbf{x} = \alpha\mathbf{a}$ expresses the fact that the vectors $\mathbf{x}$ and $\mathbf{a}$ have the same direction.

2. $\mathbf{x} = \alpha\mathbf{a}$ means that the ratio of the length of $\mathbf{x}$ to the length of $\mathbf{a}$ is α.

In Chapter 1, if we knew that two vectors $\mathbf{x}$ and $\mathbf{a}$ had the same direction, we expressed the relationship between this pair of collinear vectors by saying that their lengths had ratio α; we assumed there that numbers were known and we used them to express the relationship. We *could* proceed in the opposite direction; we can characterize a number by giving two collinear vectors. Instead of using numbers in the axioms, we could introduce them by means of collinear vector pairs.

If we want to reformulate the vector axioms, we could replace Axiom 1 of Group 2 by a set of axioms which would use collinearity of vectors as an undefined relation on vector pairs. These axioms would have to list enough properties of collinear vectors to characterize them. For example, if $C(\mathbf{a},\mathbf{b})$ means that the vectors $\mathbf{a}$ and $\mathbf{b}$ are collinear, then some of the axioms describing collinearity might be the following.

1. For any vector $\mathbf{a}$, $C(\mathbf{a},\mathbf{a})$.
2. For any two vectors $\mathbf{a}$ and $\mathbf{b}$, if $C(\mathbf{a},\mathbf{b})$, then $C(\mathbf{b},\mathbf{a})$.
3. For any three vectors $\mathbf{a},\mathbf{b}$, and $\mathbf{c}$, if $C(\mathbf{a},\mathbf{b})$ and $C(\mathbf{b},\mathbf{c})$, then $C(\mathbf{a},\mathbf{c})$.
4. For any vector $\mathbf{x}$, $C(\mathbf{0},\mathbf{x})$.

Several other axioms would be necessary to completely characterize collinearity. After this was completed, a definition of number could be developed; each number would actually be an equivalence class of certain collinear vectors (how this can be done will be clear when you have finished this section). There would have to be enough axioms to allow us to prove all of the properties of numbers that we need to get Euclidean geometry. To actually get the reals would be a difficult job, but it is not necessary. All of Euclidean geometry can be done with the positive integers and ratios of these integers if we have an axiom in our system equivalent to the postulate of Archimedes (Section 7.2). Euclid himself used only these concepts.*

We are not going to carry this development any further. It will be listed in the exercises if you would like to work out some of the details. Instead, we shall find a way to introduce numbers (which will not have all the properties of the real numbers) into three geometries—Euclidean, affine, and projective—in essentially the same way. To do this it seems better (than our approach in Chapter 2) to use points as the only primitive elements and to then define both vectors and scalars (or numbers) in terms of points.

The discussion that we have just completed about defining numbers in terms of a relation between certain collinear vector pairs is not wasted. We can still do essentially the same thing. Instead of using collinear vectors, we can think of putting the tails of the two vectors together; then the common tail and two tips give us three collinear points. We can use these three collinear points to define the scalars.

Of the three geometries that we are interested in at present (Euclidean, affine, and projective), it seems that affine geometry is the best place to begin. Once we have introduced scalars in affine geometry, we can use them in Euclidean geometry because it contains all the propositions of affine

---

* A discussion of this can be found in E. E. Moise, *Elementary Geometry from an Advanced Standpoint*, Addison-Wesley, Reading, Mass., 1963, Chapter 20.

geometry. On the other hand, if we want to introduce scalars in projective geometry we can designate a line in the projective plane as the line at infinity and reduce the projective plane to an affine plane (as we did in Section 8.6). Adjustments will then be necessary to adapt the numbers of the affine plane for projective uses. We shall discuss this at the end of this section.

Let us first introduce scalars into affine geometry. We shall assume that our affine geometry has been axiomatized using only points as the undefined objects. (Some axiom systems for affine geometry are not categorical and have various representations which contain only a finite number of points. We could even be using one of these axiom systems.) Vectors can be defined in this affine geometry if we consider them as equivalence classes of pairs of points (we did this in Section 1.1, although we did not call them that). Since there are many kinds of equivalence relations in geometry (Section 1.7), let us give the relation that we are going to use a new name to avoid confusion: *equipollence*. Equipollence is a relation between two sets of n collinear points; two sets of n collinear points are equipollent if the lines on which they are situated are parallel and there is a correspondence between the points of the two sets such that the joins of these corresponding points are parallel (we assume that the notions of line, parallel, and join have been developed in this affine geometry). It is easy to see that equipollence is an equivalence relation if the geometry contains the usual assumption that any line is parallel to itself.

A *vector* is now defined as an equivalence class of pairs of points under this equipollence relation. These vectors are essentially the same as the ones we are familiar with. The sum of two vectors can be defined as in Chapter 1, and the Desargues' theorem, which is also a proposition of affine geometry (including the cases in which the joins of the corresponding vertices of the two triangles are parallel and the meets of the corresponding sides are on the line at infinity), can be used to show that the definition is independent of the representatives of the equivalence classes (vectors).

Scalars can now be defined as equivalence classes of triples of collinear points. (Essentially, we are thinking of scalars as the ratio of two collinear vectors. The same scalar may be represented by many different pairs of collinear vectors, some of which have different directions.) We define two triples of collinear points R,S,T and U,V,W not on parallel lines to be *proportional* if R,S,T is equipollent to a collinear triple A,B,C and U,V,W is equipollent to a collinear triple A,P,Q (Figure 9.1a) such that A is common to both of these triples and the join of B and P is parallel to the join of C and Q. Two triples of collinear points on parallel lines are proportional if they are both proportional to a third triple as just defined.

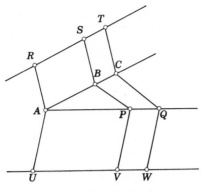

Fig. 9.1a

A *scalar* is then an equivalence class of triples of collinear points under this proportionality relation.

Before we define operations for scalars we need a lemma.

Lemma. *Given a scalar α (an equivalence class of triples of collinear points under proportionality) and a vector v (an equivalence class of pairs of points under equipollence), we can find a representative A,P,Q of α in which AP is a representative of v and also a representative A,R,S of α in which AS is a representative of v.*

Proof. Let AP be any representative of the vector v, and A,B,C be any representative of α which is not collinear with A and P. To find a representative A,P,Q of the scalar α, consider the parallel to BP through C and let the meet of this parallel with the line AP be Q (Figure 9.1b). A,P,Q is proportional to A,B,C and is the representative of α that we wanted.

The second part is proved similarly. |

Using the lemma, we can now define multiplication of a vector by a scalar, multiplication of two scalars, and addition of two scalars.

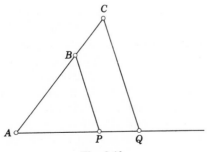

Fig. 9.1b

Definition.   *If α is a scalar and* **v** *a vector with representative AP, then* α**v** *is represented by AQ where A,P,Q is a representative of α.*

If we think of α as AQ/AP, this is a reasonable definition.

Definition.   *If α and β are scalars, then αβ is represented by the collinear triple A,P,R where A,P,Q is a representative of α and A,Q,R is a representative of β.*

Again, if we think of α as AQ/AP and β as AR/AQ, we would expect αβ to be $(AQ/AP)(AR/AQ) = AR/AP$.

Definition.   *If α and β are scalars, then α + β is represented by A,B,E where A,B,C represents α, A,B,D represents β, and AE = AC + AD (vector addition).*

If we think of α as AC/AB and β as AD/AB, then $(AC + AD)/AB$ is the reasonable choice for the definition of α + β.

Given any affine plane, if we want to represent all scalars by triples A,B,C of collinear points in a uniform way, we could fix the points A and B in the representatives of the scalars (this is possible by the lemma) and the scalars are then given by the point C. In a way, we have converted the points of a line in the affine plane into scalars. If C coincides with A, we call the scalar zero, and if C coincides with B, we call it one. Of course, any line of the affine plane can be used; the same scalars could be represented by the points of any line in the plane. However, if we consider two different affine planes, they may have different scalars (meaning there is no isomorphism preserving addition and multiplication). We cannot tell if the scalars are the same unless the planes are connected in some way (for example, two planes in the same three-dimensional affine space, or two affine planes obtained from the same projective plane).

Now let us discuss how scalars can be introduced into projective geometry. We can do this (as we mentioned before) by converting the projective plane into an affine plane by taking a line out of the projective plane. We can take out any line; thus, many affine planes are possible from the same projective plane. Since all of these affine planes arise from one projective plane and all the lines there are essentially the same, the scalars in each of these affine planes will be isomorphic.

We are not going to go into the specific details of this development of scalars in projective geometry. You may try to do this as an exercise if you are interested. We do want to mention one thing that will occur. Given a triple of collinear points in projective geometry, they will not determine a scalar because we do not know which line of the projective plane is to be eliminated. It seems that a scalar is assigned not to three collinear points in projective geometry, but to three collinear points A,B,C *and* a line ω (of course, the line cannot contain A,B, or C since then the points could not be used when we passed to the affine plane). If two lines ω and ω' meet the line of A,B,C in a point D, then the affine scalar assigned to A,B,C relative to ω and the affine scalar assigned to A,B,C relative to ω' will be identical (in Exercise 13, we shall suggest that you prove this). This means that the scalar assigned to A,B,C will be determined if we give a fourth point D on the line of A,B,C. A scalar in projective geometry is thus represented by four collinear points. This is not surprising since the simplest projective invariant, cross ratio, involves four points also.

Exercises

1. Formulate some axioms and definitions to replace Axiom 1 of Group 2 if we want the vector axioms of Chapter 2 to be stated without using the real numbers. (This is not a simple exercise.)
2. State the various forms of Desargues which hold in affine geometry.
3. Prove that equipollence is an equivalence relation on sets of n collinear points. (You may use any affine form of the Desargues' theorem.)
4. Define addition of the vectors developed from equipollence in this section and show that addition is independent of the representatives of the vectors.
5. In the proof of the lemma in this section, how do we know that a representative A,B,C of α which is not collinear with AP exists? Prove the second part of the lemma.
6. If α, β are scalars and $\mathbf{v}$ a vector, prove that $\alpha(\beta \mathbf{v}) = (\alpha\beta)\mathbf{v}$.
7. Prove that scalar multiplication is commutative.
8. Prove the associative law for scalar multiplication.
9. Prove that scalar addition is commutative.
10. Prove the distributive law for scalar multiplication over addition.
11. Prove that the scalars developed in this section form a field.
12. Explain how two different affine planes can lead to different (nonisomorphic) scalars.
13. If A,B,C,D are four distinct collinear points in projective geometry, show that any two lines ω and ω' through D, and not containing A,B, or C, lead to the same affine scalars (the same equivalence class of collinear triples if we eliminate the triples on the lines ω and ω').

9.2 NUMBERS IN INVERSIVE GEOMETRY

In Chapter 5 we assumed that a Euclidean plane was given and, from it, we built an inversive plane by adding a point Ω. In this section, we shall take the opposite approach. We shall assume that inversive geometry is defined by a set of axioms which include enough axioms to do the usual things like deal with inversions in circles and speak of orthogonal circles. On this basis, we want to introduce numbers into the inversive geometry— a type of number which will do essentially what the complex numbers did for us in Chapter 5. In order to do this, we shall be guided by the experience that we have already had of complex numbers in inversive geometry.

Unlike affine geometry, where numbers were assigned to equivalence classes of triple of collinear points and were represented by triples of points on a *line*, here we shall convert each point of the inversive *plane* (with one point Ω removed) into a number by defining the sum and product of two points (numbers).

Most of the work has been done for us in Chapter 5. Here we shall have to reformulate our procedure and make sure that we are not using anything from Euclidean geometry.

In Section 5.3 we saw that a translation is the product of two reflections in parallel lines. Here we can fix a point Ω and think of two parallels as two circles having Ω as their only common point. Instead of reflections, we shall speak of inversions, so translations will be double inversions: the product of two inversions in circles tangent to each other at Ω. We shall call such a translation *addition*. (Notice that *addition is a transformation*; ultimately, we want to define the sum of two points and the *sum will be a point*.)

A rotation was expressed as a double reflection in two intersecting lines in Section 5.3. In our present development, we shall choose a second point O (we chose Ω previously) and the intersecting lines can be thought of as two circles having O and Ω in common. A rotation about O then becomes a double inversion in these two circles.

Besides rotations, we shall need stretchings to arrive at a definition of the product of two points (numbers). Stretchings were described in Chapter 5 as double inversions in concentric circles, the common center being the point with respect to which the stretching took place. Now we replace the two concentric circles by two circles which are orthogonal to the pencil of circles through O and Ω (and in the set about O) since this is the inversive counterpart of concentric circles (see Section 5.9 where the family of circles orthogonal to two given circles was developed).

The composition of a rotation (a double inversion in two circles through O and Ω) and a stretching (a double inversion in two circles orthogonal to the family of circles through O and Ω) will be called a *multiplication*. (Notice again that *multiplication is a transformation*; we want to define the product of two points and the *product will be a point*.)

We are now ready to define the sum and product of two numbers (points) using the addition and multiplication just described.

Definition.   *The sum* $X + Y$ *of the points* X *and* Y *not equal to* Ω *is that point* Z *of the inversive plane which is the result of applying to* X *the addition which takes* O *to* Y.

In other words, if f is an addition (translation) such that $f(O) = Y$, then the point $f(X)$ is the sum $X + Y$.

Besides O and Ω, let E be a third fixed point. Then we can define the product of two numbers (points) as follows.

Definition.   *The product* XY *of the points* X *and* Y *not equal to* Ω *is that point* Z *of the inversive plane which is the result of applying to* X *the multiplication which takes* E *to* Y.

Thus, if $F(E) = Y$ and F is a multiplication (composition of a rotation and a stretching), then the point $F(X)$ is the product XY.

We can now form the sum and product of all the points of the inversive plane except Ω, so we may think of them as numbers. It remains to show that these numbers have the usual properties; these will be suggested as exercises.

Exercises

1. Using complex numbers, explain why our definitions of sum and product are reasonable.
2. Prove that, if O and E are as above, then for all points X, Y, Z of the inversive plane,
   (a) $X + Y = Y + X$.
   (b) $(X + Y) + Z = X + (Y + Z)$.
   (c) $X + O = X = O + X$.
   (d) There exists a point $-X$ such that $X + (-X) = O = (-X) + X$.
   (e) $XY = YX$.
   (f) $(XY)Z = X(YZ)$.
   (g) $EX = X = XE$.
   (h) There exists a point X^{-1} such that $XX^{-1} = E = X^{-1}X$.
   (i) $X(Y + Z) = XY + XZ$ and $(Y + Z)X = YX + ZX$.
3. Why must we exclude Ω from our numbers?
4. Formulate a definition for the conjugate of the numbers that we have just developed.

Bibliography

Adler, C. F., *Modern Geometry, an Integrated First Course*, McGraw-Hill, New York, 1958.

Artin, E., *Geometric Algebra*, Interscience, New York, 1957.

Blumenthal, L. M., *A Modern View of Geometry*, Freeman, San Francisco, 1961.

Bonola, R., *Non-Euclidean Geometry*, Open Court, LaSalle, Ill., 1912; Dover, New York, 1955.

Borsuk, K. and W. Szmielew, *Foundations of Geometry*, North-Holland, Amsterdam, 1960.

Coxeter, H. S. M., *Introduction to Geometry*, John Wiley and Sons, New York, 1961.

Coxeter, H. S. M., *Non-Euclidean Geometry*, Third Edition, University of Toronto Press, Toronto, 1957.

Coxeter, H. S. M., *Projective Geometry*, Blaisdell, New York, 1964.

Dorwart, H. L., *The Geometry of Incidence*, Prentice-Hall, Englewood Cliffs, N.J., 1966.

Eves, H., *A Survey of Geometry*, Two Volumes, Allyn and Bacon, Boston, 1963, 1965.

Fishback, W. T., *Projective and Euclidean Geometry*, John Wiley and Sons, New York, 1962.

Forder, H. G., *The Foundations of Euclidean Geometry*, Cambridge University Press, London, 1927; Dover, New York, 1958.

Graustein, W. C, *Introduction to Higher Geometry*, Macmillan, New York, 1930.

Heath, T. L., *The Thirteen Books of Euclid's Elements*, Three Volumes, Second Edition, Cambridge University Press, New York, 1926; Dover, New York, 1956.

Hilbert, D., *The Foundations of Geometry*, Open Court, Chicago, 1902.

Hilbert, D. and S. Cohn-Vossen, *Geometry and the Imagination*, Chelsea, New York, 1952.

Klein, F., *Elementary Mathematics from an Advanced Standpoint, Geometry*, Macmillan, New York, 1939; Dover, New York.

Levy, H., *Projective and Related Geometries*, Macmillan, New York, 1964.

Lieber, H. G. and L. R. Lieber, *Non-Euclidean Geometry*, Academy Press, New York, 1931.

213

Meserve, B. E., *Fundamental Concepts of Geometry*, Addison-Wesley, Reading, Mass., 1955.

Moise, E. E., *Elementary Geometry from an Advanced Standpoint*, Addison-Wesley, Reading, Mass., 1963.

Prenowitz, W. and M. Jordan, *Basic Concepts of Geometry*, Blaisdell, Waltham, Mass., 1965.

Robinson, G. de B., *Vector Geometry*, Allyn and Bacon, Boston, 1962.

Schuster, S., *Elementary Vector Geometry*, John Wiley and Sons, New York, 1962.

Seidenberg, A., *Lectures in Projective Geometry*, D. Van Nostrand, Princeton, 1962.

Veblen, O. and J. W. Young, *Projective Geometry*, Two Volumes, Ginn, Boston, 1910, 1918.

Wolfe, H. E., *Introduction to Non-Euclidean Geometry*, Holt, Rinehart, and Winston, New York, 1945.

Hints and Answers to
Some of the Exercises

SECTION 1.1

1. Let the translation send a point A to a different point A' and let it send a second point B to itself. Consider the line AB to see that this leads to a contradiction.

2. Use the definition of translation to show that lines AB and $A'B'$ are parallel. Assume that AA' and BB' intersect and show that this leads to a contradiction.

3. Yes, in three-space, the line through the center of the rotation and perpendicular to the plane of rotation. Vectors perpendicular to the plane of rotation are not changed.

5. If AB and CD represent the zero vector, use the properties of the zero vector. If AB and CD represent a nonzero vector and are on distinct lines, use Exercise 2; if AB and CD are on the same line, consider a third representative not on that line and apply Exercise 2 twice.

SECTION 1.2

3. Use Euclidean geometry.

4. Use the definition of vector addition to show that $\mathbf{a} + \mathbf{0} = \mathbf{a}$. Assume that $\mathbf{a} + \mathbf{0} = \mathbf{a}$ and $\mathbf{a} + \mathbf{0}' = \mathbf{a}$ and show that $\mathbf{0} = \mathbf{0}'$ (you may use Exercise 3).

6. Use the second definition of subtraction and Exercise 3.

7. No, find a counterexample.

SECTION 1.3

1(a) Use the definition of multiplication of vectors by numbers and Euclidean geometry; there are several cases to consider.

2. If a vector $\mathbf{a}$ has two different representatives AB and CD, show that $\alpha\mathbf{a}$ with α a real number is represented by αAB and also by αCD.

SECTION 1.4

1. If all the scalers are one. If all the scalers except possibly one are equal to zero; there are other cases.
4. Consider $\alpha(\mathbf{a} + \mathbf{b}) + \beta(\mathbf{a} + \mathbf{c}) + \gamma(\mathbf{b} + \mathbf{c}) = 0$ for real α, β, γ. Show that $\alpha = \beta = \gamma = 0$.
6. Show that there are real numbers α, β both of which are not zero such that $\alpha \mathbf{a} + \beta \mathbf{0} = \mathbf{0}$. Because vectors which are dependent have the same direction and the zero vector is dependent with a vector of *any* direction.

SECTION 1.5

1. If $\mathbf{u}$ and $\mathbf{v}$ have the same direction. If $A = B + \mu \mathbf{v}$ for some real number μ and $\mathbf{u}$ and $\mathbf{v}$ have the same direction.
2. Use the same approach as the one used in this section for proving the theorem about the medians of a triangle.
4. Let the sides of the quadrilateral represent vectors. Use linear combinations of these vectors to represent the sides of the figure that must be shown to be a parallelogram. Consider a diagonal of this figure in order to prove that a pair of opposite sides are parallel and of equal length.
6. $(m + n)/(m + 2n)$ to $n/(m + 2n)$.

SECTION 1.6

5. Consider a triangle ABC; let the altitudes from A and B meet at X. Show that $XB \cdot CA + XA \cdot BC + XC \cdot BA = 0$. Since $XB \cdot CA = 0$ and $XA \cdot BC = 0$, it follows that $XC \cdot BA = 0$.
6. Use the radius from the vertex and the diameter of the circle subtending the angle to show that the dot product of the vectors determined by the two sides is zero. (The two radii in the diameter determine vectors of equal length and opposite sense.)

SECTION 1.7

4. Use the properties of determinants.
5. Let $\mathbf{e}$ be a vector which is independent of $\mathbf{a}$ and $\mathbf{b}$. If $\mathbf{c}$ is independent of $\mathbf{a}$ and $\mathbf{b}$ and $\mathbf{a}, \mathbf{b}, \mathbf{c}$ is right-handed with respect to $\mathbf{a}, \mathbf{b}, \mathbf{e}$, put $\mathbf{c}$ in the first class and, if left-handed, put $\mathbf{c}$ in the second class. Let $\mathbf{c}$ and $\mathbf{d}$ be in the same class and show that no vector having its tip on the segment between the tips of $\mathbf{c}$ and $\mathbf{d}$ is a linear combination of $\mathbf{a}$ and $\mathbf{b}$.

SECTION 1.8

1. Use a discussion similar to the one in which the definition of cross product was developed.

6. Parallelograms with the same base and equal altitudes have equal areas.

7. Use the definition of cross product and dot product to compute the left-hand side.

SECTION 1.9

1. They do not exist.

3. Let $\mathbf{d} = \mathbf{a} \times (\mathbf{b} + \mathbf{c}) - \mathbf{a} \times \mathbf{b} - \mathbf{a} \times \mathbf{c}$ and find the dot product of both sides with an arbitrary vector $\mathbf{x}$. Remember that $\mathbf{a} \cdot (\mathbf{b} \times \mathbf{c}) = (\mathbf{a} \times \mathbf{b}) \cdot \mathbf{c}$ and use Exercise 3 of Section 1.6.

4. Vector addition has all the properties of addition of the real numbers; cross multiplication has only the property of closure; cross multiplication is distributive over vector addition.

6. Give a counterexample.

9. Calculate $(\mathbf{a} \times \mathbf{b}) \times (\mathbf{c} \times \mathbf{d})$ by setting $\mathbf{a} \times \mathbf{b} = \mathbf{x}$, using Exercise 5, and then replacing $\mathbf{x}$ by $\mathbf{a} \times \mathbf{b}$; repeat, letting $\mathbf{c} \times \mathbf{d} = \mathbf{y}$.

10. Use Exercise 1 of Section 1.8 and Exercise 9 of this section.

SECTION 2.1

4. Dot product is not associative since the axioms can be used to show that a dot product of three vectors does not exist.

5. It tells us how to add vectors geometrically.

SECTION 2.2

3. Yes, the axioms of Group 3 are not used in these proofs.

4. Yes. The parallelogram was used only to provide intuition while formulating the theorem. The proof does not depend on the parallelogram; some of the points may even coincide.

SECTION 2.3

1. To insure that we are considering all the points of the line. A finite set of collinear points would satisfy the definition if the word "maximal" were omitted.

SECTION 2.4

2. This is a generalization of the parallel postulate so you might try an approach similar to the one in this section, making the necessary modifications for the change of dimension.

SECTION 2.5

2. See Theorem 8 in Section 2.6.

3. Use $(A - C) = (A - B) + (B - C)$ and Exercise 2.

SECTION 2.6

4. If the line enters triangle ABC through vertex A, choose a point D on the line CA and on the side of A opposite C; apply the axiom of Pasch to triangle CDB.

SECTION 2.7

1. Assume that **a** and **b** are linearly dependent and show that this leads to a contradiction; similarly for **b** and **c**, and **c** and **a**.

2. See Exercise 5 of Section 1.4.

7. Assume that $X = O + x\mathbf{i} + y\mathbf{j} + z\mathbf{k} = O + r\mathbf{i} + s\mathbf{j} + t\mathbf{k}$ and use the fact that $\mathbf{i},\mathbf{j},\mathbf{k}$ are linearly independent.

SECTION 2.8

5. Use the definition of cross product.

7. If $\mathbf{u} = \{l,m,n\}$, $\mathbf{v} = \{o,p,q\}$, and $\mathbf{w} = \{r,s,t\}$, then

$$(\mathbf{uvw}) = \begin{vmatrix} l & m & n \\ o & p & q \\ r & s & t \end{vmatrix}.$$

SECTION 2.9

4. $\cos \varphi$

$$= \left[\frac{[b(lm' - ml') - c(nl' - ln')]^2 + [c(mn' - nm') - a(lm' - ml')]^2 + [a(nl' - ln') - b(mn' - nm')]^2}{(a^2 + b^2 + c^2)[(mn' - nm')^2 + (nl' - ln')^2 + (lm' - ml')^2]} \right]^{\frac{1}{2}}$$

6. $(mn' - nm')(x - a) + (nl' - ln)(y - b) + (lm' - ml')(z - c) = 0.$

7. Find three points in the plane which determine two linearly independent vectors; for example, if $\alpha,\beta,\gamma,\delta$ are all nonzero the points, $(-\delta/\alpha,0,0)$, $(0,-\delta/\beta,0)$, and $(0,0,-\delta/\gamma)$ determine $\{-\delta/\alpha,\delta/\beta,0\}$ and $\{-\delta/\alpha,0,\delta/\gamma\}$.

8. $|l|/\sqrt{l^2 + m^2 + n^2}$, $|m|/\sqrt{l^2 + m^2 + n^2}$, and $|n|/\sqrt{l^2 + m^2 + n^2}$.

9.
$$\frac{\begin{vmatrix} a - a' & b - b' & c - c' \\ l & m & n \\ l' & m' & n' \end{vmatrix}}{\sqrt{(mn' - nm')^2 + (nl' - ln')^2 + (lm' - ml')^2}}.$$

10. Use trigonometry and Exercise 3 of this section;

$$\left[\frac{[(y - b)n - (z - c)m]^2 + [(z - c)l - (x - a)n]^2 + [(x - a)m - (y - b)l]^2}{l^2 + m^2 + n^2}\right]^{1/2}.$$

SECTION 3.1

4. Trapezoid, parabola, and ellipse.

5. $P = (x,y)$ sent to $P' = (\alpha x, \beta y)$ is a composition of a stretching α in the y-axis and a stretching β in the x-axis.

6. Yes. Transform the ellipses so that the centers are at the origin and use Exercise 5.

SECTION 3.2

2. Triangle (if we overcome the difficulty of losing points), conic.

3. All the affine properties; this is a characterization of affine geometry.

SECTION 3.3

(a) In a bundle Ω of a plane Π, if there is a flat m' and a ray P' not in m', then there is one and only one flat n' in Ω containing the ray P' such that n' and m' intersect in a line parallel to Π.

SECTION 3.4

1. $[-18k,-13k,11k]$, $k \neq 0$.

2. $(3k,-10k,-k)$, $k \neq 0$.

3. $(4k,-3k,0)$, $k \neq 0$.

4. $[k,k,k]$, $k \neq 0$.

5. b,c.

6. $\begin{vmatrix} a_1 & b_1 & c_1 \\ a_2 & b_2 & c_2 \\ a_3 & b_3 & c_3 \end{vmatrix} = 0.$

SECTION 3.5

2. The line m can be external to the triangle; D and E the intersections of m with lines AC and CB are then external to the triangle; M can still be shown to be the midpoint by Euclidean geometry.

5. $N = (29/3,0,1)$.

7. D,E,N,G and M,G,C,F.

8. Three: -1, 2, and $\frac{1}{2}$.

SECTION 3.6

2. Use the invariance of the cross ratio of four collinear points.

3. If the slopes are m_1,m_2,m_3,m_4, then the cross ratio is

$$\frac{m_1 - m_3}{m_2 - m_3} \Big/ \frac{m_1 - m_4}{m_2 - m_4}.$$

7. $35/32$

8. $\frac{1}{2}$

9. $A = M$ or $B = N$; $A = B$ or $M = N$; $B = M$ or $A = N$; they are harmonic.

SECTION 3.7

2. The line at infinity $[0,0,1]$; a point not at infinity $(a,b,1)$; a line $[u,v,0]$ through the origin.

SECTION 3.8

1. The dual of a perspectivity maps four concurrent lines onto four other concurrent lines; dualize Figure 3.8a. The cross ratio of the lines is preserved since it is the same as the cross ratio of the four points of intersection of the corresponding lines of the two sets.

9. Three; one perspectivity can be used to send A,B,C to A'',B'',C'' on a different line, then A'',B'',C'' can be sent to A,B,C by a double perspectivity.

10. Assume that the mapping takes A,B,C,D to A',B',C',D' and also to A',B',C',D''. Consider the inverse mapping, taking A',B',C',D' to A,B,C,D and use Exercise 4 to show that $D' = D''$.

11. Use Exercise 10.

SECTION 3.9

5. The affine Desargues: If two triangles have two pairs of corresponding sides parallel and the joins of the corresponding vertices parallel, then the third pair of corresponding sides is parallel.

7. Let the two given triangles in the projective plane be projections of the same third triangle not in that plane.

8. If the alternate sides of a hexagon are concurrent, then the joins of the opposite vertices are concurrent; the figure for Pappus' theorem and its dual are the same.

SECTION 3.10

6. Let the five points be A,B,C,D,E. Find the meet G of the lines AB and DE. Let l be any line containing G. Let the meet of l and line BC be H, and the meet of l and CD be J. The intersection of lines EH and AJ is a sixth point.

SECTION 3.11

6. Let the diagonal lines be the diameter through the point and the chord through the point perpendicular to the diameter.

11. Consider a circle and use Exercises 6 and 10.

SECTION 3.12

1. Yes, let every point of the real line be mapped into its negative.

SECTION 4.1

3. No, because $(k\alpha, k\beta, k\gamma)$ with $k \neq 0$ will represent a vector in the same ray and, therefore, represents the same point.

SECTION 4.2

4. If A,B,C are collinear and B,C,D are collinear, then, A,B,D are collinear.

5. If A,B,C,D are cocircular and B,C,D,E are cocircular, then A,B,C,E are cocircular.

6. Use the vector equation of a conic developed at the end of this section and the relationship between homogeneous coordinates and vectors discussed in Section 3.4.

SECTION 4.3

9. Use the formula $(abc)X = (E \cdot a)X_1A + (E \cdot b)X_2B + (E \cdot c)X_3C$ developed in this section, the choice of $a \cdot E = b \cdot E = c \cdot E = 1$, and the fact that only the ratios of the coordinates are significant.

SECTION 5.1

3. Let X be any point on a circle with center S. Let X' be the image of X. Let Y be the intersection of OX with circle S, and Y' the image of Y. Let OP be the tangent from O to circle S. Use the fact that the length of a tangent from an external point is the mean proportional between the length of the secant from that point and the external segment of the secant. Show that, no matter which point X on circle S is chosen, X' is at the same distance from a fixed point T.

6. If the line PP' meets the circle at A and B, calculate the cross ratio $(AP'/BP')/(AP/BP)$. Use O the center of the circle and the fact that $AO = -OB$ to simplify the expression.

10. A circle through the center; a line not through the center; itself.

SECTION 5.2

3. $(11, -14)$.

4.
$$x' = a + \frac{R^2(x - a)}{(x - a)^2 + (y - b)^2}, \quad y' = b + \frac{R^2(y - b)}{(x - a)^2 + (y - b)^2};$$
these represent inversion in the circle of radius R about the point (a,b).

6. Any circle can be translated to the origin, the inversion performed, then the image translated back to the original position.

7. $x^2 + (y - \frac{1}{10})^2 = \frac{1}{100}$, $x = 2$, $x^2 + y^2 = 4$, $y = x$, $x^2 + (y - \frac{1}{2})^2 = \frac{1}{4}$.

SECTION 5.3

1. If AB is translated to $A'B'$, this can be accomplished by a reflection in the line which is perpendicular to BB' and through the point which is $\frac{1}{4}$ the distance from B to $A'B'$, followed by a reflection in the line perpendicular to BB' from the point which is $\frac{3}{4}$ the distance from B to $A'B'$.

3. No, give an example of an inversive transformation which does not preserve a Euclidean property.

SECTION 5.4

6. $z = (dz' - b)/(-cz' + a)$. This always exists because $bc - ad \neq 0$.

7. Use Exercises 4, 5, and 6 and the associativity of mappings under composition.

8. No, find a counterexample.

SECTION 5.5

1. A straight line $\alpha + \bar{\varepsilon}z + \varepsilon\bar{z} = 0$, or equivalently $\alpha z_2\bar{z}_2 + \bar{\varepsilon}z_1\bar{z}_2 + \varepsilon\bar{z}_1 z_2 = 0$. $\Omega = (1,0)$ is on this line because $\alpha(0 \cdot 0) + \bar{\varepsilon}(1 \cdot 0) + \varepsilon(1 \cdot 0) = 0$.

3. See Exercise 1.

5. Use Exercise 4.

SECTION 5.6

3. Tangent circles under inversion in a circle with center at the point of tangency are transformed into parallel lines.

6. Use inversion in a circle with center at one of the vertices.

SECTION 5.8

2. Let z_1, z_2, z_3 be sent to w_1, w_2, w_3 and consider the equation

$$\frac{w_1 - w}{w_2 - w} \bigg/ \frac{w_1 - w_3}{w_2 - w_3} = \frac{z_1 - z}{z_2 - z} \bigg/ \frac{z_1 - z_3}{z_2 - z_3}.$$

4. Send one of the points to Ω.

SECTION 6.2

1. $y = \pm\sqrt{7}$.

2. $\sqrt{35}$ arc cos $(13/\sqrt{35})$.

3. arc cos $(-\sqrt{14}/\sqrt{17})$. $(20/\sqrt{42}, -25/\sqrt{42}, 5/\sqrt{42})$.

4. $d = R$ arc sin $[(Ax + By + Cz)/(\sqrt{x^2 + y^2 + z^2}\sqrt{A^2 + B^2 + C^2})]$.

5. A small circle.

SECTION 6.3

1. $\rho = (\frac{2}{5}\sqrt{3})\zeta$, so the sphere may have any radius with $\rho > 0$.

2. $(\frac{1}{3}, \frac{2}{3}, 1)$.

3. No, because $\zeta > 0$.

4. $y = 0$. $(\sqrt{30} + 2\sqrt{51})x + (5\sqrt{30} - \sqrt{51})y = 11\zeta$.

5. If $x_1 y_2 - x_2 y_1 \neq 0$, then

$$A = \gamma \left. \begin{vmatrix} \zeta_1 & y_1 \\ \zeta_2 & y_2 \end{vmatrix} \middle/ \begin{vmatrix} x_1 & y_1 \\ x_2 & y_2 \end{vmatrix} \right.$$

and

$$B = \gamma \left. \begin{vmatrix} x_1 & \zeta_1 \\ x_2 & \zeta_2 \end{vmatrix} \middle/ \begin{vmatrix} x_1 & y_1 \\ x_2 & y_2 \end{vmatrix} \right.$$

with $\gamma \neq 0$ an arbitrary real number.

SECTION 6.5

2. $x = x' \cos \theta + y' \sin \theta$ $x = x'\sigma - \zeta'\tau$ $y = y'\sigma - \zeta'\tau$

$y = -x' \sin \theta + y' \cos \theta$, $\zeta = -x'\tau + \zeta\sigma$, $\zeta = -y'\tau + \zeta'\sigma$.

3. Use Exercise 2.

4. Two rotations are always sufficient to send a point to another point.

SECTION 6.6

1. $(\gamma_1 B_2 - \gamma_2 B_1)^2 + (A_1 \gamma_2 - \gamma_1 A_2)^2 \leq (A_1 B_2 - A_2 B_1)^2$.

SECTION 6.7

3. $B^2 > \gamma^2$.

SECTION 6.8

2. A right angle.

3. There are four lines parallel to both axes: $x + y = \zeta$, $x + y = -\zeta$, $x - y = \zeta$, and $-x + y = \zeta$. There are infinitely many lines divergent with respect to both axes; for example, $x + y = \frac{1}{2}\sqrt{6}\zeta$.

SECTION 6.9

3. $\cos(\alpha + \beta) \neq 1$ because $\alpha + \beta \neq 0$ and $\alpha + \beta \neq \pi$; $\cos(\alpha + \beta)$ is not greater than one because α and β are real numbers.

SECTION 6.10

2. $(\zeta'B - \gamma y')x + (x'\gamma - A\zeta')y = (x'B - Ay')\zeta.$

SECTION 6.11

1. $\zeta = \sigma$ with $\sigma > 0$ a constant real number; this is obtained by finding the locus of points equidistant from the "origin."
2. $x = \sigma. y = \sigma.$
5. They become parallel.

SECTION 6.12

2. Use the distance formula of hyperbolic geometry and apply Exercise 1 with $\alpha = \delta/i\rho$ and $\beta = (\zeta_1\zeta_2 - x_1x_2)/\rho^2.$
3. Use the fact that the transformations which take points to the "x-axis" are in the form of linear homogeneous equations; we know from Chapter 3 that they preserve collinearity and cross ratio.

SECTION 7.1

1. Show that a theorem and its negative can also be proved. You can show that one system is consistent relative to another system by finding a model of the first within the second; however, this only shows that the first system is consistent *if* the second system is consistent.
2. Find a model in which all of the axioms hold except the one that you wish to prove independent.

SECTION 7.3

2. If $P = Q$, it is possible that PR and PS are distinct lines.
7. Let the hypothesis of Desargues be as in Axiom 4. From Axiom 6, points L and M the intersections of sides AC and QR, and BC and PR exist. Show that $APMBQL$ is a Pascalian hexagon having O,R,C as the meets of the opposite sides. Apply the Pappus theorem twice to show that hexagon $ABMPQL$ is Pascalian and use this result to prove the conclusion of Desargues.

SECTION 7.5

3. Use, as one realization, vectors $\{x,y,\zeta\}$ where x,y,ζ are as in Section 6.3 and define an appropriate dot product.

4. Assume that some question formulated in terms of the axioms cannot be answered; we can assume that it is formulated so that it has both a positive and a negative answer. Each answer leads to a different realization. Show that these realizations cannot be isomorphic and, therefore, the system is not categorical. Reasoning from the contrapositive, categoricity then implies completeness.

SECTION 8.2

2. Composition of mappings is always associative.

SECTION 8.3

2. Composition of mappings is associative.
3. No, give a counterexample.

SECTION 8.5

4. $a^2 + c^2 = 1$ can be used to show that there exists a θ such that $\cos \theta = a$ and $\sin \theta = c$. Then $\tan \theta = c/a = -b/d$ from $ab + cd = 0$, and it follows that $b = \pm \sin \theta$ and $d = \mp \cos \theta$.

SECTION 9.1

7. Let A,P,Q be on one line and A,C,D on a second line and let both triples represent α. Let A,Q,R and A,B,C represent β. Essentially, this means that $AQ/AP = AD/AC$ and $AR/AQ = AC/AB$. Then $\alpha\beta$ is AR/AP and $\beta\alpha$ is AD/AB. To prove these are equal, we need RD parallel to PB; use the Pappus theorem in one of its affine forms.
13. Consider the configuration for the projective form of the definition of proportional triples of collinear points and show that the same affine configuration arises from both ω and ω'.

SECTION 9.2

4. Use inversion in the circle through O,E, and Ω.

Index